2241 / 2242 Lab Manual

D1283297

CENGAGE
Learning·

Australia • Brazil • Japan • Korea • Mexico • Singapore • Spain • United Kingdom • United States

2241 / 2242 Lab Manual

Executive Editors:
 Maureen Staudt
 Michael Stranz

Senior Project Development Manager:
 Linda deStefano

Marketing Specialist:
 Courtney Sheldon

Senior Production/Manufacturing Manager:
 Donna M. Brown

Production Editorial Manager:
 Kim Frv

Sr. Rights Acquisition Account Manager:
 Todd Osborne

For product information and technology assistance, contact us at
Cengage Learning Customer & Sales Support, 1-800-354-9706

For permission to use material from this text or product,
submit all requests online at **cengage.com/permissions**
Further permissions questions can be emailed to
permissionrequest@cengage.com

This book contains select works from existing Cengage Learning resources and was produced by Cengage Learning Custom Solutions for collegiate use. As such, those adopting and/or contributing to this work are responsible for editorial content accuracy, continuity and completeness.

Compilation © 2012 Cengage Learning
ISBN-13: 978-1-285-13654-7

ISBN-10: 1-285-13654-3

Cengage Learning
5191 Natorp Boulevard
Mason, Ohio 45040
USA

Cengage Learning is a leading provider of customized learning solutions with office locations around the globe, including Singapore, the United Kingdom, Australia, Mexico, Brazil, and Japan. Locate your local office at:
international.cengage.com/region.
Cengage Learning products are represented in Canada by Nelson Education, Ltd.
For your lifelong learning solutions, visit **www.cengage.com/custom.**
Visit our corporate website at **www.cengage.com.**

Printed in the United States of America

Acknowledgements

The content of this text has been adapted from the following product(s):

Experiment 54: Isolation Of Casein And Lactose From Milk - A Small-Scale Approach - Pavia
ISBN-10: (0-495-30553-7)
ISBN-13: (978-0-495-30553-8)

Experiment 30: Chromic Acid Oxidation Of Alcohols - A Small-Scale Approach - Pavia
ISBN-10: (0-495-30539-1)
ISBN-13: (978-0-495-30539-2)

Chromatography - Gilbert/Martin
ISBN-10: (0-495-30227-9)
ISBN-13: (978-0-495-30227-8)

Experiment 3: Extraction - A Small-Scale Approach - Pavia
ISBN-10: (0-495-30474-3)
ISBN-13: (978-0-495-30474-6)

TECH0722: Isolating Clove Oil from Cloves Using Steam Distillation
ISBN-10: (0-87540-722-6)
ISBN-13: (978-0-87540-722-7)

TECH0703: Purifying Acetanilide by Recrystallization
ISBN-10: (0-87540-703-X)
ISBN-13: (978-0-87540-703-6)

Experiment 16: Isolation Of Chlorophyll And Carotenoid Pigments From Spinach - A Small-Scale Approach - Pavia
ISBN-10: (0-495-30499-9)
ISBN-13: (978-0-495-30499-9)

TECH0701: Measuring the Melting Points of Compounds and Mixtures
ISBN-10: (0-87540-701-3)
ISBN-13: (978-0-87540-701-2)

SYNT0745: Synthesizing Aspirin: The Acetylation of Salicylic Acid
ISBN-10: (0-53497-772-3)
ISBN-13: (978-0-53497-772-6)

TECH 704: Separating Cyclohexane and Toluene by Distillation
ISBN-10: (0-87540-704-8)
ISBN-13: (978-0-87540-704-3)

TECH 700: Practicing Safety in the Organic Chemistry Laboratory
ISBN-10: (0-87540-700-5)

ISBN-13: (978-0-87540-700-5)

SYNT 718: Nucleophilic Addition to Carbonyl: Grignard Reaction with An Aldehyde
ISBN-10: (0-87540-718-8)
ISBN-13: (978-0-87540-718-0)

Experiment 46: Methyl Salicylate (Oil of Wintergreen) - Microscale - Pavia
ISBN-10: (0-495-30373-9)
ISBN-13: (978-0-495-30373-2)

Experiment 48: Sulfa Drugs: Preparation of Sulfanilamide - Microscale - Pavia
ISBN-10: (0-495-30377-1)
ISBN-13: (978-0-495-30377-0)

ANAL0727: Classifying an Unknown Compound by Functional Group
ISBN-10: (0-87540-727-7)
ISBN-13: (978-0-87540-727-2)

ANAL0728: Identifying an Unknown Aldehyde or Ketone
ISBN-10: (0-87540-728-5)
ISBN-13: (978-0-87540-728-9)

Experiment 13: Isopentyl Acetate (Banana Oil) - Microscale - Pavia
ISBN-10: (0-495-30325-9)
ISBN-13: (978-0-495-30325-1)

REAC 712: Dehydrating Cyclohexanol
ISBN-10: (0-87540-712-9)
ISBN-13: (978-0-87540-712-8)

Polymers - Gilbert/Martin
ISBN-10: (0-495-30244-9)
ISBN-13: (978-0-495-30244-5)

Table Of Contents

Practicing Safety in the Organic Chemistry Laboratory

prepared by **Michael W. Rapp**, University of Central Arkansas

PURPOSE

Review the basic rules of laboratory safety. Recognize the common hazards in an organic chemistry laboratory. Learn the proper responses to incidents that may occur in the laboratory.

SAFETY RULES FOR THE ORGANIC CHEMISTRY LABORATORY

Follow all rules. A Safety Contract is included within this module. You must hand in a completed contract to indicate your willingness to follow the standard rules of laboratory safety before you will be allowed to work in the laboratory.

1. *Wear safety goggles while in the chemistry laboratory.* Use splashproof goggles rated as ANSI Z87.1. Goggles are to be worn over prescription glasses. Supply your own goggles because sharing goggles can lead to eye infection from another wearer. Use of contact lenses under the goggles is discouraged because contact lenses may increase the damage done if an irritant gets in your eye. If you must wear contact lenses under your goggles to avoid unreasonably limited vision, indicate that need on your Safety Contract.

2. *Wear proper clothing to provide protection from reagent spills.* Long pants are required and long-sleeved shirts are preferred. A laboratory coat that extends below the knee is recommended. Shoes must be closed-toe and made of nonporous material. Do not wear loose-fitting clothing because it may catch on objects and cause spills. Avoid loosely woven or fuzzy fabrics because they increase the chances of fire hazard to the wearer. Tie back hair that is longer than shoulder length.

3. *Use good housekeeping practices to ensure a safe workplace.* Call to the attention of the laboratory instructor any conditions that seem unsafe. Avoid cluttering the work area, especially the work areas shared by many students. Place personal items, such as coats and backpacks, in separate storage areas rather than in the laboratory work space. Return items promptly to their proper locations. Disassemble and clean glassware directly after use because residues in glassware may become resistant to cleaning if not washed promptly. Allow hot glassware to cool to room temperature before washing.

4. *Do only authorized experiments, and work only when the laboratory instructor or another qualified person is present.* Do not enter the laboratory until the laboratory instructor is present. Unauthorized experimenting will waste time and may expose you and others to unreasonable risk. Authorized experimental procedures take into account the special hazards of the materials used. Do not treat laboratory reagents and equipment as playthings. Do not remove any reagents from the laboratory. Injuries from laboratory incidents most often occur from violations of the precautions given in this paragraph.

5. *Treat all laboratory reagents as if they are poisonous and corrosive, unless told otherwise. Immediately wash spills off your skin* with plenty of water. Then notify your laboratory instructor. This response is especially important for many organic compounds because their fat solubility enhances their ease of absorption through the skin. Wash your hands thoroughly with soap or detergent before leaving the laboratory. Special hazards of laboratory reagents will be indicated by appropriate labels on the reagent bottles.

Containers from chemical supply companies may use the National Fire Protection Association's diamond or some similar indicator of potential hazard, as shown in Figure 1. A number from 0 (low) to 4 (high) in each category indicates the degree of hazard.

Figure 1   National Fire Protection Association label

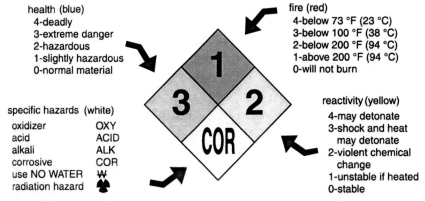

6. *Dispense reagents carefully and dispose of laboratory reagents as directed.* Do not use reagents from unidentified containers. Double check each label before dispensing a reagent. To prevent contamination, do not return any reagent to its original container. Place any excess reagent in the recovery container provided by your laboratory instructor. Dispose of reagents as directed by the laboratory instructor and the written procedure. Promptly notify the laboratory instructor of any spill. Clean up a spill *only if directed* to do so by your laboratory instructor. Spills should be cleaned up immediately to prevent contact of the chemicals with persons who are not aware of the spill. When weighing reagents, dispense them into containers so that reagents do not spill onto the balance.

7. *Do not eat, drink, use tobacco, or apply cosmetics in the laboratory.* Violation of this rule can introduce poisons into your system. Especially avoid any contamination to your mouth or eyes. Never bring food or drinks into the laboratory.

8. *Immediately report all incidents to the laboratory instructor.* An **incident** is any situation in the laboratory that might endanger those persons present. Your laboratory instructor must give prompt attention

when injuries occur. Even minor incidents may require attention. The laboratory instructor may also be able to use the information you provide to help other students avoid a similar difficulty.

9. *Be familiar with the location and use of all safety equipment in the laboratory.* All laboratories should have an eyewash station, a safety shower, a fume hood, and more than one fire extinguisher. Anticipate the steps to be taken in the event of an incident. Prompt response to an incident can make the difference between a minor event and permanent injury. The laboratory instructor may direct you to assist in responding. However, do not place yourself or others at risk in order to respond to an incident in the laboratory. A subsequent section describes proper responses to incidents in the laboratory.

10. *Become familiar with each laboratory assignment before coming to the laboratory.* Pay particular attention to cautions given in the procedure and by the laboratory instructor. Use of some equipment presents special hazards. For example, vacuum operations include the possibility of implosions, and ultraviolet light is damaging to the eyes if viewed directly. Each laboratory experiment will give special cautions for any hazardous reagents used in that experiment. Your laboratory instructor will provide other information and reminders as needed.

By law, chemical supply companies must provide a **Material Safety Data Sheet (MSDS)** with each reagent they sell. The MSDS is a technical bulletin that gives detailed information on the properties of a laboratory reagent. Some information from an MSDS for 1-propanol is shown in Figure 2 on the next page. Your laboratory instructor may have you consult the reagent MSDS as part of your laboratory work.

COMMON HAZARDS IN THE ORGANIC CHEMISTRY LABORATORY

Anticipate common hazards encountered in the laboratory. Experience has shown that ignoring the following *common concerns* will lead to mishaps.

1. Never pipet by mouth. Many organic chemicals are toxic.

2. Do not use chipped or cracked glassware, which may cause cuts or may crack and spill its contents unexpectedly.

3. Obtain approval from your laboratory instructor before starting a distillation. Make certain the apparatus has an opening. Do not heat a closed apparatus because abrupt release of the increased pressure may propel reagents or pieces of glass at persons nearby. Use a fresh boiling chip each time a liquid is boiled to avoid **bumping**, the sudden eruptive release of vapor. Such a release can burn persons nearby. Do not heat any distillation pot to dryness because the residue that remains may be heat sensitive, and overheating could cause it to detonate. Also, glassware that is superheated could crack. Before heating a flask, clamp the neck of the flask to support it in an elevated position to allow withdrawal of the heat source and rapid cooling, if needed.

4. Lubricate and clamp ground glass joints so they will not freeze or spring open in use. Use lubricant sparingly.

5. Do not point the open end of a container at anyone. Abrupt formation of bubbles, such as from boiling, could propel the contents into a person's face.

MATERIAL SAFETY DATA SHEET

**ANY SCIENTIFIC COMPANY   EMERGENCY #: (800)-555-XXXX
YOURTOWN, USA**

Section 1 (Identity): 1-PROPANOL (and synonyms given) Mol. Formula C_3H_8O Mol. Wt. 60.1
    CAS # 71-23-8   NFPA Ratings (scale 0–4):   Health = 1, Fire = 3,   Reactivity = 0

Section 2 (Hazardous Ingredients): 1-PROPANOL (100%)
        Exposure Limits: 200 ppm (492 mg/m^3) OSHA TWA
                250 ppm (614 mg/m^3) OSHA STEL

Section 3 (Physical & Chemical Characteristics): Description: Colorless liquid with mild alcohol odor
    Boiling Point: 207 F (97 C)   Melting Point –195 F (–125 C)   Vapor Pressure (20 C): 15 mm Hg
    Odor Threshold: 30 ppm

Section 4 (Physical Hazards): Dangerous fire hazard when exposed to heat or flame. Vapors are heavier
    than air and may travel a considerable distance to a source of ignition. Flash Point: 74 F (23 C) (CC)
    Upper Explosive Limit 13.7%   Fire Fighting Media: Dry chemical, carbon dioxide, water spray, or alcohol-
    resistant foam.   Transportation Data: US DOT Hazard Class 3 — flammable liq.

Section 5 (Reactivity): Stable under normal temperatures and pressures. Incompatibles: alkali & alkaline
    earth metals. Attacks coatings, plastics, and rubber.

Section 6 (Health Hazards — Inhalation, Skin Contact, Eye Contact, and Ingestion):
    INHALATION: Irritant/Narcotic. 4000 ppm is immediately dangerous to life or health.
    Acute Exposure: Inhalation of vapors may cause moderate irritation of the upper respiratory tract with
        coughing and shortness of breath. High concentrations may cause CNS depression, with dizziness,
        headache, and vomiting.
    Chronic Exposure: Reproductive effects have been reported.
    First Aid: Remove from exposure area. Perform artificial respiration if necessary. Get medical attention immed.

Section 7 (Precautions for Safe Handling and Use — Storage, Disposal, Spill & Leak Procedures):
    May be ignited by electrostatic sparks, so should be stored in grounded container, as specified in NFPA
    77-1983. Disposal must be in accordance with 40 CFR 262 (EPA Hazardous Waste Number D001). For small
    spills, take up with sand or other noncombustible absorbent and place into containers for later disposal.

Section 8 (Control Measures — Ventilation, Firefighting, Clothing, Gloves, Eye Protection): Wear
    appropriate protective clothing and equipment to prevent prolonged skin contact.

Figure 2   Selected information from MSDS for 1-propanol

6.   Place heated glass and other hot objects on an appropriate surface, such as a wire gauze or ceramic pad, until they have cooled. Hot
glass or metal may look like cool glass or metal, so cautiously touch
objects that have been heated before handling them. Place a note
nearby any hot objects remaining at the end of a laboratory period, so
students in a subsequent laboratory period will not be endangered.

7.   Use a fume hood when working with reagents whose vapors
are harmful. Except for small quantities heated by steam or a
hot-water bath, heating of highly flammable organic substances in
open containers must be done in a hood. In using a fume hood, position any apparatus well within the hood space, keeping your head
outside the hood. The flow of air through the hood must be adequate
and unobstructed. The hood sash should be lowered, except when
making manipulations within the hood. Place within the hood only
those items necessary for the operation being performed. Keep the
exhaust fan on as long as any reagents remain within the hood.

8.   When testing odors of reagents, gently waft vapors from the container toward your nose. Do not directly sniff the contents of a container.

9. Do not use open flames (Bunsen burners) in the presence of flammable materials, especially organic solvents such as acetone, diethyl ether, or petroleum ether. Use of a flameless heat source diminishes the danger of a fire, but such heat sources remain hot for quite some time after they are turned off. Overheated sand baths, hot plates, or heating wells can ignite fumes from volatile organic solvents.

10. Wear gloves when dispensing irritating reagents. This precaution is especially important for organic reagents, which can penetrate the skin readily. Your laboratory instructor will designate gloves that are appropriate for the reagents to be used. Latex surgical gloves are not appropriate because they allow passage of many organic reagents. Gloves should be inflated to check for breaks by whipping them through the air. Do not check gloves by inflating them by mouth.

11. Take special care when working with strong acids or strong bases. Contact with these materials can cause severe chemical burns. Prepare dilute acids by slowly adding the concentrated acid to a larger volume of water, with stirring. The water dissipates the evolved heat and prevents localized boiling that could spew the contents from the container.

12. If you must insert glass tubing into stoppers, follow the directions given by your laboratory instructor.

RESPONSES TO INCIDENTS IN THE ORGANIC CHEMISTRY LABORATORY

Become familiar with actions to be taken in the event of incidents in the laboratory. Provide appropriate assistance to others in emergencies. The items that follow describe the actions that should be taken in certain situations.

1. Report all incidents to the laboratory instructor, who is responsible for actions to be taken in response to incidents and for reports to be made to other authorities. As defined in Safety Rule 8, an incident is any situation in the laboratory that might endanger those persons present. An improper response may change a trivial difficulty into a much more hazardous situation. Sometimes an irritation or personal injury is not manifested immediately. A student who experiences an irritation later in the day, and who has a reasonable suspicion that contact with laboratory reagents could have caused the problem, should contact the laboratory instructor or a health care professional for advice.

The safety of persons in the laboratory has absolute priority over all other considerations. While you will not have the responsibility for directing others in the laboratory, you should be aware that the typical sequence of actions to take in the event of an incident in the laboratory is *ALERT, CONFINE,* and *EVACUATE.* If you are the first to notice a hazard in the laboratory, you should *alert* your laboratory instructor and others nearby. After you and others are clear of danger, your laboratory instructor will *confine* the hazard. If the hazard persists, the laboratory instructor may give instructions to *evacuate* the area.

Severe injuries may result from unreasonable responses to unexpected situations. For example, a person who spills a corrosive reagent on himself or herself might hope no one else notices, waiting until leaving the laboratory to wash off the spill. In the meantime, the burn from the reagent may have progressed from a superficial irritation to one that requires medical attention. Or a person who has lifted a test tube at the time the contents ignite might throw the tube through the air onto another person, catching that person's clothes on fire. Consider the consequences of your actions.

2.   Dispose of broken glass as directed by the laboratory instructor. Use a hand brush and dust pan to collect the pieces. Do not attempt to gather sharp glass by hand. Place broken glass in specially designated receptacles in order to avoid placing other persons at risk. Place very small, sharp objects—for example, syringe needles and pieces of capillary tube—in specially designated receptacles.

If a mercury thermometer is broken, step back from the work area and notify the laboratory instructor, who will use special techniques to collect the spilled mercury. The special hazard with mercury is not from contact with the skin, but from prolonged exposure to the vapor. A cut by a broken thermometer should get the same attention as other cuts.

3.   For either minor cuts or burns, wash the affected area using soap or detergent. Tissue damage from a superficial burn will be minimal if the affected area is cooled quickly, so you should flush the affected area with cold water. Then notify the laboratory instructor. When work is resumed, protect any break in the skin by wearing a glove, in order to prevent introduction of laboratory reagents.

4.   In the event of a reagent spill, notify the laboratory instructor. Appropriate steps to be taken in response to a reagent spill will vary, depending on the amount and identity of the reagent. Concerns for hazards other than the reagent itself, such as danger of shorting electrical equipment, may even take precedence. Spills of organic solvents may be a fire hazard. In such an event, remove all ignition sources, including any equipment that could produce a spark—for example, switches being turned on and off. Hot plates and sand baths at a high temperature do not cool rapidly on turning off, so move these heat sources away from the spill. If a spill creates a large amount of fumes, evacuate the laboratory. Stop any experiments, if doing so doesn't place anyone at risk.

Deal promptly with reagent spills on a person. Wash the affected area with large volumes of water. Rapid response is necessary because many organic solvents are fat soluble and can be absorbed through the skin. Use the sink or safety shower as needed, depending on the size of the spill. Remove clothing and wash skin with soap or detergent to complete the removal of the reagent. Do not remove goggles before washing any reagent spill from the face, to lessen the likelihood of getting the reagent in the eyes.

A person whose eyes have had reagents splashed into them requires assistance from others. A person's automatic response to an irritation to the eyes is closing of the lids and rubbing, actions that will only increase the irritation. Other persons should assist the person to the eyewash fountain and operate the water flow, while the person holds open his/her eyelids. The flow of water must get to the entire eye surface, continuing for twenty minutes. Cold water may be intolerable for such an uninterrupted period, so periodic washing may have to be done. Irrigation of the eye will not be adequate if contact lenses that are present are not removed. Further treatment of irritation to the eye from a reagent spill must be done only by a health care professional.

5.   Many common solvents used in the organic chemistry laboratory are highly flammable, and a small fire may occur in the laboratory. Do not react without thinking. The immediate response to a fire in the laboratory is to take those actions that remove individuals from the hazard. For example, stepping back from a small fire and cautioning neighbors of the hazard would be a reasonable response. Move flammable materials away, and turn equipment off or remove equipment from the vicinity of the fire. Shut off the gas spigot or heating element. Place a watch glass or beaker over a small container to smother the burning material. Some *small* fires, such as alcohol fires, may be allowed to burn out.

If a fire spreads to a larger area of the bench, the laboratory instructor or other authorized persons should operate the fire extinguisher. Should a fire reach a stage where it cannot be easily controlled, the laboratory instructor will direct you to evacuate the laboratory and the building.

The most distressing incidents in laboratories are those where an individual is on fire. Using small quantities of flammable substances and following safe practices in the laboratory ensure that such an event is unlikely to happen. Proper response can make the difference between loss of some clothing or, in the extreme case, loss of life. If a person's lungs are seared from inhaling flames, there will be little chance of recovery.

The safety shower or water from the sink may be sufficient to extinguish a fire on a person. In a severe situation, the proper response to fire on an individual's clothing is to *STOP, DROP,* and *ROLL.* That is, if you have fire on your body, *stop* where you are, *drop* to the floor, and *roll* to smother the flames. Staying upright will allow the flames to rise to the face. Nearby persons can use a laboratory coat to beat out the flames. When the flames are extinguished, remove any smoldering fabric. If the person has been burned, place the person under the safety shower. Other persons nearby can assist as needed, such as extinguishing fire on the bench, shutting off equipment, and cleaning up. Most other persons in the laboratory should simply move away.

6. Ingestion or inhalation of a reagent will likely require the assistance of a health care professional. In such an event, immediately notify the laboratory instructor, who will gather the information needed to report the incident to the poison control center. Space is provided at the end of this module for you to record the phone number of the poison control center in your area.

Avoid the inhalation of unsafe levels of irritating or toxic vapors by following the directions for using laboratory reagents and by using the reagents in a fume hood. While you must not depend upon your senses to alert you to inadvisable conditions, notify your laboratory instructor promptly if your eyes begin to sting or if you develop a headache that may be caused by fumes in the laboratory. Especially avoid breathing the vapors from chlorinated solvents and aromatic compounds.

7. Immediately notify the laboratory instructor if you or a neighbor feels faint. A person who has become unconscious from inhalation of fumes must be removed from the source of the fumes. Other than checking the person's airway and treatment for shock (elevating limbs, keeping warm), further treatment should only be made by a health care professional.

SAFETY INFORMATION

Complete this form and keep it for possible use.

1. **Emergency health providers** (telephone numbers to call)

Campus Health Services:

   on campus _____   off campus _____

Emergency Medical Assistance:

   on campus _____   off campus _____

State Poison Control Center: _____

Campus Police:

   on campus _____   off campus _____

City Police or Fire Department:

   on campus _____   off campus _____

2. **Contacting the laboratory instructor**

Name: _____   Office: _____

Office phone: on campus _____   off campus _____

Home phone: _____   E-mail address: _____

3. **Reporting incidents** (for reference)

The following information will be needed when communicating with health professionals and/or recording incidents.

Nature of the incident (description – including fire, substances involved, number of individuals involved and their physical conditions):

Individuals involved (identification – name, gender, age):

Location of the incident, including who will meet any emergency vehicle, and where:

Person reporting the incident (name, phone number being used to report the incident. *Note:* Do not allow this phone to be tied up for calls unrelated to control of the incident.):

Safety Contract

Complete this form and give to your laboratory instructor.

I have carefully read the organic chemical laboratory safety module. I have given my answers to the accompanying safety quiz and given that completed quiz to the laboratory instructor as an indication of my familiarity with the module. Whenever I am in an area where laboratory reagents are being used, I agree to abide by the following rules:

1. Wear safety goggles.

2. Wear proper clothing.

3. Use good housekeeping practices.

4. Do only authorized experiments, and work only when the laboratory instructor or another qualified person is present.

5. Treat laboratory reagents as if they are poisonous and corrosive.

6. Dispense reagents carefully. Dispose of laboratory reagents as directed.

7. Do not eat, drink, use tobacco, or apply cosmetics in the laboratory.

8. Report all incidents to the laboratory instructor.

9. Be familiar with the location and use of all safety equipment.

10. Become familiar with each laboratory assignment before coming to the laboratory.

11. Anticipate the common hazards that may be encountered in laboratory.

12. Become familiar with actions to be taken in the event of incidents in the laboratory.

_____   _____
student signature   date

_____   _____
laboratory instructor   date

In the space below, give any health information, such as pregnancy or other circumstance, that might help the laboratory instructor provide a safer environment for you, or that could aid the laboratory instructor in responding to an incident involving you in the laboratory.

1. I do/do not (circle one) expect to wear contact lenses during laboratory work. [*Note:* Goggles must still be worn when contact lenses are worn.]

2. List any known allergies to medication or other chemicals.

_____   _____   _____
name   section   date

Safety Quiz

1. On a separate sheet of paper, sketch the layout of the laboratory. (a) Note the location of each important safety feature (fire extinguisher, fume hood, eye wash, safety shower, and exits). (b) Draw a line from your work location, showing the path you would take to evacuate the laboratory. (c) Indicate the nearest location where you can activate the fire alarm.

2. Describe the steps to be taken in the event 10 mL of ethanol in a 50-mL beaker ignites in the laboratory.

3. Identify two important reasons for notifying the laboratory instructor of any incidents that occur in laboratory.

4. Why is unauthorized experimenting by a student in the laboratory not allowed?

5. Describe the steps to be taken in the laboratory if a large bottle of acetone (noncorrosive, nontoxic, highly volatile, water-soluble, flammable solvent) is broken and spilled.

6. According to the information in the MSDS (Figure 2), which hazardous category (health, fire, or reactivity) is of greatest concern for 1-propanol?

7. What is the first action to be taken in the event a person spills some reagent on himself or herself? What is the second action to be taken?

8. Identify three precautions to be taken before beginning the distillation of an organic liquid.

ISBN 0-87540-700-5

© 1997 by Chemical Education Resources

Classifying an Unknown Compound by Functional Group

Prepared by Jan William Simek, California Polytechnic State University

PURPOSE OF THE EXPERIMENT

Identify the functional group in an unknown organic compound by solubility tests and qualitative chemical tests.

BACKGROUND REQUIRED

You should be familiar with techniques for weighing, measuring by volume, and mixing in a test tube.

BACKGROUND INFORMATION

Organic qualitative analysis is an exercise in spectroscopy. Nuclear magnetic resonance spectroscopy and infrared spectroscopy are the major spectroscopic techniques used by organic chemists. However, much insight can be gained from using simple qualitative tests to determine the identity of unknowns. Structures of unknown compounds can be determined by comparing physical properties, performing functional group tests, and checking melting points of derivatives against those of known compounds reported in the literature. Solubility properties and chemical reactivity become apparent during these qualitative tests.

Organic qualitative analysis involves four types of tests.

1. *Measurement of physical properties* includes determining refractive index, boiling points, melting points, and density.
2. *Solubility tests* can suggest the size and polarity of an unknown compound and the presence of basic or acidic functional groups. A compound's solubility in aqueous acid or base involves ionization of the compound and, therefore, a chemical reaction. The salts produced are water-soluble.
3. *Chemical tests* transform an unknown into a different compound with an accompanying change in appearance. These tests are often called

classification tests because they identify the possible functional groups present.

4. *Formation of a solid derivative* is a critical step in identifying an unknown. Many compounds have similar physical properties and give similar results in qualitative tests. However, an unknown can undergo reaction to form another compound called a **derivative**. The melting point of the purified derivative allows identification of the unknown.

Unknown, monofunctional organic compounds can be classified into their functional group categories. For this experiment, the possible categories are alkane, alkene, alkyl halide, alcohol, phenol, amine, aldehyde, ketone, and carboxylic acid. Each of these functional groups has a unique combination of solubility and reactivity that allows it to be distinguished from the others. The results of solubility tests reduce the number of classification tests that must be conducted.

Solubility Tests

Organic compounds follow three interdependent rules of solubility:

1. *small organic molecules are more soluble in water than are large organic molecules;*

2. *polar organic molecules, especially those capable of hydrogen bonding, are more soluble in water than are nonpolar molecules; and*

3. *compounds in their ionic forms are more soluble in water than their neutral forms.*

For example, benzoic acid is not soluble in water, yet it is soluble in sodium hydroxide solution and in sodium hydrogen carbonate solution because these bases react with benzoic acid to form the water-soluble benzoate ion. The solubility of carboxylic acids and amines is so characteristic that solubility tests alone differentiate these functional groups from all the others in this experiment.

The solubility flowchart shown in Figure 1 provides the scheme for this experiment. The first test to perform on all unknowns is water solubility.

Water

Small, polar organic compounds such as alcohols, aldehydes, ketones, amines, carboxylic acids, and a few phenols are soluble in water. Water-soluble compounds are tested with pH paper to see if they are acidic or basic. A pH of 4 or lower indicates a carboxylic acid. A pH of 8 or higher indicates an amine.

Water-soluble compounds are tested with 5% sodium hydrogen carbonate ($NaHCO_3$) to determine whether or not they are carboxylic acids. Carboxylic acids react with $NaHCO_3$ to produce carbon dioxide bubbles, as shown below in Equation 3.

Large alcohols, aldehydes, ketones, amines, carboxylic acids, and phenols are not soluble in water. Alkanes, alkyl halides, and alkenes are not soluble in water, regardless of their size. These water-insoluble compounds are tested for their solubility in the following reagents.

5% Sodium Hydroxide

Water-insoluble compounds are first tested with 5% sodium hydroxide (NaOH). Sodium hydroxide is a strong base that ionizes strong or weak

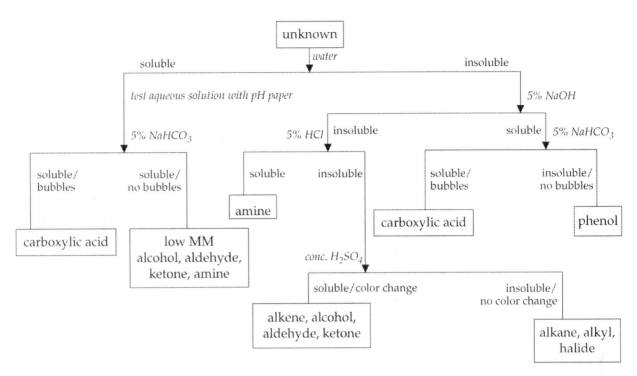

Figure 1
Solubility flowchart

acids. Thus, both carboxylic acids and phenols are converted to salts and dissolve in aqueous solution. Non-acidic compounds will not dissolve. The reactions of carboxylic acids and phenols are shown in Equations 1 and 2, respectively.

$$R-\overset{\overset{\text{O}}{\|}}{C}-OH \quad + \quad NaOH(aq) \quad \longrightarrow \quad R-\overset{\overset{\text{O}}{\|}}{C}-O^-Na^+ \quad + \quad H_2O \qquad (Eq.\ 1)$$
carboxylic acid   *water soluble*

$$\text{(substituted phenol)} \quad + \quad NaOH(aq) \quad \longrightarrow \quad \text{(phenolate)} \quad + \quad H_2O \qquad (Eq.\ 2)$$
substituted phenol   *water soluble*

5% Sodium Hydrogen Carbonate

Water-insoluble compounds that are soluble in 5% NaOH are then tested with 5% sodium hydrogen carbonate ($NaHCO_3$). Strongly acidic compounds such as carboxylic acids react with $NaHCO_3$ to form water-soluble salts, as shown in Equation 3. The reaction also produces bubbles of carbon dioxide (CO_2).

This test is commonly misinterpreted because the CO_2 bubbles are tiny. Careful observation is essential.

Phenols are less acidic than carboxylic acids and do not react with $NaHCO_3$ to form water-soluble salts. As a result, phenols are insoluble in 5% $NaHCO_3$.

$$R-\overset{\overset{\displaystyle O}{\|}}{C}-OH \;+\; NaHCO_3(aq) \;\longrightarrow\; R-\overset{\overset{\displaystyle O}{\|}}{C}-O^-Na^+ \;+\; H_2CO_3$$

carboxylic acid   water soluble

$$\longrightarrow\; R-\overset{\overset{\displaystyle O}{\|}}{C}-O^-Na^+ \;+\; H_2O \;+\; CO_2 \qquad (Eq.\;3)$$

water soluble   bubbles

5% Hydrochloric Acid

Water-insoluble compounds that are insoluble in 5% NaOH are tested with 5% hydrochloric acid (HCl). If a compound is soluble in 5% HCl, it is an amine. Amines are organic bases that react with HCl to form water-soluble amine salts, as shown in Equation 4.

$$R-\overset{\overset{\displaystyle ..}{N}}{\underset{\displaystyle R}{|}}-R \;+\; HCl(aq) \;\longrightarrow\; R-\overset{\overset{\displaystyle H}{|}}{\underset{\displaystyle R}{N^+}}-R\;\;Cl^- \qquad (Eq.\;4)$$

amine   water soluble

Concentrated Sulfuric Acid

Water-insoluble compounds that are insoluble in 5% HCl are tested with concentrated sulfuric acid (H_2SO_4). Virtually all organic compounds containing alkene functional groups or oxygen or nitrogen atoms are soluble in concentrated H_2SO_4. These functional groups typically react with H_2SO_4 to form new compounds. Only alkanes, alkyl halides, and some aromatic compounds are insoluble in H_2SO_4.

Classification Tests

Solubility tests alone can indicate whether an unknown compound in this experiment is a carboxylic acid, a phenol, or an amine. The other functional groups must be identified or verified by classification tests.

Classification tests are based on the chemical reactivity characteristic of particular functional groups. The results are intended to be visual and obvious, such as a color change, formation of a precipitate, or evolution of bubbles. Sometimes the results are difficult to interpret or are borderline between positive and negative.

There are two inviolable rules when performing classification tests. First, perform the test exactly as described. If the procedure says add 3 drops, do not add 4 or 5. Second, always perform tests in triplicate. Perform the test on a known compound that will result in a positive test (**known positive**); perform the test on a known compound that will result in a negative test (**known negative**); and perform the test on the unknown compound. This direct visual comparison of the results of testing the unknown against a known positive test and a known negative test confirms that the reagents are good and you are performing the test properly.

No classification test is always accurate in every case. A compound may produce a **false positive** if the test is positive even though the compound giving the test *is not* of the expected type. For example, some phenols give a positive test for aldehydes. A **false negative** occurs if the test is negative even though the compound undergoing the test *is* the expected type.

For example, less reactive aldehydes or very insoluble aldehydes may fail to give a positive test for aldehydes.

The following classification tests are performed in this experiment and are among those tests commonly performed in qualitative organic analysis.

Bromine in Cyclohexane

Alkenes react with bromine (Br_2) in cyclohexane, an orange solution, to produce colorless vicinal dibromides, as shown in Equation 5. This test is commonly used for water-insoluble compounds. Alkenes with strong electron-withdrawing groups may fail to react. Phenols, phenyl ethers, and some aldehydes and ketones also react to decolorize bromine in cyclohexane.

$$\underset{\text{alkene}}{\text{C=C}} \quad + \quad \underset{\text{orange}}{Br_2} \quad \xrightarrow{\text{cyclohexane solvent}} \quad \underset{\text{colorless}}{\overset{Br}{\underset{Br}{-C-C-}}} \qquad \text{(Eq. 5)}$$

Potassium Permanganate

Alkenes are oxidized to diols by dilute potassium permanganate ($KMnO_4$), as shown in Equation 6. The purple color of $KMnO_4$ disappears and is replaced by the brown color of manganese dioxide (MnO_2). Because $KMnO_4$ is a strong oxidizing agent, aldehydes, some primary and secondary alcohols, phenols, and aromatic amines can also react.

$$\underset{\text{alkene}}{\text{C=C}} \quad + \quad \underset{\text{purple}}{KMnO_4(aq)} \quad \longrightarrow \quad \overset{OH\ OH}{-C-C-} \quad + \quad \underset{\text{brown}}{MnO_2} \qquad \text{(Eq. 6)}$$

Silver Nitrate in Ethanol

Alkyl halides react with silver nitrate ($AgNO_3$) in ethanol by the S_N1 mechanism. Tertiary, allylic, and benzylic halides give an immediate precipitate at room temperature, as shown in Equation 7. Secondary halides require several minutes to give a precipitate, and primary halides require hours.

$$\underset{\text{alkyl halide}}{R-X} \ + \ AgNO_3 \ + \ HOCH_2CH_3 \ \longrightarrow \ R-OCH_2CH_3 \ + \ HNO_3 \ + \ \underset{\text{precipitate}}{AgX(s)} \qquad \text{(Eq. 7)}$$

Sodium Iodide in Acetone

A saturated solution of sodium iodide (NaI) in acetone reacts rapidly with primary, allylic, and benzylic chlorides or bromides by the S_N2 mechanism. Secondary halides react slowly, while tertiary halides are unreactive. The corresponding alkyl iodides and a precipitate of sodium chloride or sodium bromide result, as shown in Equation 8.

$$\underset{X\,=\,Br,\,Cl}{R-X} \quad + \quad NaI \quad \xrightarrow{\text{acetone}} \quad R-I \quad + \quad \underset{\text{precipitate}}{NaX(s)} \qquad \text{(Eq. 8)}$$

Beilstein Test

An organic halide placed on a copper wire and then exposed to a flame produces the blue–green flame of the volatile copper halide.

TCICA Test

In acid solution, 1,3,5-trichloroisocyanuric acid (TCICA) slowly releases chlorine, which is an oxidizing agent. The reaction is rapid in the presence of an oxidizable compound such as a primary or secondary alcohol, as shown in Equation 9. The product is isocyanuric acid, which is very soluble in water but precipitates from the solvent acetonitrile. The time it takes for isocyanuric acid precipitate to appear is characteristic of the type of alcohol. Secondary alcohols react fastest, within 15–30 seconds; primary alcohols produce a precipitate usually within 3–7 minutes, although some can take up to 20 minutes; tertiary alcohols are not oxidizable at room temperature and produce no precipitate within an hour.

$$3 \text{ alcohol} + \text{TCICA} \xrightarrow[\text{CH}_3\text{CN}]{\text{1 drop HCl (aq)}} 3 \text{ carbonyl compound} + \text{isocyanuric acid precipitate} + 3 \text{ HCl} \quad (\text{Eq. 9})$$

Iron(III) Chloride

Many phenols react with iron(III) chloride ($FeCl_3$) solution to give brightly colored complexes. Many of these complexes are short-lived; the color may fade soon after it forms. Some phenols may not react at all, so a negative iron(III) chloride test is inconclusive. Aldehydes or ketones with significant enolic character can also give colored complexes with $FeCl_3$.

Bromine in Water

Phenols are activated toward electrophilic aromatic substitution and react with Br_2 in the absence of catalyst, as shown in Equation 10. The disappearance of the bromine color, and often the appearance of a precipitate of the brominated phenol, constitute a positive test. Other activated aromatic compounds, such as phenyl ethers and anilines, can also react with Br_2.

$$\text{phenol} + n \text{ Br}_2 \longrightarrow \text{phenol-Br}_n + n \text{ HBr} \quad (\text{Eq. 10})$$

phenol   orange   usually
              $n = 1\text{–}3$ colorless

2,4-Dinitrophenylhydrazine

Aldehydes and ketones rapidly form yellow, orange, or red precipitates with 2,4-dinitrophenylhydrazine (DNP) reagent, as shown in Equation 11.

aldehyde or
ketone

2,4-dinitrophenylhydrazine

a 2,4-dinitrophenylhydrazone
(a 2,4-DNP derivative)
red to yellow solid

$$R\text{C(O)}R' + H_2NNH\text{-}C_6H_3(NO_2)_2 \xrightarrow{H^+} \text{(2,4-DNP derivative)} + H_2O \quad (Eq.\ 11)$$

Tollens Silver Mirror Test

Aldehydes are easily oxidized by silver ion, a mild and selective oxidizing agent. This reaction works best in basic solution. However, silver salts precipitate in basic solution unless ammonia is present to form the diaminesilver(I) complex ion, as shown in Equation 12. As shown in Equation 13, silver ion is reduced to silver metal, which plates out on *clean* glass, producing a mirror.

Some aldehydes are slow to react and require a few minutes to produce a silver mirror. Occasionally, the silver appears as a heavy black precipitate instead of adhering to the glass as a mirror.

$$Ag^+ + 2NH_3\ (aq) \longrightarrow Ag(NH_3)_2^+\ (aq) \quad (Eq.\ 12)$$

$$R\text{-}\overset{O}{\overset{\|}{C}}\text{-}H + 2\ Ag(NH_3)_2^+\ OH^- \xrightarrow[H_2O]{NH_3}$$

$$R\text{-}\overset{O}{\overset{\|}{C}}\text{-}O^-NH_4^+ + 2Ag\ (s) + 3NH_3\ (aq) + H_2O \quad (Eq.\ 13)$$

aldehyde

In this experiment, you will identify two unknowns by functional groups using solubility tests and classification tests. Tables 1 and 2 list known positive and known negative compounds for solubility tests and classification tests.

Equipment

250-mL beaker	microspatula
Bunsen burner	glass stirring rod
copper wire	6–10 test tubes, 15 × 125-mm
10-mL graduated cylinder	6–10 test tubes, 10 × 75-mm
hot plate	test tube rack
pH paper	thermometer, −10 to 260 °C
1.0-mL transfer pipet	tongs
Pasteur pipet, with latex bulb	

Table 1 *Known positive and known negative test compounds for solubility tests*

	liquid compound		solid compound	
solvent	positive test	negative test	positive test	negative test
water	glycerol	benzaldehyde	2,2-dimethyl-1,3-propanediol	benzoic acid
5% NaOH	eugenol	benzaldehyde	vanillin	biphenyl
5% NaHCO$_3$	octanoic acid	benzaldehyde	benzoic acid	biphenyl
5% HCl	diisobutylamine	benzaldehyde	4-N,N-dimethyl-aminobenzaldehyde	biphenyl
H$_2$SO$_4$	cyclohexene	cyclohexane	vanillin	biphenyl

Table 2 *Known positive and known negative test compounds for functional group classification tests*

functional group	test	liquid compound		solid compound	
		positive test	negative test	positive test	negative test
alkane	by exclusion—alkanes are insoluble in aqueous reagents and in H_2SO_4, and are negative for alkyl halide tests				
alkene	bromine/cyclohexane	cyclohexene	cyclohexane	none	none
	$KMnO_4$	cyclohexene	cyclohexane	none	none
alkyl halide	Beilstein	1-bromohexane	2-propanol	none	none
	$AgNO_3$/ethanol	2-chloro-2-methylpropane	2-propanol	none	none
	NaI/acetone	1-bromohexane	2-propanol	none	none
alcohol	TCICA test	2-propanol	2-chloro-2-methylpropane	2,2-dimethyl-1,3-propanediol	benzoic acid
phenol (to confirm)	$FeCl_3$	eugenol	benzyl alcohol	vanillin	benzoic acid
	bromine/H_2O	2-isopropylphenol	2-propanol	2-naphthol	benzoic acid
amine	soluble in HCl—this group is determined by the series of solubility tests: if water soluble, solution is basic to pH paper; if water-insoluble, then soluble in HCl				
aldehyde	2,4-DNP	benzaldehyde	1-butanol	piperonal	benzoic acid
	Tollens test	benzaldehyde	1-butanol	piperonal	4-methoxy-acetophenone
ketone	2,4-DNP	acetone	1-butanol	4-methoxy-acetophenone	benzoic acid
carboxylic acid	soluble in NaOH and in $NaHCO_3$—this group is determined by the series of solubility tests: if water-soluble, solution is acidic to pH paper; if water-insoluble, then soluble in NaOH and soluble in $NaHCO_3$ with gas evolution				

Reagents and Properties (amounts estimated for two unknowns)

substance	quantity	molar mass (g/mol)	mp (°C)	bp (°C)
acetone	10 mL	58.1		56
acetonitrile	1 mL	41.0		82
ammonium hydroxide, conc.	6 mL	17.0		
benzaldehyde	1 mL	106.1		179
benzoic acid	1 g	122.1	123	
benzyl alcohol	0.2 mL	108.1		205
biphenyl	0.5 g	154.2	72	255
bromine in water, satd.	6 mL	159.8		
1-bromohexane	0.2 mL	165.1		158
1-butanol	0.5 mL	74.1		118
2-chloro-2-methylpropane	0.2 mL	92.6		52
cyclohexane	8 mL	84.2		81
cyclohexene	0.25 mL	82.2		83
diethyl ether	6 mL	74.1		35
diisobutylamine	0.2 mL	129.2		139
4-(dimethyl-amino) benzaldehyde	0.1 g	149.2	75	
2,2-dimethyl-1,3-propanediol	0.2 g	104.2	127	
2,4-dinitrophenylhydrazine	2 mL			
ethanol, 95%	6 mL	46.1		78
eugenol	0.2 mL	164.2		254
iron(III) chloride, 3%	1 mL	162.2		
glycerol	0.2 mL	92.1	20	182
hydrochloric acid, 5%	6 mL	36.5		
2-isopropylphenol	0.2 mL	136.2	16	213
4-methoxyacetophenone	0.2 g	150.2	38	
2-methyl-2-propanol	0.5 mL	74.1	26	83
2-naphthol	0.1 g	144.2	123	286
nitric acid, 3M	10 mL	63.0		
octanoic acid	0.2 mL	144.2	16	237
piperonal	0.2 g	150.1	37	264
potassium permanganate, 1%	0.5 mL	158.0		
2-propanol	0.5 mL	60.1		82
silver nitrate, 5%	12 mL	169.9		
silver nitrate in ethanol, 2%	6 mL	169.9		
sodium hydrogen carbonate, 5%	6 mL	84.0		
sodium hydroxide, 5%	6 mL	40.0		
sodium iodide in acetone	6 mL	149.9		
sulfuric acid, concentrated	6 mL	98.1		
TCICA in acetonitrile, 3%	3 mL	232.4	251	
unknown organic compound	1 mL/1 g			
vanillin	0.5 g	152.2	83	

Preview

- Perform the water solubility test on the known positive, known negative, and unknown
- Perform subsequent solubility tests
- If the solubility tests point to a carboxylic acid or amine, the classification is complete
- If the solubility tests suggest any other functional groups, perform the classification tests appropriate to those groups until the unknown is narrowed to only one functional group

---

PROCEDURE

CAUTION

Wear departmentally approved safety goggles at all times while in the chemistry laboratory.

　　　Always use caution in the laboratory. Many chemicals are potentially harmful. Follow safety precautions given for all reagents used in this experiment. Prevent contact with your eyes, skin, and clothing. Avoid ingesting any of the reagents.

Perform all tests in triplicate using an unknown, a known positive, and a known negative. Mix well to make certain that liquid samples are not floating at the meniscus. Allow several minutes for compounds to dissolve. Be patient and observe closely.

　　Conduct the solubility tests following the pattern shown in Figure 1 earlier in this experiment. *Verify your solubility test results with your laboratory instructor before performing the classification tests.* Conduct the classification tests indicated by your solubility results. Use clean test tubes for each test.

1. Performing the Water Solubility Test

CAUTION

Unknowns may be flammable, toxic, corrosive, or irritating. Keep away from flames or other heat sources.

Add 2–3 drops of a liquid sample or about 50 mg of a solid sample to 1 mL of distilled or deionized water in a test tube. Tap the tube with your finger to mix or stir gently with a glass stirring rod. Record the sample as soluble or insoluble.

　　If the unknown is water-soluble, test the solution with pH paper. Also test the pH of water as a control.

　　A solution at pH 4 or lower suggests a carboxylic acid. A solution at pH 8 or higher suggests an amine.

2. Performing the 5% Sodium Hydroxide Solubility Test

CAUTION

Sodium hydroxide (NaOH) and hydrochloric acid (HCl) are toxic and corrosive.

If your compound is water-soluble, proceed to Part 3.

For water-insoluble compounds, add 2–3 drops of a liquid sample or about 50 mg of a solid sample to 1 mL of 5% NaOH in a test tube. Tap the tube with your finger to mix or stir gently with a glass stirring rod. Record the sample as soluble or insoluble.

To verify that a compound has dissolved, add 5% HC1 to the NaOH mixture until the solution is acidic to pH paper. Look for a precipitate, indicating that the water-soluble salt has converted back into the water-insoluble compound.

Solubility in NaOH indicates either a carboxylic acid or phenol.

3. Performing the 5% Sodium Hydrogen Carbonate Solubility Test

A. For Water-Soluble Compounds

Put 2–3 drops of liquid sample or about 50 mg of solid sample in a dry test tube. Add 1 mL of 5% sodium hydrogen carbonate (NaHCO₃). Do not stir. Watch for bubbles at the interface of the phases. Then tap the tube with your finger to mix or stir gently with a glass stirring rod. Record the sample as soluble or insoluble.

Generation of bubbles and solubility indicates a carboxylic acid. Solubility without generation of bubbles indicates a low molar mass alcohol, aldehyde, ketone, or amine. Conduct classification tests to determine which functional group is present.

CAUTION

Diethyl ether (ether) is highly flammable and toxic. Keep away from flames or other heat sources. Use a *fume hood*.

If no bubbles were observed, put 2–3 drops of liquid sample or about 50 mg of solid sample in a dry test tube. Using a ***fume hood,*** add about 1 mL of ether. Then immediately add 1 mL of 5% NaHCO₃. Observe whether or not bubbles are generated at the ether–water interface.

Generation of bubbles indicates a carboxylic acid.

B. For Water-Insoluble Compounds

Put 2–3 drops of liquid sample or about 50 mg of solid sample in a dry test tube. Add 1 mL of 5% sodium hydrogen carbonate (NaHCO₃). Do not stir. Watch for bubbles at the interface of the phases. Then tap the tube with your finger to mix or stir gently with a glass stirring rod. Record the sample as soluble or insoluble.

Generation of bubbles or solubility indicates a carboxylic acid.

If the compound is not soluble in NaHCO₃ but is soluble in NaOH, it is likely a phenol. Confirm the presence of phenol with a phenol classification test.

4. Performing the 5% Hydrochloric Acid Solubility Test

CAUTION

Hydrochloric acid (HCl) is toxic and corrosive.

For compounds insoluble in water and insoluble in 5% NaOH, add 2–3 drops of a liquid sample or about 50 mg of a solid sample to 1 mL of 5% HCl in a test tube. Tap the tube with your finger to mix or stir gently with a glass stirring rod. Record the sample as soluble or insoluble.

If the compound is soluble in 5% HCl, it is most likely an amine.

5. Performing the Concentrated Sulfuric Acid Solubility Test

CAUTION

Concentrated sulfuric acid (H_2SO_4) is toxic and oxidizing. Use a *fume hood* when working with H_2SO_4.

If the compound is insoluble in 5% HCl and 5% NaOH, add 2-3 drops of a liquid sample or about 50 mg of a solid sample to 1 mL of concentrated sulfuric acid (H_2SO_4) in a dry test tube. Tap the tube with your finger to mix or stir gently with a glass stirring rod. Do not use a metal spatula.

Record the sample as soluble or insoluble. Interpret a color change or a precipitate as soluble.

If the compound is soluble in H_2SO_4, the sample is an alkene, an alcohol, an aldehyde, or a ketone. Conduct classification tests for each compound type.

If the compound is insoluble in H_2SO_4, the sample is an alkane or an alkyl halide. Conduct classification tests for alkyl halides.

If alkyl halide tests are negative, the compound is an alkane.

6. Performing the Bromine in Cyclohexane Test for Alkenes

CAUTION

Bromine (Br_2) is toxic and oxidizing. It causes severe burns. Always use a *fume hood* when working with Br_2. Acetone and cyclohexane are flammable and irritating. Keep away from flames or other heat sources.

Place 1 mL of cyclohexane in a small test tube. Add 3 drops of Br_2/H_2O. Mix until the bromine color appears in the top cyclohexane layer.

For liquid samples, add 2 drops of sample to the Br_2/H_2O. Tap the tube with your finger to mix or stir gently with a glass stirring rod. Note and record whether or not the orange color disappears.

For solid samples, place 30 mg of solid into a test tube. Add 5 drops of acetone. Add the acetone solution to the Br_2/H_2O. Tap the tube with your finger to mix or stir gently with a glass stirring rod. Note and record whether or not the orange color disappears.

NOTE 1: Phenols, phenyl ethers, and some aldehydes and ketones may test positive.

If the orange color disappears quickly, the sample may be an alkene. [NOTE 1]

7. Performing the Potassium Permanganate Test for Alkenes

CAUTION

1% Potassium permanganate ($KMnO_4$) is corrosive and oxidizing.

If your sample is water-soluble, place 1–2 mL of water into a small test tube. If your sample is water-insoluble, place 1–2 mL of 95% ethanol into a small test tube.

Add 2 drops of a liquid sample or about 30 mg of a solid sample. Add 2 drops of 1% $KMnO_4$. Tap the tube with your finger to mix or stir gently

NOTE 2: The brown color or precipitate may not appear. Aldehydes, some primary and secondary alcohols, phenols, and aromatic amines may test positive.

with a glass stirring rod. Let the mixture stand 10–20 s. Note and record whether or not the purple color disappears.

If the purple color disappears and a brown color or precipitate appears, the compound may be an alkene. [NOTE 2]

8. Performing the Silver Nitrate in Ethanol Test for Alkyl Halides

CAUTION

Silver nitrate (AgNO₃) in ethanol is flammable, toxic, and oxidizing. It also stains the skin. Keep away from flames or other heat sources.

Place 1 mL of 2% $AgNO_3$ in ethanol into a small test tube.

For liquid samples, add 2 drops of sample to the 2% $AgNO_3$. Tap the tube with your finger to mix or stir gently with a glass stirring rod.

For solid samples, place 30 mg of solid into a test tube. Add 5 drops of ethanol. Add this ethanol solution to the 2% $AgNO_3$ in ethanol. Tap the tube with your finger to mix or stir gently with a glass stirring rod. Note and record whether or not a precipitate forms.

An immediate precipitate indicates a tertiary, allylic, or benzylic halide.

9. Performing the Sodium Iodide in Acetone Test for Alkyl Halides

CAUTION

Sodium iodide (NaI) in acetone is flammable and irritating. Keep away from flames or other heat sources.

Place *exactly* 1.0 mL of NaI in acetone into a small test tube. Add 3 drops of a liquid sample. Tap the tube with your finger to mix or stir gently with a glass stirring rod. Allow the tube to stand 3–6 min at room temperature. Note and record whether or not a precipitate forms.

A white precipitate indicates a primary, allylic, or benzylic halide.

10. Performing the Beilstein Flame Test for Alkyl Halides

CAUTION

Make certain no flammable compounds are near when using a flame.

Obtain a coiled piece of pure copper wire from your laboratory instructor. Light a Bunsen burner. Using tongs, hold the copper wire in the flame to burn the wire clean. Remove the wire from the flame and allow the wire to cool for 1–2 min.

Use a dropper to put 1 drop of liquid sample or a few mg of a solid sample on the coiled wire. Quickly insert the wire into the lower part of the flame. Note and record the color of the flame.

A blue–green color indicates the presence of chlorine, bromine, or iodine in the compound.

11. Performing the TCICA Test for Alcohols

CAUTION

1,3,5-trichloroisocyanuric acid (TCICA) is corrosive and oxidizing. Acetonitrile is toxic. 5% Hydrochloric acid (HCl) is toxic and corrosive.

Place 0.5 mL of the TCICA test solution into a small test tube. Add 1 drop of 5% HCl. Tap the tube with your finger to mix or stir gently with a glass stirring rod.

For liquid samples, add 1 drop of the sample. Tap the tube with your finger to mix or stir gently with a glass stirring rod.

For solid samples, dissolve about 20 mg of solid in 1–2 drops of acetonitrile. Add this solution to the TCICA/HCl solution.

Note and record whether or not a precipitate forms.

The formation of a precipitate within 1 min indicates a secondary alcohol; the formation of a precipitate between 3–20 min indicates a primary alcohol.

12. Performing the Iron(III) Chloride Test for Phenols

CAUTION

Iron(III) chloride (FeCl₃) is toxic and corrosive. Ethanol is flammable and toxic. Keep away from flames or other heat sources.

Place 1 mL of 95% ethanol into a small test tube. Add 2 drops of a liquid sample or about 30 mg of a solid. Add 3–5 drops of 3% $FeCl_3$. Tap the tube with your finger to mix or stir gently with a glass stirring rod. Note and record any formation of a brightly colored solution.

NOTE 3: Some aldehydes or ketones also give colored complexes with $FeCl_3$.

The presence of bright color, even briefly, indicates a phenol. [NOTE 3]

13. Performing the Bromine in Water Test for Phenols

CAUTION

Bromine (Br₂) is toxic and oxidizing. It causes severe burns. Always use a *fume hood* when working with Br₂. Ethanol is flammable. Keep away from flames or other heat sources.

Place 1 mL of 95% ethanol into a small test tube. Add 5 drops of a liquid sample or about 30 mg of a solid.

Add a drop of water. Tap the tube with your finger to mix or stir gently with a glass stirring rod.

Add 1 drop of Br_2/H_2O. Tap the tube with your finger to mix or stir gently with a glass stirring rod.

Note and record whether or not the orange color disappears.

The disappearance of the orange color indicates a phenol.

14. Performing the 2,4-DNP Test for Aldehydes and Ketones

CAUTION

2,4-Dinitrophenylhydrazine (2,4-DNP) solution is corrosive and irritating. It stains skin and clothing.

For liquid samples, place 1 drop of sample into a clean, dry test tube. Add up to 20 drops of 2,4-DNP solution. Tap the tube with your finger to mix or stir gently with a glass stirring rod.

For solid samples, add about 30 mg of solid into a clean, dry test tube. Add 0.5 mL of ethanol. Tap the tube with your finger to mix or stir gently with a glass stirring rod. If the unknown does not dissolve, prepare a warm-water bath by placing 175–200 mL of tap water into a 250-mL beaker.

Use a hot plate to heat the water to 40 °C. Place the test tube into a warm-water bath and swirl the tube until the unknown is dissolved. Cool the solution to room temperature. Add up to 20 drops of 2,4-DNP solution. Tap the tube with your finger to mix or stir gently with a glass stirring rod.

Note and record whether or not a precipitate forms.

An immediate, brightly colored precipitate indicates an aldehyde or ketone.

15. Performing the Tollens Silver Mirror Test for Aldehydes

CAUTION

Silver nitrate (AgNO₃) and nitric acid (HNO₃) are toxic and oxidizing. AgNO₃ will stain skin and clothing. Sodium hydroxide (NaOH) is toxic and corrosive. Ammonium hydroxide (NH₄OH) is corrosive and a lachrymator. Use a *fume hood* when working with NH₄OH.

NOTE 4: The test tubes must be *very clean* for a silver mirror to form.

Thoroughly wash 3 test tubes with soap and water. [NOTE 4] Rinse the test tubes with distilled or deionized water. Do not rinse the test tubes with acetone.

CAUTION

Prepare the Tollens reagent just before use. A highly explosive precipitate forms upon standing several hours. When you are finished with the Tollens tests, rinse each test tube with ~1 mL of 3*M* HNO₃ to destroy any residual Tollens reagent.

Add 2 mL of 5% AgNO₃ to each test tube. Add 1 mL of 5% NaOH solution to each test tube. In a *fume hood,* add concentrated NH₄OH dropwise, with mixing, until the black Ag₂O precipitate just dissolves.

For liquid samples, add 1 drop of liquid to the Tollens reagent. Tap the tube with your finger to mix or stir gently with a glass stirring rod. Allow the solution to stand for 5 min.

For solid samples, dissolve about 30 mg of solid in 0.5 mL ethanol. If necessary, heat the solution in a 40 °C warm-water bath to dissolve the sample. Cool the solution to room temperature. Add the sample solution to the Tollens reagent. Tap the tube with your finger to mix or stir gently with a glass stirring rod. Allow the solution to stand for 5 min.

Record whether or not a silver mirror or a black precipitate forms.

Formation of a silver mirror or heavy black precipitate indicates an aldehyde.

If there is no visible change within 5 min, place the tube in a 80 °C hot-water bath for 15 s. Allow the solution to stand for 5 min.

When the tests are complete, pour the contents of each tube into the "Recovered Silver Solution" container, provided by your laboratory instructor. Rinse each test tube with ~1 mL of 3*M* HNO₃ to destroy any residual Tollens reagent. Add this rinse to the "Recovered Silver Solution" container. Wash the test tubes with soap and water.

16. Cleaning Up

Use the labeled collection containers provided by your laboratory instructor.

Turn in your remaining unknown to your laboratory instructor. Clean your glassware with soap or detergent.

CAUTION

Wash your hands with soap or detergent before leaving the laboratory.

POST-LABORATORY QUESTIONS

1. Record the solubility results for each unknown that you tested. Describe your observations and briefly explain your conclusions.

2. Record the results of the classification tests that you conducted for each unknown you tested. Describe your observations and briefly explain your conclusions.

3. For each of your unknowns, list the functional group to which it belongs next to its identification code.

4. You suspect that your unknown contains halogen, so you perform the silver nitrate in ethanol test and the sodium iodide in acetone test, both of which are negative. Do these results prove that your compound does not contain a halogen? Briefly explain.

Name   _Section_   _Date_

Pre-Laboratory Assignment

1. Why is it important to rinse test tubes used in the Tollens test with $3M$ HNO_3?

2. What risks do you run by not performing the qualitative tests in triplicate?

3. (a) Why is it important to have clean test tubes before running a test?

(b) Before which tests should acetone _not_ be used to clean the test tubes?

4. Why is water solubility the first test to run?

5. Why run solubility tests before running the functional group classification tests?

6. Determine the functional group present in these unknowns:

(a) Unknown A is soluble in water and gives bubbles with 5% $NaHCO_3$.

(b) Unknown B is insoluble in water, insoluble in 5% NaOH, but soluble in 5% HCl.

(c) Unknown C is insoluble in water, insoluble in 5% NaOH, insoluble in 5% HCl, soluble with a color change in conc. H_2SO_4, and decolorizes both $KMnO_4$ (aq) and bromine in cyclohexane.

(d) Unknown D is soluble in water, does not produce bubbles with 5% $NaHCO_3$, gives a precipitate with 2,4-DNP, and gives a silver mirror in the Tollens test.

7. In each of the following cases, describe the *next* test you would perform.

(a) Unknown X is insoluble in water, 5% NaOH, 5% HCl, and conc. H_2SO_4.

(b) Unknown Y is insoluble in water, soluble in 5% NaOH, and insoluble in 5% $NaHCO_3$.

(c) Unknown Z is insoluble in water, insoluble in 5% NaOH, insoluble in 5% HCl, and soluble in conc. H_2SO_4.

8. If your unknown is soluble in water and does not produce bubbles with 5% $NaHCO_3$, what steps would you follow to determine if your unknown is an amine?

Identifying an Unknown Aldehyde or Ketone

Prepared by Jan William Simek, California Polytechnic State University

PURPOSE OF THE EXPERIMENT

Identify an unknown aldehyde or ketone by qualitative chemical tests and by comparison of a derivative melting point to literature values.

BACKGROUND REQUIRED

You should be familiar with melting point measurement, refractive index measurement, recrystallization, and vacuum filtration.

BACKGROUND INFORMATION

Organic qualitative analysis is an exercise in spectroscopy. Nuclear magnetic resonance spectroscopy and infrared spectroscopy are the major spectroscopic techniques used by organic chemists. However, much insight can be gained from using simple qualitative tests to determine the identity of unknowns. Structures of unknown compounds can be determined by comparing physical properties, performing functional group tests, and checking melting points of derivatives against those of known compounds reported in the literature. Solubility properties and chemical reactivity become apparent during these qualitative tests.

Classification Tests

Qualitative tests are called **classification tests** because they support or refute the presence of certain structural features of a molecule. For example, certain classification tests indicate the presence of a particular functional group, such as an aldehyde or an alcohol. Other tests indicate a functional group that easily undergoes oxidation. Still other tests show the presence of an acidic hydrogen or other specific feature. A feature common to all classification tests is that the results of a test are readily visible. For example, the color may change, a precipitate may form, a gas may evolve, or a separate layer may form.

There are two inviolable rules when performing classification tests. First, perform the test exactly as described. If the procedure says add

3 drops, do not add 4 or 5. Second, always perform tests in triplicate. Perform the test on a known compound that will result in a positive test (**known positive**); perform the test on a known compound that will result in a negative test (**known negative**); and perform the test on the unknown compound. This direct visual comparison of the results of testing the unknown against a known positive test and a known negative test confirms that the reagents are good and you are performing the test properly.

No classification test is always accurate in every case. A compound may produce a **false positive** if the test is positive even though the compound giving the test *is not* of the expected type. For example, some phenols give a positive test for aldehydes. A **false negative** occurs if the test is negative even though the compound undergoing the test *is* the expected type. For example, less reactive aldehydes or very insoluble aldehydes may fail to give a positive test for aldehydes.

The following classification tests are performed in this experiment and are among those tests commonly done when an unknown is thought to be an aldehyde or ketone.

Tollens Silver Mirror Test

Aldehydes are easily oxidized by silver ion, a mild and selective oxidizing agent. This reaction works best in basic solution. However, silver salts precipitate in basic solution unless ammonia is present to form the diaminesilver(I) complex ion, as shown in Equation 1. Equation 2 shows that silver ion is reduced to silver metal, which plates out on *clean* glass, producing a mirror.

$$Ag^+ + 2\,NH_3(aq) \rightarrow Ag(NH_3)_2{}^+(aq) \qquad \text{(Eq. 1)}$$

$$\underset{\text{aldehyde}}{R-\overset{\overset{\displaystyle O}{\|}}{C}-H} + 2\,Ag(NH_3)_2{}^+\,OH^- \xrightarrow[\text{H}_2\text{O}]{NH_3} R-\overset{\overset{\displaystyle O}{\|}}{C}-O^-\;NH_4{}^+ + 2\,Ag\,(s) + 3NH_3\,(aq) + H_2O$$
$$\text{(Eq. 2)}$$

Some aldehydes are slow to react and require a few minutes to produce a silver mirror. Occasionally, silver appears as a heavy black precipitate instead of adhering to the glass as a mirror. Questionable results are verified using another test, such as the Schiff test.

Schiff Test

In a complex series of reactions that is not completely understood, Schiff reagent reacts only with aldehydes to produce a purple fuchsia solution. A faint pink color results from the initial reagent and does not constitute a positive test. The Schiff test is the most sensitive test for aldehydes. However, the Schiff test is subject to giving false positives and false negatives.

Iodoform Test

Methyl ketones can be oxidized with iodine (I_2) in basic solution to generate iodoform, a bright yellow solid, as shown in Equation 3. Elemental I_2 is generated by oxidizing iodide (I^-) with hypochlorite (OCl^-), as shown in Equation 4.

$$R-\overset{\overset{\textstyle O}{\|}}{C}-CH_3 \xrightarrow[\text{NaOH}]{\text{excess } I_2} R-\overset{\overset{\textstyle O}{\|}}{C}-O^- + CHI_3(s) \qquad \text{(Eq. 3)}$$

methyl ketone

$$2\,I^-(aq) + OCl^-(aq) + H_2O(\ell) \rightarrow I_2 + Cl^-(aq) + 2\,OH^-(aq) \qquad \text{(Eq. 4)}$$

Methyl ketones are not the only compounds that result in a positive iodoform test. Secondary alcohols having an adjacent methyl group are oxidized to methyl ketones by the iodoform test reagent. These methyl ketones then give a positive iodoform test.

Acetone is a methyl ketone, so acetone must not be used to rinse test tubes before the iodoform test. Also, a false negative can occur with methyl ketones that have a very low solubility in the iodoform test reagent.

Derivatives

Unknown compounds can be reacted with various reagents to give new compounds called **derivatives**. Stable, crystalline derivatives can be used to help identify unknowns by comparing the derivative melting point with literature values. For any derivative, purity is more important than yield. Only a small amount of derivative is needed for a melting point, but it must be pure to give accurate results.

Several derivatives can be made to confirm an unknown aldehyde or ketone. One such derivative, a semicarbazone, is rapidly formed and easily crystallized.

A **semicarbazone** is made by reacting a semicarbazide with an aldehyde or ketone, as shown in Equation 5. Semicarbazide is produced by reacting semicarbazide hydrochloride with sodium acetate, as shown in Equation 6.

$$\underset{\substack{\text{aldehyde}\\\text{or ketone}}}{R-\overset{\overset{\textstyle O}{\|}}{\underset{}{C}}-R'} + \underset{\text{semicarbazide}}{H_2NHN-\overset{\overset{\textstyle O}{\|}}{C}-NH_2} \xrightarrow{H^+} \underset{\text{a semicarbazone}}{R-\overset{\overset{\textstyle C=N-NH}{\underset{}{}}}{C}-R'} + H_2O(\ell) \qquad \text{(Eq. 5)}$$

$$\underset{\text{semicarbazide hydrochloride}}{Cl^-\overset{+}{H_3}NHN-\overset{\overset{\textstyle O}{\|}}{C}-NH_2} + CH_3COO^-Na^+ \xrightarrow{H^+} \underset{\text{semicarbazide}}{H_2NHN-\overset{\overset{\textstyle O}{\|}}{C}-NH_2} + CH_3COOH + NaCl$$

$$\text{(Eq. 6)}$$

In this experiment, you will analyze an unknown aldehyde or ketone by performing qualitative tests, by measuring the refractive index, and by preparing a derivative and measuring its melting point. You will identify your unknown by comparing its data with the data shown in Table 1 on the next page.

Table 1 *Physical properties of aldehydes and ketones*

name	bp (°C)	n_D^{20}	semicarbazone mp (°C)
aldehydes			
2-furaldehyde	161	1.5260	202
cyclohexane-carbaldehyde	162	1.4500	173
3-cyclohexene-carbaldehyde	164	1.4745	154
octanal	171	1.4183	101
phenylacetaldehyde	194	1.5290	156
salicylaldehyde	196	1.5720	231
p-tolualdehyde	204	1.5460	221
2-phenylpropanal	205	1.5170	154
o-chlorobenzaldehyde	208	1.5660	233
3-phenylpropanal	224	1.5230	127
m-methoxybenzaldehyde	230	1.5530	205
cinnamaldehyde	252	1.6220	215
ketones			
2-heptanone	150	1.4080	127
cyclohexanone	155	1.4500	166
2-methylcyclohexanone	163	1.4480	195
3-methylcyclohexanone	169	1.4450	180
cycloheptanone	181	1.4610	163
5-nonanone	187	1.4190	90
acetophenone	200	1.5325	198
propiophenone	218	1.5258	174
butyrophenone	230	1.5195	187
valerophenone	242	1.5143	166

Equipment

250-mL beaker
400-mL beaker
Büchner funnel, with adapter*
125-mL filter flask,
   with vacuum tubing
filter paper
glass stirring rod
10-mL graduated cylinder
*or Hirsch funnel

100-mL graduated cylinder
melting point capillary tube
microspatula
4 Pasteur pipets, with latex bulb
1.0-mL pipet
12 test tubes, 13 × 100-mm
thermometer, –10 to 260 °C
watch glass

Reagents and Properties

substance	quantity	molar mass (g/mol)	mp (°C)	bp (°C)
ammonium hydroxide, conc.	1 mL			
2-butanone	0.25 mL	72.1		80
95% ethanol	5–10 mL	46.0		78
iodoform test solution	6 mL			

substance	quantity	molar mass (g/mol)	mp (°C)	bp (°C)
3M nitric acid	5 mL			
Schiff test solution	6 mL			
semicarbazide hydrochloride	0.15 g	111.5	175–177	
5% silver nitrate	6 mL			
sodium acetate, anhydrous	0.15 g	82.0		
10% sodium hydroxide	3 mL			
5% sodium hypochlorite (bleach)	6 mL			
o-tolualdehyde	0.25 mL	120.2		199–200

Preview

- Prepare and recrystallize a semicarbazone derivative of your unknown
- Filter the derivative and allow it to dry
- Perform a Tollens silver mirror test on a known positive, a known negative, and your unknown
- Perform a Schiff test on a known positive, a known negative, and your unknown
- Perform an iodoform test on a known positive, a known negative, and your unknown
- Measure the refractive index of your unknown
- Measure the melting point of your derivative
- Compare your data with the data of Table 1 to deduce the identity of your unknown

PROCEDURE

CAUTION

Wear departmentally approved safety goggles at all times while in the chemistry laboratory.

Always use caution in the laboratory. Many chemicals are potentially harmful. Follow safety precautions given for all reagents used in this experiment. Prevent contact with your eyes, skin, and clothing. Avoid ingesting any of the reagents.

1. Preparing a Semicarbazone Derivative [NOTE 1]

NOTE 1: For efficient use of laboratory time, begin by forming the semicarbazone derivative. Perform other tests while waiting for the semicarbazone to crystallize and dry.

CAUTION

95% Ethanol is flammable and toxic. Do not use near flames or other heat sources. Semicarbazide hydrochloride is toxic. Your unknown may be corrosive, toxic, and irritating.

Prepare a hot-water bath by placing 100 mL of tap water in a 250-mL beaker and heating the water to 80 °C.

Prepare an ice-water bath by mixing ice and tap water in a 400-mL beaker.

Obtain an unknown compound from your laboratory instructor. Record its identification code.

Label a test tube "ethanol–water". Mix 3 mL of 95% ethanol and 3 mL of distilled or deionized water in the test tube. Cool the ethanol–water mixture in the ice-water bath for later use.

Label a second test tube "unknown". Place 1 mL of 95% ethanol into the test tube. Add 5 drops of the unknown. Mix the solution until it is homogeneous.

Weigh 0.15 g of semicarbazide hydrochloride and place it into a third test tube. Weigh 0.15 g of anhydrous sodium acetate and add it to the semicarbazide hydrochloride. Add 2 mL of distilled or deionized water to dissolve the solids.

Pour the aqueous solution of semicarbazide into the test tube containing the ethanol solution of the unknown. Mix well by shaking the test tube. Shake the test tube for 5–10 s every minute for approximately 5 min until a precipitate forms. Cool the test tube in the ice-water bath for 5 min.

Use a Büchner funnel to vacuum filter the semicarbazone. Measure 25 mL of distilled or deionized water. Use the water to rinse the test tube and to wash the precipitate in the Büchner funnel.

CAUTION

If the hot-water bath is too hot, ethanol can boil out and cause burns.

To recrystallize the semicarbazone, transfer the semicarbazone precipitate to a clean test tube. Add 2 mL of distilled or deionized water, 2 mL of 95% ethanol, and a boiling chip. Heat the tube in the hot-water bath until the semicarbazone dissolves.

If some of the semicarbazone remains undissolved, add 1 mL of 95% ethanol and heat again. Continue adding 1-mL amounts of ethanol until the semicarbazone dissolves in hot ethanol–water solution. Do not add more than a total of 8 mL of 95% ethanol.

When the semicarbazone dissolves, remove the tube from the hot-water bath. Allow the solution to cool to room temperature.

If the cooling solution turns cloudy and the compound starts coming out of solution as a liquid instead of a solid, quickly put the test tube in an ice-water bath and rapidly swirl the tube until a solid is visible. Then remove the tube from the ice-water bath and allow the recrystallization to continue at room temperature.

When the semicarbazone has crystallized completely, vacuum filter the semicarbazone. Remove the boiling chip. Rinse the semicarbazone with the 6 mL of chilled 1:1 95% ethanol–water mixture.

Spread the semicarbazone on a watch glass. Allow the semicarbazone to dry for 30 min.

Measure the melting point of the semicarbazone. Compare the melting point with the melting points in Table 1 earlier in this experiment.

2. Performing the Tollens Silver Mirror Test for an Aldehyde

CAUTION

Silver nitrate ($AgNO_3$) and nitric acid (HNO_3) are toxic and oxidizing. $AgNO_3$ will stain skin and clothing. Sodium hydroxide (NaOH) is toxic and corrosive. Ammonium hydroxide (NH_4OH) is corrosive and a lachrymator. Use a *fume hood* when working with NH_4OH. 2-Butanone is flammable and irritating. Do not use near flames or other heat sources.

CAUTION

Prepare the Tollens reagent just before use. A highly explosive precipitate forms upon standing. Upon completion of the tests, rinse each test tube with ~1 mL of 3*M* HNO_3 to destroy any residual Tollens reagent.

NOTE 2: When performing the Tollens test, the test tubes must be *very clean* for a silver mirror to form.

Thoroughly wash 3 test tubes with soap and water. [NOTE 2] Then rinse the test tubes with distilled water. Do not rinse the test tubes with acetone.

Label the test tubes "known positive", "known negative", and "unknown", respectively. Label all 3 tubes "Tollens Test".

Add 2 mL of 5% $AgNO_3$ to each test tube. Add 1 mL of 10% NaOH to each test tube. A precipitate will form. To each test tube, add concentrated NH_4OH dropwise, with mixing, until the black Ag_2O precipitate just dissolves.

Add 2 drops of *o*-tolualdehyde to the tube labeled "known positive". Mix well.

Add 2 drops of 2-butanone to the tube labeled "known negative". Mix well.

Add 2 drops of the unknown to the tube labeled "unknown". Mix well.

For each tube, note whether or not a silver mirror or a heavy black precipitate forms. Record your observation. If there is no visible change within 5 min, place the tube in the 80 °C hot-water bath for 15 s. *Do not overheat the tube.*

When the tests are complete, pour the contents of each tube into the "Recovered Silver Solution" container, provided by your laboratory instructor. Rinse each test tube with ~1 mL of 3*M* HNO_3 to destroy any residual Tollens reagent. Add this rinse to the "Recovered Silver Solution" container. Wash the test tubes with soap and water.

3. Performing the Schiff Test for an Aldehyde

CAUTION

2-Butanone is flammable and irritating. Do not use near flames or other heat sources. Schiff solution contains pararosaniline hydrochloride, sodium hydrogen sulfite and HCl. Schiff solution is toxic, irritating, and a suspected carcinogen. Use chemically resistant gloves when working with Schiff solution.

Label 3 test tubes "known positive", "known negative", and "unknown", respectively. Label all 3 tubes "Schiff Test". Add 2 mL of Schiff solution to each test tube.

Add 1 drop of *o*-tolualdehyde to the tube labeled "known positive". Mix well.

Add 1 drop of 2-butanone to the tube labeled "known negative". Mix well.

Add 1 drop of the unknown to the tube labeled "unknown". Mix well.

Constantly shake each tube to speed up the reaction. After 5 min, note the color in each tube and record your observation. [NOTE 3]

When the tests are complete, pour the contents of each tube into the "Recovered Schiff Solution" container, provided by your laboratory instructor.

NOTE 3: A faint pink color results from the initial reagent and does not constitute a positive test. A purple fuchsia color constitutes a positive test. Several minutes may be required for color development.

4. Performing the Iodoform Test for a Methyl Ketone

CAUTION

2-Butanone is flammable and irritating. Do not use near flames or other heat sources. Iodoform test solution contains potassium iodide and acetonitrile. Iodoform test solution is toxic and irritating.

Check the temperature of the hot-water bath to make certain it remains at 80 °C.

Label 3 test tubes "known positive", "known negative", and "unknown", respectively. Label all 3 tubes "Iodoform Test."

Add 2 mL of iodoform test solution to each test tube. Warm the tubes in the hot-water bath for 30 s.

Add 1 drop of 2-butanone to the tube labeled "known positive". Mix well. [NOTE 4]

Add 1 drop of o-tolualdehyde to the tube labeled "known negative". Mix well.

Add 1 drop of the unknown to the tube labeled "unknown". Mix well.

Immediately add 2 mL of fresh chlorine bleach (5% sodium hypochlorite, NaOCl) to each tube and mix. Note whether or not a yellow precipitate forms immediately and record your observation.

When the tests are complete, pour the contents of each tube into the "Recovered Iodoform Test Solution" container, provided by your laboratory instructor.

NOTE 4: Notice that the known positive and known negative compounds for the iodoform test are in reverse order from the aldehyde tests.

NOTE 5: The refractive index at 20 °C is calculated by using the following equation, where T is the ambient temperature in degrees Celsius and n_D^T is the refractive index measured at ambient temperature.

$$n_D^{20} = n_D^T + 0.00045(T - 20\,°C)$$

5. Measuring the Refractive Index

Measure the refractive index of your unknown. Note and record the laboratory temperature. Correct the refractive index to 20 °C, if necessary. [NOTE 5]

6. Cleaning Up

Turn in any unused unknown to your laboratory instructor. Use the labeled collection containers provided by your laboratory instructor. Clean your glassware with soap or detergent.

CAUTION

Wash your hands with soap or detergent before leaving the laboratory.

POST-LABORATORY QUESTIONS

1. Discuss the results of your classification tests and semicarbazone derivative formation. What is your unknown? How do your data exclude other possibilities?

2. How will the melting point of your semicarbazone derivative be affected if the derivative is not dry enough? Briefly explain.

3. Show your calculation for correcting the refractive index to 20 °C.

Pre-Laboratory Assignment

1. Why is it important to use gloves when handling Schiff reagent?

2. Why is it important not to use acetone to clean the test tubes used in this experiment?

3. Why is it important to perform the qualitative tests in triplicate?

4. In the procedure for preparing semicarbazone derivatives, what is the purpose of adding sodium acetate to semicarbazide hydrochloride?

5. In the iodoform test, why is it necessary to add sodium hypochlorite?

6. If an unknown forms a silver mirror in the Tollens test, forms a purple color in the Schiff test, produces no precipitate in the iodoform test, has a refractive index of 1.5250, and forms a semicarbazone melting at 124–126 °C, what is its identity? Support your conclusions.

modular · laboratory · program · in · chemistry

publisher: H.A. Neidig

organic editor: Joe Jeffers

Nucleophilic Addition to Carbonyl: Grignard Reaction with an Aldehyde

prepared by **Jan William Simek**,
California Polytechnic State University

PURPOSE OF THE EXPERIMENT

Demonstrate formation of a carbon–carbon bond using the addition of a Grignard reagent across the carbonyl of an aldehyde. Characterize the product using thin-layer chromatography, infrared spectroscopy, and nuclear magnetic resonance spectroscopy.

BACKGROUND REQUIRED

You should be familiar with using a Bunsen burner, packing a drying tube, and drying organic layers. You should also be familiar with techniques for magnetic stirring, reflux, distillation, extraction, solvent evaporation, thin-layer chromatography, infrared spectroscopy, and nuclear magnetic resonance spectroscopy.

BACKGROUND INFORMATION

Victor Grignard began his investigations into the reaction of organic halides with magnesium at the turn of the twentieth century. For this work, he received the 1912 Nobel Prize in Chemistry. In the history of organic chemistry, no other reaction has had greater significance than the Grignard reaction for its scope, simplicity, and versatility.

Common nonmetals such as oxygen, nitrogen, and the halogens are more electronegative than carbon. As a result, a carbon bonded to these atoms has a partial positive character. When magnesium is inserted between the carbon and a halogen, however, the polarity is reversed because carbon is more electronegative than magnesium. This process transforms carbon from an electrophilic atom to a nucleophilic one, as shown in Equation 1. The Grignard reaction was the first reaction to generalize the use of carbon as a nucleophile to make carbon–carbon bonds.

$$\overset{\delta+}{C}\!\!-\!\!X^{\delta-} \quad \xrightarrow[\text{ether}]{\text{Mg}} \quad \overset{\delta-}{C}\!\!-\!\!\overset{\delta+}{Mg}\!\!-\!\!X^{\delta-} \qquad \text{(Eq. 1)}$$

X=Cl, Br, I

a Grignard reagent

The structure of a Grignard reagent in solution has been the subject of much study. In fact, a Grignard reagent cannot be isolated without a solvent present. The nonbonded electrons from the oxygen in an ether solvent or the nitrogen in an amine solvent are necessary to stabilize a Grignard reagent. The standard way of indicating a Grignard reagent, RMgX, is not an accurate representation of the larger aggregate in solution. The stoichiometry works, however, as if RMgX were the actual reactive species. For simplicity, chemists continue to use this designation.

The nucleophilic carbon of a Grignard reagent rapidly adds to the carbonyl carbon of an aldehyde or ketone, as shown in Equation 2. A Grignard reagent can also react with esters, acid chlorides, nitriles, epoxides, and carbon dioxide.

$$\text{R—Mg—X} \quad + \quad \overset{:O:}{\underset{R' \quad R''}{C}} \quad \longrightarrow \quad \overset{:O:^-}{\underset{\underset{R}{R' \overset{|}{C} R''}}{}} \quad [\text{MgX}]^+ \qquad \text{(Eq. 2)}$$

Hydrolysis of the resulting complex with aqueous acid produces an alcohol, as shown in Equation 3. The reaction of a Grignard reagent with formaldehyde produces a primary alcohol. With any other aldehyde, the Grignard reaction produces a secondary alcohol. With a ketone, the Grignard reaction produces a tertiary alcohol.

$$\overset{:O:^-}{\underset{\underset{R}{R' \overset{|}{C} R''}}{}} \quad [\text{MgX}]^+ \quad \xrightarrow[\text{H}_2\text{O}]{\text{H}^+} \quad \overset{:OH}{\underset{\underset{R}{R' \overset{|}{C} R''}}{}} \quad + \quad \text{Mg}^{2+} \quad + \quad \text{X}^- \qquad \text{(Eq. 3)}$$

The greatest practical challenge in preparing a Grignard reagent is to keep water out of the reaction. The negative charge of the carbon in the Grignard reagent makes the carbon very basic. Water can donate a proton to the carbon, destroying the nucleophilic character of the Grignard reagent, as shown in Equation 4. Several precautions are taken in the procedure to exclude water: the reaction flask is flame-dried before adding solvent; a drying tube keeps moisture from entering the apparatus; iodine is vaporized in the flask to tie up traces of water and to activate the surface of the magnesium; the diethyl ether solvent is specially dried and packaged to guarantee that it is anhydrous.

$$\text{R—Mg—X} \quad + \quad \text{H—OH} \quad \longrightarrow \quad \text{R—H} \quad + \quad \text{Mg(OH)X} \qquad \text{(Eq. 4)}$$

In this experiment, you will prepare the Grignard reagent isopropylmagnesium bromide from 2-bromopropane. You will react this Grignard reagent with 4-methoxybenzaldehyde to form a secondary alcohol, 1-(4-methoxyphenyl)-2-methylpropan-1-ol, as shown in Equation 5.

2-bromopropane	isopropyl magnesium bromide	4-methoxybenzaldehyde	1-(4-methoxyphenyl)-2-methylpropan-1-ol

Equipment

50-mL beaker	magnetic stir bar
100-mL beaker	magnetic stirrer
250-mL beaker*	magnetic wand‡
boiling chip	microspatula
Bunsen burner	paper towel
capillary tubes†	Pasteur pipet, with latex bulb
condenser, with tubing	pencil
cotton	pH paper
distilling head	1.0-mL pipet
drying tube, with stopper	product vial
2 Erlenmeyer flasks, 25-mL	2 round-bottom flasks, 50-mL
2 Erlenmeyer flasks, 50-mL,	ruler
with stopper	125-mL separatory funnel
250-mL Erlenmeyer flask	3 ×7-cm silica gel TLC plate
filter funnel	2 support stands
fluted filter paper	2 utility clamps
25-mL graduated cylinder	2.0-mL vial, with cap
4-oz jar, with lid§	

*or concentric ring bath for hot-water bath
†for preparing micropipets
‡or glass stirring rod
§or 250-mL beaker with foil or plastic wrap as cover for TLC developing chamber

Reagents and Properties

substance	quantity	molar mass (g/mol)	mp (°C)	bp (°C)
2-bromopropane	1.48 g	123.0		59
calcium chloride, anhydrous	8 g*	110.99		
dichloromethane	5 mL	84.93		40
diethyl ether, anhydrous	20 mL	74.12		34.6
diethyl ether, solvent grade	22 mL	74.12		34.6
iodine	0.02 g	253.8	113	184
magnesium	0.36 g	24.3		
magnesium sulfate, anhydrous	2 g	120.37		
4-methoxybenzaldehyde	0.68 g	136.15	−1	248
1-(4-methoxyphenyl)-2-methylpropan-1-ol†		180.21		
phosphoric acid, 1M	15 mL			
sodium chloride, saturated solution	10 mL			
sodium hydroxide, 5%	10 mL			

*amount varies, depending on size of drying tube
†product

Preview

- Assemble the reflux apparatus

- Flame-dry a round-bottom flask

- Weigh magnesium turnings

- Add magnesium and iodine to the dried round-bottom flask

- Heat the reflux apparatus to flood the apparatus with iodine vapor

- Weigh 2-bromopropane and dissolve it in *anhydrous* diethyl ether

- Add 2-bromopropane solution to the magnesium turnings and reflux to make the Grignard reagent

- Weigh 4-methoxybenzaldehyde and dissolve it in *anhydrous* diethyl ether

- Add 4-methoxybenzaldehyde portions to the Grignard reagent

- Heat 10 min with a hot-water bath

- Pour the mixture into ice water and acidify it with phosphoric acid

- Separate the layers

- Extract the product into ether and wash it with 5% NaOH and saturated NaCl solution

- Dry the ether layer with anhydrous magnesium sulfate

- Remove the ether from the product

- Weigh the product

- Characterize the product using TLC, IR, and NMR

PROCEDURE   ***Chemical Alert***

2-bromopropane—*flammable and irritant*

calcium chloride—*irritant and hygroscopic*

dichloromethane—*toxic and irritant*

diethyl ether—*flammable and toxic*

iodine—*toxic and corrosive*

magnesium—*flammable*

4-methoxybenzaldehyde—*irritant*

phosphoric acid—*corrosive*

5% sodium hydroxide—*toxic and corrosive*

Caution: Wear departmentally approved safety goggles at all times while in the chemistry laboratory.

1. **Drying the Apparatus**   ***Caution:***   Iodine (I_2) is toxic and corrosive. Magnesium (Mg) is flammable. Keep away from flames or other heat sources. Calcium chloride ($CaCl_2$) is irritating and hygroscopic. Prevent eye, skin, and clothing contact. Avoid inhaling and ingesting these compounds. Use a ***fume hood***.

Place two 25-mL Erlenmeyer flasks in a drying oven. Pack a drying tube with anhydrous $CaCl_2$.

Clamp a dry 50-mL round-bottom flask to a support stand. Add a magnetic stir bar. Using a medium flame from a Bunsen burner, flame (heat) all outer surfaces of the flask, starting at the bottom and working up until no more water vapor condenses on the flask.

Insert the drying tube into the neck of the flask and cool the flask for 5 min. Remove the drying tube.

Weigh 0.36 g of Mg turnings. Add the turnings and 3–4 crystals of I_2 to the flask.

Insert the dry condenser into the round-bottom flask. Place the drying tube in the top of the condenser.

Use the Bunsen burner flame to gently heat the round-bottom flask until I_2 vapor fills the flask. Allow the apparatus to cool to room temperature.

When the apparatus is cool, place a magnetic stirrer under the round-bottom flask of the apparatus, as shown in Figure 1. Attach tubing to the condenser and begin a slow flow of tap water through the condenser.

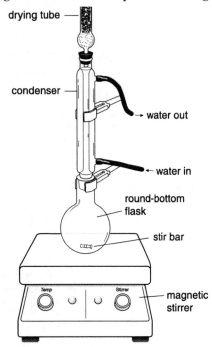

Figure 1   Reflux apparatus for the Grignard reaction

2.   Preparing the Grignard Reagent

Caution: 2-Bromopropane is flammable and irritating. Diethyl ether is highly flammable and toxic. Do not use near flames or other heat sources. *Make certain all burners in the laboratory are extinguished before opening the container of diethyl ether.* Prevent eye, skin, and clothing contact. Avoid breathing fumes and ingesting these compounds. Use a *fume hood*.

In a cool, *dry* 25-mL Erlenmeyer flask, weigh 1.48 g (1.13 mL) of 2-bromopropane. [NOTE 1] *Immediately* add approximately 10 mL of *anhydrous* diethyl ether by pouring directly from the ether container.

Remove the drying tube from the top of the reflux condenser. Pour the 2-bromopropane solution through the condenser into the round-bottom flask. [NOTE 2] When you observe rapid boiling, adjust the magnetic stirrer to slow or medium speed.

When the boiling begins to subside, prepare a hot-water bath by filling a 250-mL beaker with *hot* tap water. Place the bath under the round-bottom flask. Immerse the flask until the water level in the bath is even with the reaction mixture level in the flask.

NOTE 1:   2-Bromopropane is volatile. Product yield will be low if ether is not added immediately after weighing 2-bromopropane.

NOTE 2:   The reaction should begin within 2 min and produce enough heat to boil the ether. If the reaction does not begin within 5 min, notify your laboratory instructor.

Warm the flask for 10–15 min to complete the formation of the Grignard reagent. Remove the hot-water bath and allow the solution to cool to room temperature.

3. Reacting the Grignard Reagent and the Aldehyde

Caution: 4-Methoxybenzaldehyde is irritating. Prevent contact with eyes, skin, and clothing. Avoid breathing fumes and ingesting the compound.

Weigh 0.68 g of 4-methoxybenzaldehyde (*p*-anisaldehyde) into a cool, *dry* 25-mL Erlenmeyer flask. Add approximately 10 mL of *anhydrous* diethyl ether by pouring from the container.

Remove the drying tube from the top of the reflux condenser. Over 5–10 min, use a Pasteur pipet to add the 4-methoxybenzaldehyde solution in approximately 0.5-mL portions through the condenser into the round-bottom flask. Replace the drying tube after each addition. Add the solution at such a rate that the stirred reaction mixture refluxes gently.

After all of the solution is added, warm the stirred reaction mixture with a hot-water bath for 10 min. Then allow the reaction mixture to cool to room temperature.

4. Isolating the Product

Caution: Phosphoric acid (H_3PO_4) is corrosive. Sodium hydroxide (NaOH) is toxic and corrosive. Prevent contact with eyes, skin, and clothing. Avoid breathing fumes and ingesting the compounds.

Prepare an ice-water mixture by filling a 250-mL Erlenmeyer flask with ice to the 50-mL mark. Add distilled or deionized water to the 50-mL mark.

Set the Erlenmeyer flask containing the ice water on the magnetic stirrer. Add a stir bar. [NOTE 3]   Adjust the stirrer to a rapid rate.

NOTE 3: Use a magnetic wand to transfer the stir bar from the round-bottom flask to the Erlenmeyer flask.

Remove the round-bottom flask from the apparatus. Then gradually pour the reaction mixture into the ice water.

Rinse the round-bottom flask with 4–5 mL of 1*M* H_3PO_4 and add the rinse to the reaction mixture in the ice water. Rinse the round-bottom flask with 10 mL of solvent grade diethyl ether. Add this rinse to the reaction mixture.

Continue to stir the mixture rapidly. Gradually add enough 1*M* H_3PO_4 until the mixture is acid to pH paper.

Place a filter funnel in the top of a 125-mL separatory funnel. Place a *loose* piece of cotton in the filter funnel. Pour the mixture through the cotton into the separatory funnel. Then remove the filter funnel.

Allow the layers to separate. Drain the aqueous layer from the separatory funnel into a 100-mL beaker. Pour the ether layer into a 50-mL Erlenmeyer flask and stopper the flask.

Return the aqueous layer to the empty separatory funnel and extract with a second 10-mL portion of ether. Again drain the aqueous layer into the beaker. Pour the aqueous layer into the container labeled "Acidic Aqueous Layer", provided by your laboratory instructor. Rinse the beaker with water.

Add the original ether solution to the second ether layer in the separatory funnel. Wash the combined ether layer with 10 mL of 5% aqueous NaOH. Drain the NaOH layer into the 100-mL beaker. Pour the NaOH layer into the container labeled "Recovered 5% NaOH", provided by your laboratory instructor. Rinse the beaker with water.

NOTE 4: Add anhydrous MgSO$_4$ to the solution gradually until the solution is no longer cloudy or until the MgSO$_4$ no longer clumps. Approximately 2 g will be required.

Wash the ether layer with 10 mL of saturated NaCl solution. Drain off the aqueous layer into the 100-mL beaker.

Transfer the ether solution to a dry 50-mL Erlenmeyer flask. Add enough anhydrous magnesium sulfate (MgSO$_4$) to dry the solution. [NOTE 4]   Stopper the flask and allow the solution to dry for 5 min. Then filter the solution through a fluted filter paper into a *tared* 50-mL round-bottom flask.

5. Removing the Ether
[NOTE 5]

NOTE 5: Use the separation method designated by your laboratory instructor.

Using a Rotary Evaporator

Use a rotary evaporator to collect the ether from the product, as directed by your laboratory instructor. Weigh the round-bottom flask containing your liquid product and record the mass. Place your product in a product vial labeled "Grignard Product".

Using Distillation

Set up a simple distillation apparatus in the *fume hood*. Use the 50-mL round-bottom flask containing your product as the distilling flask. Add a boiling chip. Use a hot-water bath to distill the ether from the product. Collect the ether in a 50-mL beaker.

Allow the apparatus to cool. Remove the boiling chip. Weigh the round-bottom flask containing your liquid product and record the mass. Place your product in a product vial labeled "Grignard Product".

6. Characterizing the Product

Caution: Dichloromethane is toxic and irritating. Prevent eye, skin, and clothing contact. Avoid inhaling vapors and ingesting the compound. Use a *fume hood*.

Using TLC

Place 0.1 mL of your product into a 2.0-mL vial. Add 1.9 mL of anhydrous diethyl ether. Cap the vial to prevent evaporation.

Obtain a 3 × 7-cm silica gel thin-layer chromatography (TLC) plate from your laboratory instructor. Draw a *very faint* pencil line 1 cm from the bottom to mark the origin. Make two vertical marks that intersect the pencil line 0.5 cm from each edge of the plate and a third mark 1.5 cm from one edge.

Prepare micropipets for spotting the TLC plate by drawing out melting point capillary tubing. Using a micropipet, spot a standard sample of 4-methoxybenzaldehyde once on the middle mark, keeping the spot as small as possible. Using a new micropipet, spot your product–diethyl ether sample once on the left-hand mark. Using the same micropipet, spot your sample twice on the right hand mark, allowing the ether to evaporate between spottings.

Prepare a developing chamber by pouring 5 mL of dichloromethane into a 4-oz jar. Place the TLC plate into the chamber, making certain the origin is higher than the eluent. Attach the lid. Allow the eluent to develop the plate.

Caution: Ultraviolet radiation can cause severe eye damage. Wear goggles. Do not look directly into the UV lamp.

After developing the plate, mark the eluent front. Visualize the chromatogram under short-wave UV light. Use a pencil to circle the spots on your plate.

Using IR Spectroscopy

Obtain an IR spectrum of your sample. Identify the major peaks and compare your spectrum with a spectrum of 4-methoxybenzaldehyde, provided by your laboratory instructor.

Using NMR

Obtain an NMR spectrum of your sample. Compare your spectrum with a spectrum of 4-methoxybenzaldehyde, provided by your laboratory instructor.

7. **Cleaning Up**   Use the labeled collection containers as directed by your laboratory instructor. Clean your glassware with soap or detergent.

> **Caution:** Wash your hands with soap or detergent before leaving the laboratory.

Post-Laboratory Questions

1. Calculate the percent yield for your product.
2. What is the purpose of adding anhydrous $MgSO_4$ to the ether solution? What would occur if this step were omitted?
3. Calculate the R_fs for all spots on your chromatogram.
4. (a) Identify the spots in the TLC.
   (b) Does TLC indicate the presence of any unreacted aldehyde?
   (c) What does the TLC show about the polarity of the product compared with the polarity of the aldehyde?
5. What peak in the IR spectrum most clearly demonstrates the presence of alcohol product? If the product had unreacted aldehyde remaining, what IR peak would indicate the presence of this contaminant?
6. (a) What peaks in the NMR spectrum most clearly demonstrate the presence of the predicted product?
   (b) If the product had unreacted aldehyde remaining, what NMR peak would indicate the presence of this contaminant?
7. Draw a Newman projection along C(1)–C(2), with the OH group attached to C(1). Are the two methyl groups equivalent? What evidence do you find from the NMR spectrum to support your conclusion?

NAME _____   SECTION _____   DATE _____

SYNT 718/Nucleophilic Addition to Carbonyl: Grignard Reaction with an Aldehyde

Pre-Laboratory Assignment

1. Describe the safety hazards for diethyl ether.

2. Write the chemical reactions for the formation of the respective Grignard reagents from the reaction of magnesium with the following organic halides:
    (a)   iodomethane

    (b)   bromobenzene

    (c)   chlorocyclohexane

3. Write the reactions of methylmagnesium iodide with the following aldehydes and ketones. Assume that all reactions include a hydrolysis in aqueous acid.
    (a)   formaldehyde (methanal), CH_2O

    (b)   acetone

    (c)   cyclohexanone

4. (a)   What is the common purpose of these precautions: flaming the apparatus before running the reaction; using a drying tube to separate the atmosphere inside the apparatus from the outside air; and using anhydrous ether as the solvent?

    (b)   What could be the undesired result if these precautions were not followed?

5. Why is the Grignard reagent prepared in excess relative to the aldehyde?

6. Show the reaction of excess Grignard reagent with aqueous acid.

7. Calculate the theoretical yield of the product, 1-(4-methoxyphenyl)-2--methylpropan-1-ol. Show your calculation here and in your laboratory notebook.

8. (a)   When analyzing the product using TLC, why is it helpful to spot the reactant on the same plate as the product?

    (b)   Why not spot just the product?

9. Indicate the major differences between the IR spectra of the reactant aldehyde and the product alcohol.

ISBN 0-87540-718-8

© 1998 Chemical Education Resources

5

Isopentyl Acetate (Banana Oil)

Esterification
Heating under reflux
Extraction
Simple distillation
Microscale boiling point

In this experiment you will prepare an ester, isopentyl acetate. This ester is often referred to as banana oil because it has the familiar odor of this fruit.

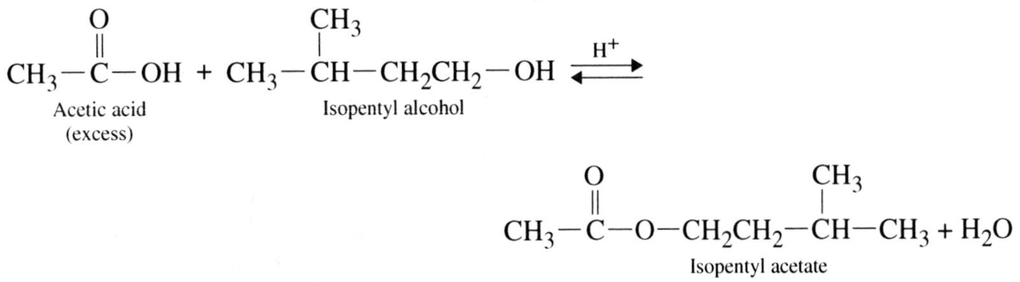

$$CH_3-\overset{\overset{O}{\|}}{C}-OH \ + \ CH_3-\overset{\overset{CH_3}{|}}{CH}-CH_2CH_2-OH \ \underset{\longleftarrow}{\overset{H^+}{\longrightarrow}}$$

Acetic acid (excess)   Isopentyl alcohol

$$CH_3-\overset{\overset{O}{\|}}{C}-O-CH_2CH_2-\overset{\overset{CH_3}{|}}{CH}-CH_3 \ + \ H_2O$$

Isopentyl acetate

Isopentyl acetate is prepared by the direct esterification of acetic acid with isopentyl alcohol. Because the equilibrium does not favor the formation of the ester, it must be shifted to the right, in favor of the product, by using an excess of one of the starting materials. Acetic acid is used in excess because it is less expensive than isopentyl alcohol and more easily removed from the reaction mixture.

In the isolation procedure, much of the excess acetic acid and the remaining isopentyl alcohol are removed by extraction with sodium bicarbonate and water. After drying with anhydrous sodium sulfate, the ester is purified by distillation. The purity of the liquid product is analyzed by performing a microscale boiling point determination or infrared spectroscopy.

REQUIRED READING

Review: Experiment 1   Introduction to Microscale Laboratory (pp. 2–13)

Techniques 5 and 6

New: Technique 7   Reaction Methods, Sections 7.2–7.4 and 7.6

Technique 13   Physical Constants, Boiling Points

Technique 12   Extractions, Separations, and Drying Agents

Technique 14   Simple Distillation

Essay   Esters—Flavors and Fragrances

If performing the optional infrared spectroscopy, also read:

Technique 25   Preparation of Samples for Spectroscopy

SPECIAL INSTRUCTIONS

Be careful when dispensing sulfuric and glacial acetic acids. They are corrosive and will attack your skin if you make contact with them. If you get one of these acids on your skin, wash the affected area with copious quantities of running water for 10–15 minutes.

Because a 1-hour reflux is required, you should start the experiment at the beginning of the laboratory period. During the reflux period, you may perform other work.

SUGGESTED WASTE DISPOSAL

Any aqueous solutions should be placed in a container specially designated for dilute aqueous waste. Place any excess ester in the nonhalogenated organic waste container.

NOTES TO THE INSTRUCTOR

Choose either Experiment 13A or Experiment 13B, but not both. The semi-microscale procedure requires the use of equipment not found in the typical microscale kit: a 20-mL round-bottom flask, a distillation head, and a vacuum takeoff adapter. The purpose of Experiment 13B is to allow an alternative to the use of a Hickman head for the distillation step.

This experiment has been carried out successfully using Dowex 50×2-100 ion-exchange resin instead of the sulfuric acid. Amberlyst-15 resin will also work.

EXPERIMENT 13A

Isopentyl Acetate (Microscale Procedure)

PROCEDURE

Apparatus

Using a 5-mL conical vial, assemble a reflux apparatus using a water-cooled condenser (Fig. 7.2A, p. 599). Top the condenser with a drying tube (Fig. 7.10B, p. 599) that contains a loose plug of glass wool. The purpose of the drying tube is to control odors rather than to protect the reaction from water. Use a hot plate and an aluminum block for heating.

Preparation

Remove the empty 5-mL conical vial, weigh it, and record its weight. Place approximately 1.0 mL of isopentyl alcohol (MW = 88.2, d = 0.813 g/mL) in the vial using an automatic pipet or a dispensing pump. Reweigh the vial containing the alcohol and subtract the tare weight to obtain an accurate weight for the alcohol. Add 1.5 mL of glacial acetic acid (MW = 60.1, d = 1.06 g/mL) using an automatic pipet or dispensing pump. Using a disposable Pasteur pipet, add two to three drops of concentrated sulfuric acid. Swirl the liquid to mix. Add a small boiling stone (or a magnetic spin vane) and reattach the vial to the apparatus.

Reflux

Bring the mixture to a boil (aluminum block at about 150–160°C). Be sure to stir the mixture if you are using a spin vane instead of a boiling stone. Continue heating under reflux for 60–75 minutes. Remove the heating source and allow the mixture to cool to room temperature.

Workup

Disassemble the apparatus and, using a forceps, remove the boiling stone (or spin vane). Using a calibrated Pasteur pipet (p. 11), slowly add 1.0 mL of 5% aqueous sodium bicarbonate to the cooled mixture in the conical vial. Stir the mixture in the vial with a microspatula until carbon dioxide evolution is no longer vigorous. Then cap the vial and shake *gently* with venting until the evolution of gas is complete. Using a Pasteur pipet, remove the lower aqueous layer and discard it. Repeat the extraction two more times, as outlined previously, using a fresh 1.0-mL portion of 5% sodium bicarbonate solution each time.

If droplets of water are evident in the vial containing the ester, transfer the ester to a dry conical vial using a dry Pasteur pipet. Dry the ester over granular anhydrous sodium sulfate (see Technique 12, Section 12.9, p. 680). Allow the capped solution to stand for 10–15 minutes. Transfer the dry ester with a Pasteur pipet into a 3-mL conical vial while leaving the drying agent behind. If necessary, pick out any granules of sodium sulfate with the end of a spatula.

Distillation

Add a boiling stone (or a magnetic spin vane) to the dry ester. Clamping the glassware, assemble a distillation apparatus using a Hickman still and a water-cooled condenser on top of a hot plate with an aluminum heating block (Fig. 14.5, p. 708). In order to control odors, rather than to keep the reaction dry, top the apparatus with a drying tube packed loosely with a small amount of calcium chloride held in place by bits of cotton or glass wool. Begin the distillation by turning on the hot plate (about 180°C). Stir the mixture if you are using a spin vane instead of a boiling stove. Continue the distillation until only one or two drops of liquid remain in the distilling vial. If the Hickman head fills before the distillation is complete, it may be necessary to empty it using a Pasteur pipet (see Fig. 14.6A, p. 709) and transfer the distillate to a tared (preweighed) conical vial. Unless you have a sideported Hickman still, it will be necessary to remove the condenser in order to perform the transfer. When the distillation is complete, transfer the final portion of the distillate to this same vial.

Determination of Yield

Weigh the product and calculate the percentage yield of the ester. Determine its boiling point (bp 142°C) using a microscale boiling-point determination (Technique 13, Section 13.2, p. 695). See page 107 for a spectral analysis.

EXPERIMENT 13B

Isopentyl Acetate
(Semimicroscale Procedure)

PROCEDURE

Apparatus

Assemble a reflux apparatus on top of your hot plate using a 20- or 25-mL round-bottom flask and a water-cooled condenser (refer to Fig. 7.6A, p. 601, but use a round-bottom flask instead of the conical vial). To control vapors, place a drying tube packed with calcium chloride on top of the condenser. Use a hot plate and the aluminum block with the larger set of holes for heating.

Reaction Mixture

Weigh (tare) an empty 10-mL graduated cylinder and record its weight. Place approximately 2.5 mL of isopentyl alcohol in the graduated cylinder and reweigh it to determine the weight of the alcohol. Disconnect the round-bottom flask from the reflux apparatus and transfer the alcohol into it. Do not clean or wash the graduated cylinder. Using the same graduated cylinder, measure approximately 3.5 mL of glacial acetic acid ($MW = 60$, $d = 1.06$ g/mL) and add it to the alcohol already in the flask. Using a calibrated Pasteur pipet, add 0.5 mL of concentrated sulfuric acid, mixing *immediately* (swirl), to the reaction mixture contained in the flask. Add a corundum (black) boiling stone or stirring bar and reconnect the flask. Do not use a calcium carbonate (white, marble) boiling stone, because it will dissolve in the acidic medium.

Reflux

Start water circulating in the condenser and bring the mixture to a boil. Continue heating under reflux for at least 60 minutes. Be sure to stir the mixture if you are using a stirring bar instead of a boiling stone. When the reflux period is complete, disconnect or remove the heating source and let the mixture cool to room temperature.

Extractions

Disassemble the apparatus and transfer the reaction mixture to a 15-mL capped centrifuge tube. Avoid transferring the boiling stone or stirring bar. Add 5 mL of water, cap the centrifuge tube, and mix the phases by careful shaking and venting. Allow the phases to separate and then open the cap and remove the lower aqueous layer (see a similar procedure for a conical vial in Workup on page 105). Next, extract the organic layer with 2.5 mL of aqueous sodium bicarbonate, just as you did previously with water. Extract the organic layer once again, this time with 2.5 mL of saturated aqueous sodium chloride.

Drying

Transfer the crude ester to a clean, dry, 25-mL Erlenmeyer flask and add approximately 0.5 g of anhydrous sodium sulfate. Cork the mixture and let it stand for about 10 minutes while you prepare the apparatus for distillation. If the mixture does not appear dry (the drying agent clumps and does not "flow," the solution is cloudy, or drops of water are obvious), transfer the ester to a new, clean, dry,

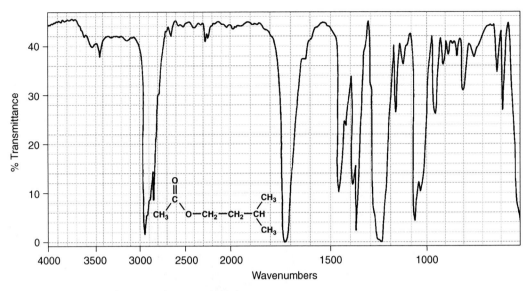

Infrared spectrum of isopentyl acetate (neat).

25-mL Erlenmeyer flask and add a new 0.25-g portion of anhydrous sodium sulfate to complete the drying.

Distillation

Assemble a distillation apparatus using your smallest round-bottom flask to distill from (Fig. 14.10, p. 713, but insert a water condenser as shown on p. 54). Use a hot plate with an aluminum block to heat. Preweigh (tare) and use a 5-mL conical vial to collect the product. Immerse the collection vial in a beaker of ice to ensure condensation and to reduce odors. Distill your ester and record its boiling-point *range* in your notebook.

Yield Determination

Weigh the product and calculate the percentage yield of the ester. At the option of your instructor, determine the boiling point using one of the methods described in Section 13.2, page 695. See below for a spectral analysis.

Infrared Spectroscopy

At your instructor's option, obtain an infrared spectrum using salt plates (Technique 25, Section 25.2, p. 834). Compare the spectrum with the one reproduced in this experiment and include it with your report to the instructor. If any of your sample remains after performing the determination of the infrared spectrum, submit it in a properly labeled vial along with your report.

QUESTIONS

1. One method for favoring the formation of an ester is to add excess acetic acid. Suggest another method, involving the right-hand side of the equation, that will favor the formation of the ester.
2. Why is it easier to remove excess acetic acid from the products than excess isopentyl alcohol?
3. Why is the reaction mixture extracted with sodium bicarbonate? Give an equation and explain its relevance.
4. Which starting material is the limiting reagent in this procedure? Which reagent is used in excess? How great is the molar excess (how many times greater)?

5. How many grams are there in 1.00 mL of isopentyl acetate? You will need to look up the density of isopentyl acetate in a handbook.

6. How many moles of isopentyl acetate are there in 1.00 g of isopentyl acetate? You will need to calculate the molecular weight of isopentyl acetate.

7. Suppose that 1.00 mL of isopentyl alcohol was reacted with excess acetic acid and that 1.00 g of isopentyl acetate was obtained as product. Calculate the percentage yield.

8. Outline a separation scheme for isolating pure isopentyl acetate from the reaction mixture.

9. Interpret the principal absorption bands in the infrared spectrum of isopentyl acetate. (Technique 25 may be of some help in answering this question.)

10. Write a mechanism for the acid-catalyzed esterification of acetic acid with isopentyl alcohol. You may need to consult the chapter on carboxylic acids in your lecture textbook

EXPERIMENT 48

6

Sulfa Drugs: Preparation of Sulfanilamide

Crystallization
Protecting groups
Testing the action of drugs on bacteria
Preparation of a sulfonamide
Aromatic substitution

In this experiment, you will prepare the sulfa drug sulfanilamide by the following synthetic scheme. The synthesis involves converting acetanilide to the intermediate *p*-acetamidobenzenesulfonyl chloride in Step 1. This intermediate is converted to sulfanilamide by way of *p*-acetamidobenzenesulfonamide in Step 2.

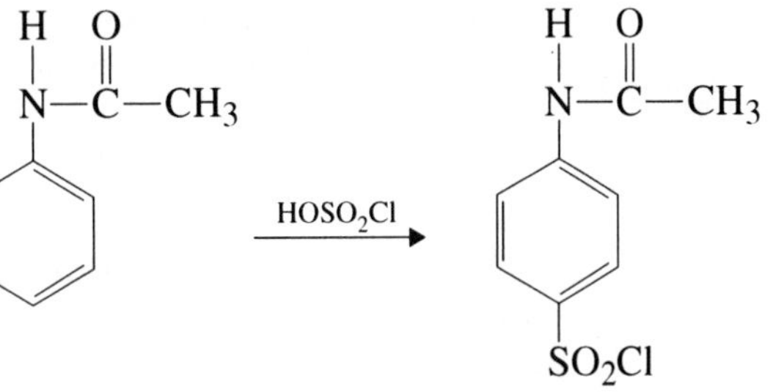

Acetanilide   *p*-Acetamidobenzenesulfonyl chloride

[1]

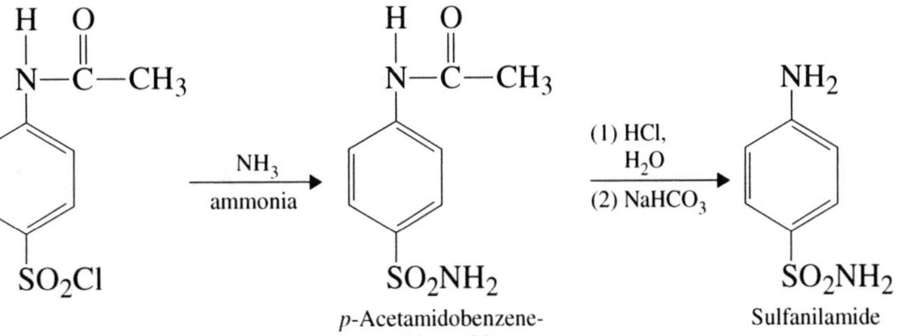

p-Acetamidobenzene-sulfonamide   Sulfanilamide

[2]

Acetanilide, which can easily be prepared from aniline, is allowed to react with chlorosulfonic acid to yield *p*-acetamidobenzenesulfonyl chloride. The acetamido group directs substitution almost totally to the *para* position. The reaction is an example of an electrophilic aromatic substitution reaction. Two problems would result if aniline itself were used in the reaction. First, the amino group in aniline would be protonated in strong acid to become a *meta* director; and, second, the chlorosulfonic acid would react with the amino group rather than with the ring, to give C_6H_5—$NHSO_3H$. For these reasons, the amino group has been "protected" by acetylation.

The acetyl group will be removed in the final step, after it is no longer needed, to regenerate the free amino group present in sulfanilamide.

p-Acetamidobenzenesulfonyl chloride is isolated by adding the reaction mixture to ice water, which decomposes the excess chlorosulfonic acid. This intermediate is fairly stable in water; nevertheless, it is converted slowly to the corresponding sulfonic acid ($Ar-SO_3H$). Thus, it should be isolated as soon as possible from the aqueous medium by filtration.

p-Acetamidobenzenesulfonyl chloride → (H₂O) → p-Acetamidobenzenesulfonic acid + HCl

The intermediate sulfonyl chloride is converted to p-acetamidobenzene-sulfonamide by a reaction with aqueous ammonia (Step 2). Excess ammonia neutralizes the hydrogen chloride produced. The only side reaction is the hydrolysis of the sulfonyl chloride to p-acetamidobenzenesulfonic acid.

The protecting acetyl group is removed by acid-catalyzed hydrolysis to generate the hydrochloride salt of the product, sulfanilamide. Note that of the two amide linkages present, only the carboxylic acid amide (acetamido group) was cleaved, not the sulfonic acid amide (sulfonamide). The salt of the sulfa drug is converted to sulfanilamide when the base, sodium bicarbonate, is added.

p-Acetamidobenzene-sulfonamide → (HCl, H₂O) → + CH₃—C(=O)—OH → (NaHCO₃) → Sulfanilamide + CH₃C(=O)—O⁻

REQUIRED READING

Review: Technique 7   Reaction Methods

Technique 8   Filtration, Sections 8.3 and 8.7

Technique 11   Crystallization, Section 11.4

Technique 25   Infrared Spectroscopy, Sections 25.4 and 25.5

New: Essay   Sulfa Drugs

SPECIAL INSTRUCTIONS

Chlorosulfonic acid must be handled with care because it is a corrosive liquid and reacts violently with water. The *p*-acetamidobenzenesulfonyl chloride should be used during the same laboratory period in which it is prepared. It is unstable and will not survive long storage. The sulfa drug may be tested on several kinds of bacteria (Instructor's Manual).

SUGGESTED WASTE DISPOSAL

Aqueous filtrates should be placed in the container provided for this purpose. Place organic wastes in the nonhalogenated waste container.

PROCEDURE

Part A.
***p*-Acetamidobenzenesulfonyl Chloride**

The Reaction Apparatus

Assemble the apparatus as shown in Figure 7.6A (inset) on page 601 using dry glassware. You will need a 5-mL conical vial, an air condenser, and a drying tube, which will be used as a gas trap. Prepare the drying tube for use as a gas trap by packing the tube loosely with dry glass wool (Technique 7, Section 7.8A, p. 607). Moisten the glass wool slightly with several drops of water. The moistened glass wool traps the hydrogen chloride that is evolved in the reaction. Attach the 5-mL conical vial after the acetanilide and chlorosulfonic acid have been added, as directed in the following paragraph. You should adjust the temperature of the aluminum block to about 110°C for use later in the experiment.

Reaction of Acetanilide with Chlorosulfonic Acid

Place 0.18 g of acetanilide in the dry 5-mL conical vial and connect the air condenser but not the drying tube. Melt the acetanilide (mp 113°C) by heating the vial in a community sand bath or aluminum block set to about 160°C. Remove the vial from the heating source and swirl the heavy oil while holding the vial at an angle so that it is deposited uniformly on the cone-shaped bottom of the vial. Allow the conical vial to cool to room temperature and then cool it further in an ice-water bath. (Don't place the hot vial directly into the ice-water bath without prior cooling, or the vial will crack.)

CAUTION

Chlorosulfonic acid is an extremely noxious and corrosive chemical and should be handled with care. Use only dry glassware with this reagent. Should the chlorosulfonic acid be spilled on your skin, wash it off immediately with water. Be very careful when washing any glassware that has come in contact with chlorosulfonic acid. Even a small amount of the acid will react vigorously with water and may splatter. Wear safety glasses.

Remove the air condenser. In a hood, transfer 0.50 mL of chlorosulfonic acid $ClSO_2OH$ ($MW = 116.5$, $d = 1.77$ g/mL) to the acetanilide in the conical vial using the graduated pipet provided. Reattach the air condenser and drying tube. Allow the mixture to stand for 5 minutes and then heat the reaction vial in the aluminum block at about 110°C for 10 minutes to complete the reaction. Remove the vial from the aluminum block. Allow the vial to cool to the touch and then cool it in an ice-water bath.

Isolation of p-Acetamidobenzenesulfonyl Chloride

The operations described in this paragraph should be conducted as rapidly as possible because the p-acetamidobenzenesulfonyl chloride reacts with water. Add 3 g of crushed ice to a 20-mL beaker. In a hood, transfer the cooled reaction mixture dropwise (it may splatter somewhat) with a Pasteur pipet onto the ice while stirring the mixture with a glass stirring rod. (The remaining operations in this paragraph may be completed at your laboratory bench.) Rinse the conical vial with a few drops of cold water and transfer the contents to the beaker containing the ice. Stir the precipitate to break up the lumps and then filter the p-acetamidobenzene-sulfonyl chloride on a Hirsch funnel (Technique 8, Section 8.3, p. 621, and Fig. 8.5, p. 622). Rinse the conical vial and beaker with two 1-mL portions of ice water. Use the rinse water to wash the crude product on the funnel. Any remaining solid in the conical vial should be left there because this vial is used again in the next section. Do not stop here. Convert the solid into p-acetamidobenzenesulfonamide in the same laboratory period.

Part B. Sulfanilamide

Preparation of p-Acetamidobenzenesulfonamide

Prepare a hot waterbath at 70°C. Place the crude p-acetamidobenzenesulfonyl chloride into the original 5-mL conical vial and add 1.1 mL of dilute ammonium hydroxide solution.[1] Stir the mixture well with a spatula and reattach the air condenser and drying tube (gas trap) using fresh, moistened glass wool. Heat the mixture in the hot waterbath for 10 minutes. Allow the conical vial to cool to the touch and place it in an ice-water bath for several minutes. Collect the p-acetamidobenzenesulfonamide on a Hirsch funnel and rinse the vial and product with a small amount of ice water. You may stop here.

Hydrolysis of p-Acetamidobenzenesulfonamide

Transfer the solid into the conical vial and add 0.53 mL of dilute hydrochloric acid solution.[2] Attach the air condenser and heat the mixture in an aluminum block at about 130°C until all the solid has dissolved. Then heat the solution for an additional 5 minutes. Allow the mixture to cool to room temperature. If a solid (unreacted starting material) appears, heat the mixture for several minutes at 130°C. When the vial has cooled to room temperature, no further solids should appear.

Isolation of Sulfanilamide

With a Pasteur pipet, transfer the solution to a 20-mL beaker. While stirring with a glass rod, cautiously add dropwise a slurry of 0.5 g of sodium bicarbonate in about 1 mL of water to the mixture in the beaker. Foaming will occur after each addition of the bicarbonate solution because of carbon dioxide evolution. Allow gas evolution to cease before making the next addition. Eventually, sulfanilamide will begin to precipitate. At this point, begin to check the pH of the solution. Add the aqueous sodium bicarbonate until the pH of the solution is between 4 and 6. Cool the mixture thoroughly in an ice-water bath. Collect the sulfanilamide on a Hirsch funnel and rinse the beaker and solid with about 0.5 mL of cold water. Allow the solid to air dry on the Hirsch funnel for several minutes using suction.

---

[1] Prepared by mixing 11.0 mL of concentrated ammonium hydroxide with 11.0 mL of water.

[2] Prepared by mixing 7.0 mL of water with 3.6 mL of concentrated hydrochloric acid.

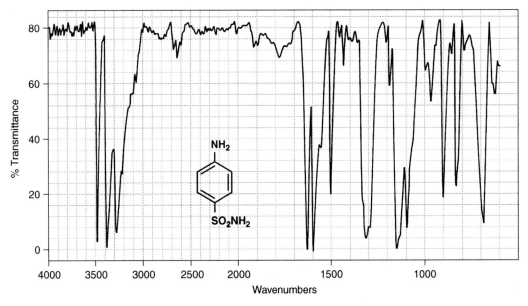

Infrared spectrum of sulfanilamide, KBr.

Crystallization of Sulfanilamide

Weigh the crude product and crystallize it from hot water (use 1.0 to 1.2 mL water/ 0.1 g) using a Craig tube (Technique 11, Section 11.4, p. 656, and Fig. 11.6, p. 657). Step 2 in Figure 11.6 (removal of insoluble impurities) should not be required in this crystallization. Let the purified product dry until the next laboratory period.

Yield Calculation, Melting Point, and Infrared Spectrum

Weigh the dry sulfanilamide and calculate the percentage yield (*MW* = 172.2). Determine the melting point (pure sulfanilamide melts at 163–164°C). At the option of the instructor, obtain the infrared spectrum using the dry film method (Technique 25, Section 25.4, p. 838) or as a KBr pellet (Technique 25, Section 25.5, p. 838). Compare your infrared spectrum with the one reproduced here. Submit the sulfanilamide to the instructor in a labeled vial or save it for the tests with bacteria (see Instructor's Manual).

QUESTIONS

1. Write an equation showing how excess chlorosulfonic acid is decomposed in water.

2. In the preparation of sulfanilamide, why was aqueous sodium bicarbonate, rather than aqueous sodium hydroxide, used to neutralize the solution in the final step?

3. At first glance, it might seem possible to prepare sulfanilamide from sulfanilic acid by the set of reactions shown here.

$$\text{H}_2\text{N}-\text{C}_6\text{H}_4-\text{SO}_3\text{H} \xrightarrow{\text{PCl}_5} \text{H}_2\text{N}-\text{C}_6\text{H}_4-\text{SO}_2\text{Cl} \xrightarrow{\text{NH}_3} \text{H}_2\text{N}-\text{C}_6\text{H}_4-\text{SO}_2\text{NH}_2$$

When the reaction is conducted in this way, however, a polymeric product is produced after Step 1. What is the structure of the polymer? Why does *p*-acetamidobenzenesulfonyl chloride not produce a polymer?

7

Methyl Salicylate (Oil of Wintergreen)

Synthesis of an ester

Heating under reflux

Extraction

Vacuum distillation

In this experiment, you will prepare a familiar-smelling organic ester, oil of wintergreen. Methyl salicylate was first isolated in 1843 by extraction from the wintergreen plant (*Gaultheria*). It was soon found that this compound had analgesic and antipyretic character almost identical to that of salicylic acid (see the essay "Aspirin") when taken internally. This medicinal character probably derives from the ease with which methyl salicylate is hydrolyzed to salicylic acid under the alkaline conditions found in the intestinal tract. Salicylic acid is known to have analgesic and antipyretic properties. Methyl salicylate can be taken internally or absorbed through the skin; thus, it finds much use in liniment preparations. Applied to the skin, it produces a mild tingling or soothing sensation, which probably comes from the action of its phenolic hydroxyl group. This ester also has a pleasant odor, and it is used to a small extent as a flavoring principle.

Salicylic acid + CH$_3$OH $\underset{}{\overset{H^+}{\rightleftharpoons}}$ Methyl salicylate (oil of wintergreen) + H$_2$O

Methyl salicylate will be prepared from salicylic acid, which is esterified at the carboxyl group with methanol. You should recall from your organic chemistry lecture course that esterification is an acid-catalyzed equilibrium reaction. The equilibrium does not lie far enough to the right to favor the formation of the ester in high yield. More product can be formed by increasing the concentrations of one of the reactants. In this experiment, a large excess of methanol will shift the equilibrium to favor a more complete formation of the ester.

This experiment also illustrates the use of distillation under reduced pressure for purifying high-boiling liquids. Distillation of high-boiling liquids at atmospheric pressure is often unsatisfactory. At the high temperatures required, the material being distilled (the ester, in this case) may partially or even completely decompose, causing loss of product and contamination of the distillate. When the total pressure inside the distillation apparatus is reduced, however, the boiling point of the substance is lowered. In this way, the substance can be distilled without being decomposed.

REQUIRED READING

Review: Techniques 5 and 6

Technique 13 — Physical Constants of Liquids, Part A, Boiling Points and Thermometer Correction

New: Technique 16 — Vacuum Distillation

Technique 25 — Preparation of Samples for Spectroscopy

Essay — Esters—Flavors and Fragrances

SPECIAL INSTRUCTIONS

The experiment must be started at the beginning of the laboratory period because a long reflux time is needed to esterify salicylic acid and obtain a respectable yield. Perform a supplementary experiment during the reaction period or complete work that is pending from previous experiments. Enough time should remain at the end of the period to perform the extractions, place the product over the drying agent, assemble the apparatus, and perform the vacuum distillation.

CAUTION

Handle the concentrated sulfuric acid carefully; it can cause severe burns.

When a distillation is conducted under reduced pressure, it is important to guard against the dangers of an implosion. Inspect the glassware for flaws and cracks and replace any that is defective.

CAUTION

Wear your safety glasses.

Because the amount of methyl salicylate obtained in this experiment is small, your instructor may want two students to combine their products for the final vacuum distillation.

SUGGESTED WASTE DISPOSAL

The aqueous extracts from this experiment should be placed in the container designated for this purpose. Place any remaining methylene chloride in the container designated for halogenated waste.

PROCEDURE

Assemble equipment for reflux using a 5-mL conical vial and a water-cooled condenser (Fig. 7.6A, p. 601). Top the apparatus with a calcium chloride drying tube. Use a hot plate with an aluminum block. Place 0.65 g of salicylic acid, 2.0 mL of methanol (d = 0.792 g/mL), and a spin vane in the vial. Stir the mixture until the salicylic acid dissolves. Carefully add 0.75 mL of concentrated sulfuric acid, *in small portions*, to the mixture in the vial while stirring. A white precipitate may form, but it will redissolve during the reflux period. Complete assembly of the apparatus and, while stirring, gently boil the mixture (aluminum block 80°C) for 60–75 minutes.

After the mixture has cooled, extract it with three 1-mL portions of methylene chloride (Technique 12, Section 12.4, p. 674). Add the methylene chloride, cap the vial, shake it, and then loosen the cap. When the layers separate, transfer the lower layer with a filter-tip pipet to another container. After completing the three extractions, discard the aqueous layer and return the three methylene chloride extracts to the vial. Extract the methylene chloride layers with a 1-mL portion of 5% aqueous sodium bicarbonate. Transfer the lower organic layer to a clean, dry conical vial. Discard the aqueous layer. Dry the organic layer over anhydrous sodium sulfate (see Technique 12, Section 12.9, p. 680). When the solution is dry, transfer it to a clean, dry, 3-mL, conical vial with a filter-tip pipet. Evaporate the methylene chloride using a warm waterbath (40–50°C) in the hood. A stream of nitrogen or air will accelerate the evaporation (Fig. 7.17A, p. 612). The product may be stored in the capped vial and saved for the next period, or it may be distilled under vacuum during the same period.

Vacuum Distillation

Using the procedure described in Technique 16, Section 16.4, page 737, distill the product by vacuum distillation using an apparatus fitted with a Hickman still and a water-cooled condenser (Fig. 16.5, p. 736). Place a small piece of a stainless steel sponge in the lower stem of the Hickman still to prevent bumpover and stir vigorously with a magnetic spin vane. Use an aspirator for the vacuum source and attach a manometer if one is available (see Fig. 16.10, p. 742). You may use an aluminum block to heat the distillation mixture. The aluminum block temperature will be about 130°C (with 20 mm Hg vacuum). If you have less than 0.75 mL, you should combine your product with that of another student.

When the distillation is complete, transfer the distillate to a tared 3-mL conical vial with a Pasteur pipet and weigh it to determine the percentage yield. Determine a microscale boiling point (Technique 13, Section 13.2, pp. 695) for your product.

Spectroscopy

At your instructor's option, obtain an infrared spectrum using salt plates (Technique 25, Section 25.2, p. 834). Compare your spectrum with the one reproduced on page 376. Interpret the spectrum and include it in your report to the instructor. You may also be required to determine and interpret the proton and carbon-13 NMR spectra (Technique 26, Part A, p. 870, and Technique 27, p. 906). Submit your sample in a properly labeled vial with your report.

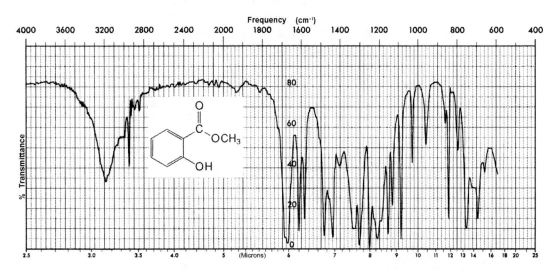

Infrared spectrum of methyl salicylate (neat).

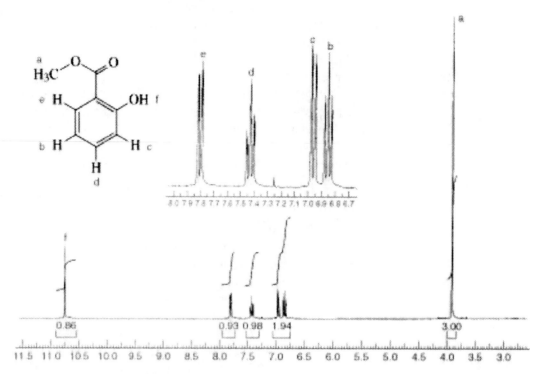

300-MHz proton NMR of methyl salicylate (CDCl₃).

QUESTIONS

1. Write a mechanism for the acid-catalyzed esterification of salicylic acid with methanol. You may need to consult the chapter on carboxylic acids in your lecture textbook.

2. What is the function of the sulfuric acid in this reaction? Is it consumed in the reaction?

3. In this experiment, excess methanol was used to shift the equilibrium toward the formation of more ester. Describe other methods for achieving the same result.

4. How are sulfuric acid and the excess methanol removed from the crude ester after the reaction has been completed?

5. Why was 5% NaHCO₃ used in the extraction? What would have happened if 5% NaOH had been used?

6. Interpret the principal absorption bands in the infrared spectrum of methyl salicylate. Also interpret the proton NMR spectrum shown on page 376.

Separating Cyclohexane and Toluene by Distillation

prepared by **Jerry Manion**, University of Central Arkansas

PURPOSE OF THE EXPERIMENT

Separate two miscible liquids, either by macroscale or microscale process, using simple and fractional distillation. Compare the efficiencies of simple and fractional distillation.

EXPERIMENTAL OPTIONS

Macroscale Distillation
Microscale Distillations
   A. Using Glassware with Elastomeric Connectors
   B. Using the Hickman Still
   C. Using Test Tube Reflux

BACKGROUND REQUIRED

You should be familiar with basic laboratory techniques for measuring volumes of chemical compounds. You should know how to prepare a bent-tip Pasteur pipet for microscale distillations. You should know how to use a refractometer to measure refractive index.

BACKGROUND INFORMATION

Distillation is a technique widely used in organic chemistry for separating compounds based on differences in their boiling points. Many organic compounds are **volatile**; that is, they have relatively high vapor pressures and low boiling points. During distillation, such volatile compounds are heated to boiling in one container, called the **pot**. The vapors produced are then cooled and reliquefied by passing them through a water-cooled **condenser**, and collected in a separate container, called the **receiver**. This technique can be used to remove a volatile solvent from a nonvolatile product; to separate a volatile product from nonvolatile impurities; or to separate two or more volatile products that have sufficiently different boiling points.

When a liquid is placed in a closed container, some of the molecules evaporate into any unoccupied space in the container. **Evaporation**, which occurs at temperatures below the boiling point of a compound, involves the transition from liquid to vapor of *only* those molecules at the liquid surface. Evaporation continues until an equilibrium is reached between molecules entering and leaving the liquid and vapor states. The pressure exerted by these gaseous molecules on the walls of the container is the **equilibrium vapor pressure**. The magnitude of this vapor pressure depends on the physical characteristics of the compound and increases as temperature increases.

If the liquid is heated to its boiling point, quite a different phenomenon occurs. The **boiling point** is the temperature at which the vapor pressure of the liquid is equal to the external pressure applied to the surface of the liquid. This external pressure is commonly atmospheric pressure. At the boiling point, bubbles of vapor are produced throughout the liquid, and the vapor pressure inside the bubbles is sufficiently high to allow them to grow in size. The escape of these bubbles results in the characteristic chaotic motion of the liquid identified as **boiling**.

Liquid is converted to vapor more rapidly by boiling than by evaporation. If the heating rate is increased, the temperature of the boiling liquid does not change, but the rate at which vapor is produced from the liquid increases. This increase occurs because the energy that is supplied by the increased heating rate is absorbed as more liquid molecules overcome intermolecular interactions and enter the vapor phase.

When a mixture of two or more volatile compounds is heated, the vapor pressure of the mixture equals the sum of the vapor pressures of each compound in the mixture. The magnitude of the vapor pressure exerted by each compound is determined by the vapor pressure of that compound (P^0) and the mole fraction of that compound present in the mixture (X). For an ideal two-compound solution, the solution vapor pressure is expressed by Raoult's law, shown in Equation 1.

$$P_T = X_1 P_1^{\,0} + X_2 P_2^{\,0} \qquad \text{(Eq. 1)}$$

In this equation, P_T is the total vapor pressure of the solution, $P_1^{\,0}$ is the vapor pressure of pure compound 1, X_1 is the mole fraction of compound 1, $P_2^{\,0}$ is the vapor pressure of pure compound 2, and X_2 is the mole fraction of compound 2.

When two liquids form a homogeneous solution, they are said to be **miscible**. Such a homogeneous mixture will boil at a temperature between the boiling points of the pure compounds. The exact boiling point of the mixture depends upon the relative amounts of the compounds present. Figure 1 shows the relationship between boiling point and composition for a two-compound mixture of cyclohexane and toluene.

When vapor is produced from such a liquid mixture, the composition of the vapor mixture is different from the composition of the liquid mixture from which it forms, as shown in Figure 2. The vapor contains a larger percent of the more volatile compound of the mixture, in this case cyclohexane. For example, a liquid composed of 50 percent cyclohexane and 50 percent toluene would boil at 90 °C and yield a vapor composed of 70 percent cyclohexane and 30 percent toluene.

This composition change that accompanies the vaporization process is the basis for the separation of mixtures by distillation. As the vapors produced by the distillation move into the water-cooled condenser, these vapors condense to a liquid, the **distillate**, which has the same composition as the vapor from which it is formed. The distillate collected in the receiver will contain more of the more volatile compound than was present in the original mixture.

If one compound is much more volatile than the other, the compounds can be separated in one vaporization step. Such a step is called **simple distillation** and uses an apparatus that consists of only a pot, a distilling head, a condenser, an adapter, and a receiver, as shown in Figure 3.

When the boiling points of two compounds differ by less than 40 °C, they cannot be separated by simple distillation. **Fractional distillation**, a process that has the effect of many simple distillations, must be used. A fractional distillation apparatus includes a fractionating column placed between the pot and the distilling head, as shown in Figure 4. Typically, any one of a variety of materials, including glass beads and metal sponge, fill the fractionating column.

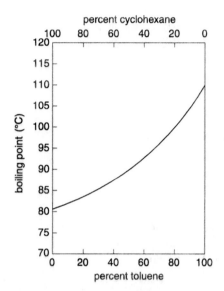

Figure 1 The boiling point of a miscible mixture is between the boiling points of the pure compounds

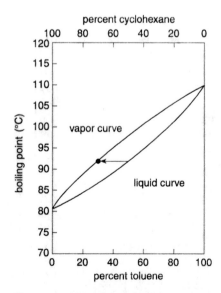

Figure 2 Vaporizing a mixture of cyclohexane and toluene produces a vapor that is enriched in cyclohexane

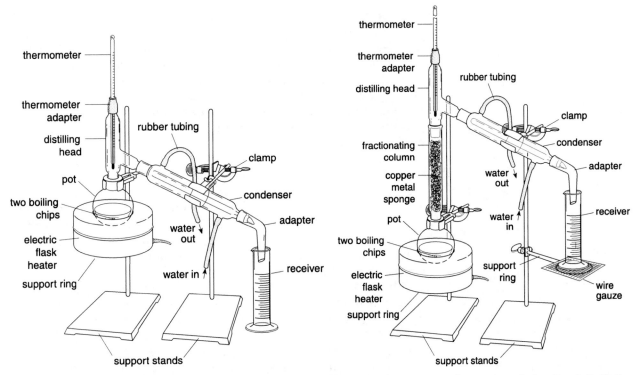

Figure 3 An apparatus for macroscale simple distillation

Figure 4 An apparatus for macroscale fractional distillation

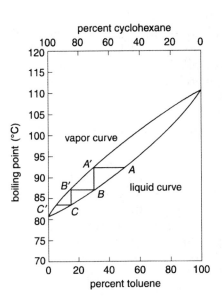

Figure 5 Each condensation and revaporization increases the concentration of the more volatile compound

The vapors generated in the pot rise up the fractionating column and encounter cooler surfaces, upon which they condense. The condensed liquid is then reheated by rising hot vapors and revaporizes. This process of condensation and revaporization, shown graphically in Figure 5, may occur again and again as the vapors rise up the column.

Each vaporization is represented by a horizontal line connecting the liquid composition curve to the vapor composition curve. Each condensation is represented by a vertical line connecting the vapor curve to the liquid curve. For example, the 50:50 liquid mixture (*A*) vaporizes to produce a 30:70 vapor mixture (*A'*). The 30:70 vapor mixture condenses to a 30:70 liquid mixture (*B*). The 30:70 liquid mixture, in turn, vaporizes to produce a 15™:85 vapor mixture (*B'*), and so on. Each condensation–revaporization results in an increase in the concentration of the more volatile compound. These composition changes are reflected by a *decrease* in boiling temperature as the mixture moves up the fractionating column. If the condensation–revaporization is repeated a sufficient number of times, the vapors of the more volatile compound reach the top of the fractionating column in a pure form. As these vapors move into the condenser, the compound condenses and is collected as a liquid.

At the same time, the less volatile compound is enriched in the opposite direction. As the condensed liquid falls toward the pot, the pot gradually contains a higher and higher percent of the less volatile compound. Thus, a separation of the two compounds is achieved.

Each condensation and revaporization that occurs on a fractionating column is called a **theoretical plate**. A fractionating column with a large number of theoretical plates accomplishes many condensation–revaporization steps and very efficiently separates the compounds in a mixture.

The fractionating column must be positioned vertically so that condensed liquid can percolate down through the rising hot vapors. This percolation promotes equilibrium between the liquid and vapor phases, a condition that allows the column to operate at maximum efficiency and provide an optimum separation.

An equally important factor affecting separation of the compounds is the distillation rate. If the distillation is conducted too rapidly, liquid–vapor equilibria will not be established in the fractionating column, and poor separation of the compounds will result.

As the liquid boils, a **condensation line** of vapor can be observed as it moves up the distilling head. Once these vapors reach the thermometer bulb, a dramatic temperature increase is observed. The temperature of the vapors in the distilling head provides information regarding the progress of the distillation. Initially, the vapors are rich in the more volatile compound, and the observed temperature is close to the boiling point of that compound. In a distillation with an efficient separation, the initial temperature remains relatively constant until all of that compound is collected. After the compound with the lower boiling point is completely distilled, the temperature rises sharply as the vapors of the higher-boiling compound reach the thermometer bulb. At this time, the boiling point of the higher-boiling compound is observed as it distills into the receiver.

When no fractionating column is used, or when the fractionating column is inefficient, mixtures of the distilled compounds are incompletely separated. This inefficiency is indicated by a very gradual increase in the temperature measured during the distillation. Samples collected at temperatures between the boiling points of the two compounds will consist of mixtures of the two compounds. A comparison of the results of simple and fractional distillation is shown in Figure 6.

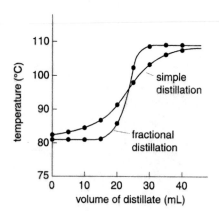

Figure 6 Distillation curves for simple and fractional distillation

Microscale Distillation

Distillation is a difficult organic laboratory technique to use when separating microscale volumes, because significant amounts of distillate are commonly left adhering to the glass surfaces of the apparatus. However, specialized equipment has been designed to permit the simple distillation of volumes less than one milliliter. One such apparatus, the Hickman still, is shown in Figure 10 later in this module. Another apparatus for microscale distillations uses special glassware with elastomeric connectors, as shown in Figure 8 later in this module. Microscale distillations may also be conducted in a test tube using a Pasteur pipet as a condenser and receiver.

Microscale distillations are especially useful when small volumes of a liquid must be purified for spectral or refractive index analyses. The relative amounts of cyclohexane and toluene present in a sample may be determined by measuring the refractive index of the sample. Figure 7 shows a graph that correlates the refractive index of mixtures of cyclohexane and toluene with their composition.

Refractive index measurements are typically reported at 20 °C. A refractive index measured at a temperature higher or lower than 20 °C must be corrected to 20 °C. To make this correction, Equation 2 is used, where n^{20} is the refractive index at 20 °C, n^T is the refractive index at the measured temperature, and T is the measured temperature.

$$n^{20} = n^T + 0.00045(T - 20\ °C) \qquad (Eq.\ 2)$$

For example, if the refractive index of a cyclohexane–toluene mixture is measured as 1.4752 at 26 °C, then the refractive index at 20 °C can be calculated:

$$n^{20} = 1.4752 + 0.00045(26 - 20\ °C) = 1.4779$$

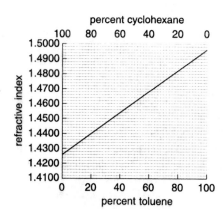

Figure 7 A correlation curve relating refractive index to the composition of cyclohexane–toluene mixtures

Locating the point on the graph in Figure 7 corresponding to $n^{20} = 1.4779$ indicates that the sample contains 74 percent toluene and 26 percent cyclohexane.

Macroscale Distillation

Equipment

aluminum foil	2 support rings
boiling chips	2 support stands
copper metal sponge*	2 utility clamps
electric flask heater, with regulator	wire gauze, ceramic center*
50-mL graduated cylinder	

standard taper glassware:
    condenser, with adapter and rubber tubing
    distilling head
    fractionating column*
    100-mL round-bottom flask
    –10 to 260 °C thermometer, with adapter[†]

*for fractional distillation
[†]adapter may be required to hold thermometer in place

Reagents and Properties

substance	quantity (mL)	mol mass (g/mol)	bp (°C)
cyclohexane	25	84.16	80.7
toluene	25	92.14	110.6

Preview

- Assemble macroscale simple distillation apparatus
- Place cyclohexane–toluene mixture in pot
- Distill the mixture, recording the temperature at 5-mL intervals
- Assemble macroscale fractional distillation apparatus and repeat as for simple distillation

PROCEDURE

Caution: Wear departmentally approved safety goggles at all times while in the chemistry laboratory.

Always use caution in the laboratory. Many chemicals are potentially harmful. Prevent contact with your eyes, skin, and clothing. Avoid ingesting any of the reagents.

General Considerations

Exercise care when assembling a distillation apparatus. Support the flask heater with a support ring attached to a support stand so that the heater can be quickly lowered away from the apparatus, if necessary.

Use a utility clamp to attach the neck of the pot to the support stand to support the apparatus in the event you remove the flask heater. Support the condenser with a second clamp and support stand.

Carefully adjust the angle of the clamp supporting the condenser. Lubricate the joints by using your finger to apply stopcock grease lightly along the interior joint section. Rotate the joint after connection to distribute the grease uniformly. Check the joints immediately before beginning the distillation, and reconnect any joints that are loose.

Select a pot size so that the pot is one-half to two-thirds full of liquid. Add two boiling chips to the pot. [NOTE 1]

Insert the thermometer into a thermometer adapter so that the top of the thermometer bulb is even with or slightly below the bottom of the side arm on the distilling head, as shown in Figure 3 earlier in this module. [NOTE 2]

NOTE 1: Overfilling the pot can result in bumping or foaming of material into the receiver. Boiling chips provide a surface on which vapor bubbles can form. This bubble formation helps prevent superheating and bumping of the liquid.

NOTE 2: Carefully positioning the thermometer ensures that the bulb is submerged in any vapors that pass through the distilling head and that the vapor temperature is measured accurately.

NOTE 3:   Water should enter the condenser at the bottom and exit from the top so that no air remains in the cooling jacket. A moderate flow of water is sufficient for cooling.

Use rubber tubing to attach the condenser to a water tap and to discharge water from the condenser to the drain. [NOTE 3]

Place the end of the adapter inside the receiver to minimize the release of vapors into the room.

Caution: Heating a closed apparatus can cause the apparatus to rupture. Make certain the distillation apparatus has an opening to the atmosphere. *Do not heat a closed container.*

     Discontinue the distillation before all of the liquid is gone from the pot. Some organic compounds explode when heated to dryness. *Do not distill to dryness.*

1. Conducting Simple Distillation

Caution: Cyclohexane is flammable and irritating. Toluene is flammable and toxic. If possible, use a ***fume hood***.

     Do not add boiling chips to a hot liquid. The large surface area of the boiling chip can cause the hot liquid to foam out of the apparatus and cause burns.

Assemble the simple distillation apparatus shown in Figure 3 earlier in this module, using a 100-mL round-bottom flask for the pot and a 50-mL graduated cylinder for the receiver. Place two boiling chips and 25 mL each of cyclohexane and toluene into the pot, taking care not to spill any chemicals onto the flask heater. Start the flow of water through the condenser. Check the apparatus and reconnect any joints that are loose.

NOTE 4:   As the liquid boils, watch for the condensation line of vapor as it moves up the distilling head. To observe and record an accurate temperature reading, the *entire thermometer bulb must be immersed in vapor.*

Heat the mixture to boiling. [NOTE 4]   Adjust the heater to produce distillate at a rate that is no greater than one drop per s. Record the temperature when you collect the first drop of distillate and again after every 5 mL of distillate you collect. Continue the distillation until the temperature reaches 110 °C or until fewer than 5 mL of liquid remains in the pot.

Turn off the heater and lower it away from the pot. Allow the pot to cool for a few minutes. Then turn off the water to the condenser.

2. Conducting Fractional Distillation

Caution: Cyclohexane is flammable and irritating. Toluene is flammable and toxic. If possible, use a ***fume hood***.

     Do not add boiling chips to a hot liquid. The large surface area of the boiling chip can cause the hot liquid to foam out of the apparatus and cause burns.

Assemble the fractional distillation apparatus shown in Figure 4 earlier in this module, using a 100-mL round-bottom flask for the pot and a 50-mL graduated cylinder for the receiver. Pack the fractionating column with copper metal sponge, as directed by your laboratory instructor. [NOTE 5]

Place two boiling chips and 25 mL each of cyclohexane and toluene into the pot. Start the water flow through the condenser. Check the apparatus and reconnect any joints that are loose.

Heat the mixture in the pot to boiling. Observe the condensation line as it moves up the fractionating column.

NOTE 5:   Be careful to position the fractionating column vertically to promote mixing of the liquid and vapor phases. The fractionating column looks much like a condenser, but has indentations in the inner jacket to support the column packing. Be careful; these indentations are easily broken. The outer jacket insulates against heat loss from the inner jacket during distillation. *Do not pass water through the fractionating column.*

When the vapors reach the top of the column packing, reduce the heating rate so the vapor condensation line remains just above the column packing and below the side arm of the distilling head. Maintain the vapor condensation line in this position for 5 min to allow the vapor and liquid in the column to reach equilibrium.

Wrap the fractionating column and distilling head with aluminum foil to minimize the temperature fluctuations during the distillation. Then adjust the heating rate to produce distillate at a rate no greater than 1 drop per s.

Record the temperature when you collect the first drop of distillate and again after every 5 mL of distillate you collect. Continue the distillation until the temperature reaches 110 °C or until fewer than 5 mL of liquid remains in the pot.

Turn off the heater and lower it from the pot. Allow the pot to cool for a few minutes. Then turn off the water to the condenser.

3. **Cleaning Up** Use the labeled collection containers provided by your laboratory instructor. Clean your glassware with soap or detergent.

Caution: Wash your hands thoroughly with soap or detergent before leaving the laboratory.

Microscale Distillations

A. Using Glassware with Elastomeric Connectors

Equipment

aluminum foil	microspatula
100-mL beaker	2 receiver vials, 5-mL,
boiling chips	with screw caps
copper metal sponge*	sand bath†
glassware with elastomeric	2 support rings
connectors	support stand
5-mL boiling flask	−10 to 260 °C thermometer,
distilling head with	with adapter
air condenser	2 utility clamps
distilling column*	wire gauze, ceramic center

*for fractional distillation

†sand in crystallizing dish on electric hot plate or sand in electric heating well with heat controller

Reagents and Properties

substance	quantity (mL)	mol mass (g/mol)	bp (°C)
cyclohexane	1.5	84.16	80.7
toluene	1.5	92.14	110.6

Preview

• Assemble microscale simple distillation apparatus

• Place cyclohexane–toluene mixture in pot

• Distill the mixture

• Collect the distillate, recording the temperature as a function of the number of drops

• Assemble microscale fractional distillation apparatus and repeat as for simple distillation

PROCEDURE

Caution: Wear departmentally approved safety goggles at all times while in the chemistry laboratory.

Always use caution in the laboratory. Many chemicals are potentially harmful. Prevent contact with your eyes, skin, and clothing. Avoid ingesting any of the reagents.

General Considerations

Exercise care when assembling a distillation apparatus. Support the flask heater with a support ring attached to a support stand so that the heater can be quickly lowered away from the apparatus, if necessary.

NOTE 1: Overfilling the pot can result in bumping or foaming of material into the receiver. A boiling chip provides a surface on which vapor bubbles can form. This bubble formation helps prevent superheating and bumping of the liquid.

Use a utility clamp to attach the neck of the pot to the support stand to support the apparatus in the event you remove the flask heater.

Select a pot size so that the pot is one-half to two-thirds full of liquid. Add a boiling chip to the pot. [NOTE 1]

Insert the thermometer into a thermometer adapter so that the top of the thermometer bulb is even with or slightly below the bottom of the side arm on the distilling head–condenser, as shown in Figure 8. [NOTE 2]

NOTE 2: Carefully positioning the thermometer ensures that the bulb is submerged in any vapors that pass through the distilling head and that the vapor temperature is measured accurately.

Place the end of the distilling head–condenser side arm inside the receiver to minimize the release of vapors into the room. Support the ice-filled beaker with wire gauze on a support ring.

Caution: Heating a closed apparatus can cause the apparatus to rupture. Make certain the distillation apparatus has an opening to the atmosphere. *Do not heat a closed container.*

Discontinue the distillation before all of the liquid is gone from the pot. Some organic compounds explode when heated to dryness. *Do not distill to dryness.*

1. Conducting Simple Distillation

Caution: Cyclohexane is flammable and irritating. Toluene is flammable and toxic. If possible, use a ***fume hood***.

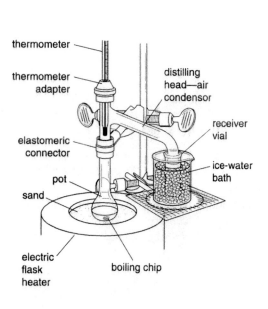

Figure 8 An apparatus using elastomeric connectors for microscale simple distillation

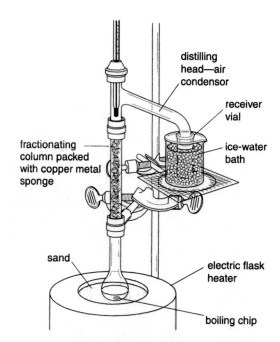

Figure 9 An apparatus using elastomeric connectors for microscale fractional distillation

Assemble the simple distillation apparatus as shown in Figure 8, using a 5-mL boiling flask for the pot and a 5-mL vial for the receiver. Place a boiling chip and 1.5 mL each of cyclohexane and toluene into the pot.

Position the thermometer bulb below the side arm of the distilling head–condenser, and place the end of the air condenser as deeply as possible into the receiver. Place the receiver into a 100-mL beaker and surround the receiver with ice. Check the apparatus and reconnect any joints that are loose.

Heat the mixture to boiling. Adjust the heating rate by using a spatula to move the hot sand either around or away from the pot. Control the heating rate to produce distillate at a rate of about 2–4 drops per min. [NOTE 3]

NOTE 3:   As the liquid boils, watch for the condensation line of vapor as it moves up the distilling head. To observe and record an accurate temperature reading, the *entire thermometer bulb* must be immersed in vapor.

Read and record the temperature when you collect the first drop of distillate and again after every 5 drops of distillate you collect. Continue the distillation until the temperature remains constant at 110 °C or until the pot is almost dry. Discontinue the heating before all of the mixture distills and the pot becomes completely dry. Lower the heater away from the pot.

2.   Conducting Fractional Distillation

Caution: Cyclohexane is flammable and irritating. Toluene is flammable and toxic. If possible, use a ***fume hood***.

Assemble the fractional distillation apparatus shown in Figure 9, using a 5-mL boiling flask for the pot and a 5-mL vial for the receiver. Place a boiling chip and 1.5 mL each of cyclohexane and toluene into the pot. Tightly pack the fractionating column with copper metal sponge.

Position the thermometer bulb below the side arm of the distilling head–condenser, and place the end of the air condenser as deeply as possible into the receiver. Place the receiver into a 100-mL beaker and surround the receiver with ice. Check the apparatus and reconnect any joints that are loose.

Heat the mixture to boiling. Observe the condensation line as it moves up the fractionating column. When the vapors reach the top of the column packing, reduce the heating rate so the vapor condensation line remains just above the column packing and below the side arm of the distilling head. Maintain the vapor condensation line in this position for about 5 min to allow the vapor and liquid in the column to reach equilibrium.

Wrap the fractionating column and distilling head with aluminum foil to minimize the temperature fluctuations during the distillation. Then adjust the heating rate to produce distillate at a rate of about 2–4 drops per min.

Read and record the temperature when you collect the first drop of distillate and again after every 5 drops of distillate you collect. Continue the distillation until the temperature remains constant at 110 °C or until the pot is almost dry. Discontinue the heating before the boiling flask becomes completely dry, and lower the heater away from the pot.

3.   Cleaning Up

Use the labeled collection containers provided by your laboratory instructor. Clean your glassware with soap or detergent.

Caution: Wash your hands thoroughly with soap or detergent before leaving the laboratory.

Microscale Distillations

B. Using the Hickman Still

Equipment

boiling chips	support stand
2 conical vials, 3-mL	–10 to 150 °C thermometer,
Hickman still	small size to fit Hickman still
magnetic spinning band*	–10 to 260 °C thermometer,
microburner	for sand bath
microspatula	tongs
3 Pasteur pipets, with latex bulb	3 utility clamps
sand bath†	6 vials, 2-mL, with screw caps

*for fractional distillation

†sand in crystallizing dish on electric hot plate or sand in electric heating well with heat controller

Reagents and Properties

substance	quantity (mL)	mol mass (g/mol)	bp (°C)
cyclohexane	1.0	84.16	80.7
toluene	1.0	92.14	110.6

Preview

- Prepare a bent-tip Pasteur pipet
- Assemble Hickman apparatus and add cyclohexane–toluene mixture
- Conduct the distillation, collecting samples from 80–90 °C, 90–100 °C, and 100–110 °C
- Repeat the Procedure using a Teflon spinning band for fractional distillation
- Determine the percent composition of the samples, using refractive index

PROCEDURE

Caution: Wear departmentally approved safety goggles at all times while in the chemistry laboratory.

Always use caution in the laboratory. Many chemicals are potentially harmful. Prevent contact with your eyes, skin, and clothing. Avoid ingesting any of the reagents.

Caution: Cyclohexane is flammable and irritating. Toluene is flammable and toxic. If possible, use a *fume hood*.

1. Conducting a Simple Distillation

Prepare a bent-tip Pasteur pipet by heating the pipet in a microburner flame. Use tongs to bend the pipet to a 30° angle 1 cm from the tip. [NOTE 1]

NOTE 1:   A standard Pasteur pipet can be used in a Hickman still model that has a built-in side port.

Transfer 1.0 mL each of cyclohexane and toluene into a 3-mL conical vial, and add a small boiling chip. Attach the Hickman still head and clamp the apparatus vertically in a sand bath, as shown in Figure 10.

Place a thermometer through the center opening of the still head so that the thermometer bulb is positioned as shown in Figure 10. Raise the sand-bath temperature to about 90 °C. Then gradually increase the sand-bath temperature at a rate of 2 °C per min. Collect the material that distills when the Hickman still thermometer registers 80–90 °C. Using a bent-tip Pasteur pipet, remove the distillate that condenses in the collar of the still head. Transfer the distillate to an appropriately labeled sample vial. [NOTE 2]

NOTE 2: Cyclohexane and toluene are quite volatile. Cap the vials to ensure that the small samples do not evaporate.

Collect a second sample that distills in the range 90–100 °C and a third sample in the range 100–110 °C.

2. Conducting Fractional Distillation

Transfer 1.0 mL each of cyclohexane and toluene into a 3-mL conical vial. Attach the Hickman still head containing a magnetic spinning band, and clamp the apparatus vertically in a sand bath, as shown in Figure 11.

Place a thermometer through the center opening of the still head so that the thermometer bulb is positioned, as shown in Figure 11. Raise the sand-bath temperature to 90 °C. When the mixture begins to boil, turn on the magnetic stirrer to a low setting to start the spinning band. Then gradually increase the sand-bath temperature at a rate of 2 °C per min. As the vapor enters the bottom of the still column, increase the spinning band rate to a middle range setting. Once liquid begins to collect in the collar of the still, increase the spinning band rate to the maximum setting.

Collect the material that distills when the Hickman still thermometer registers in the range 80–90 °C. Using a bent-tip Pasteur pipet, remove the distillate that condenses in the collar of the still head. Transfer the distillate to an appropriately labeled sample vial. [NOTE 3]

Collect a second sample that distills in the range 90–100 °C and a third that distills in the range 100–110 °C.

NOTE 3: Cyclohexane and toluene are quite volatile. Cap the vials to ensure that the small samples do not evaporate.

3. Measuring Refractive Index

Using a refractometer, measure the refractive index of the compounds in each vial. Correct the refractive indices for temperature, using Equation 2.

Using the correlation curve shown in Figure 7 earlier in this experiment and the corrected refractive index for the solution in each collection vial, determine the percent of cyclohexane and toluene in each sample.

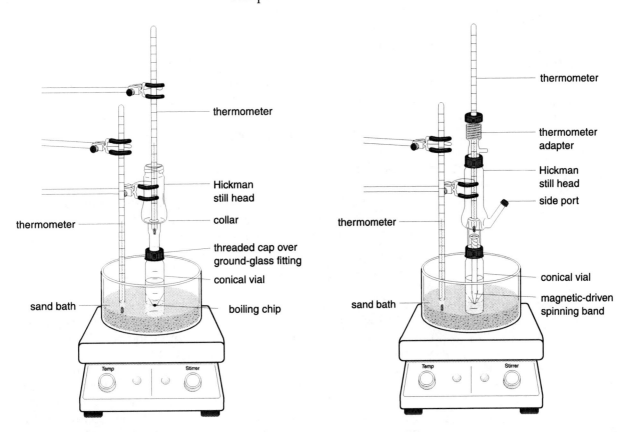

Figure 10 A Hickman still assembly for simple distillation   **Figure 11** A Hickman still assembly for fractional distillation

4. Cleaning Up   Use the labeled collection containers provided by your laboratory instructor. Clean your glassware with soap or detergent.

Caution: Wash your hands thoroughly with soap or detergent before leaving the laboratory.

Microscale Distillations

C. Using Test Tube Reflux

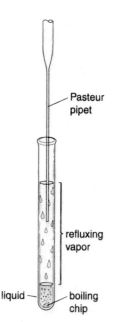

Pasteur pipet

refluxing vapor

liquid — boiling chip

Figure 12   Simple distillation of very small samples using a test tube and a Pasteur pipet

Equipment

boiling chips	support stand
copper metal sponge*	2 test tubes, 13 × 100-mm
microspatula	−10 to 260 °C thermometer
2 Pasteur pipets, with latex bulb	utility clamp
sand bath†	6 vials, 2-mL, with screw caps

*for fractional distillation

†sand in crystallizing dish on electric hot plate or sand in electric heating well with heat controller

Reagents and Properties

substance	quantity (mL)	mol mass (g/mol)	bp (°C)
cyclohexane	1.0	84.16	80.7
toluene	1.0	92.14	110.6

Preview

- Assemble apparatus and add cyclohexane–toluene mixture
- Save sample of original simple distillation mixture for analysis
- Distill approximately half of the mixture
- Transfer residue to vial
- Using refractive index, analyze the composition of the original mixture, the distillate, and the pot residue
- Repeat the Procedure for fractional distillation, using a test tube packed with copper metal sponge

PROCEDURE   *Caution:*   Wear departmentally approved safety goggles at all times while in the chemistry laboratory.

Always use caution in the laboratory. Many chemicals are potentially harmful. Prevent contact with your eyes, skin, and clothing. Avoid ingesting any of the reagents.

Caution: Cyclohexane is flammable and irritating. Toluene is flammable and toxic. If possible, use a *fume hood.*

1. Conducting Simple Distillation

Place 1.0 mL each of cyclohexane and toluene into a 13 × 100-mm test tube. Mix well and add one small boiling chip. Using a Pasteur pipet, remove about 5 drops of the mixture, and place the drops into a small vial labeled "Original Mixture–Simple". [NOTE 1]

Clamp the test tube in a vertical position. Use a sand bath to heat the liquid until the liquid boils and the condensation line for the vapor is about 2 cm from the top of the test tube, as shown in Figure 12.

Squeeze the bulb of a Pasteur pipet, place the pipet tip into the hot vapors, and *very slowly* draw the vapors into the cool pipet, where the vapors will condense. Transfer this distillate to a small vial labeled

NOTE 1:   Cyclohexane and toluene are volatile. Cap the vials to ensure that the small samples do not evaporate.

"Distillate–Simple". Repeat the process until you collect about half of the mixture in the distillate vial.

Remove the test tube from the sand bath, allow it to cool, and transfer the remaining liquid into a vial labeled "Pot Residue–Simple".

2. Conducting Fractional Distillation

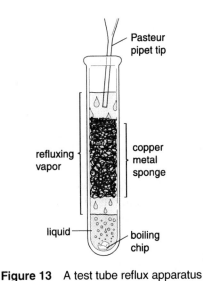

Figure 13 A test tube reflux apparatus for conducting a fractional distillation

Place 1.0 mL each of cyclohexane and toluene into a 13 × 100-mm test tube, mix well, and add one small boiling chip. Using a Pasteur pipet, remove 5–10 drops of the mixture and place the drops into a small vial labeled "Original Mixture–Fractional". [NOTE 1]

Prepare a plug of copper sponge approximately 4 cm long. Tightly pack the copper plug into the test tube so that the bottom of the plug is about 1 cm above the top of the liquid and 3 cm below the mouth of the test tube, as shown in Figure 13.

Clamp the test tube in a vertical position and heat the liquid with a sand bath until the liquid boils. Observe the vapor condensation line as it moves through the copper sponge, and adjust the heat so that the condensation line reaches a point about 1 cm above the top of the copper.

Squeeze the bulb of a Pasteur pipet, place the tip into the hot vapors, and *very slowly* draw the vapors into the cool pipet, where they will condense. Transfer this distillate to a small vial labeled "Distillate–Fractional", and repeat the process until you collect about half of the mixture in the distillate vial.

Remove the test tube from the sand bath. Cool the test tube, remove the copper plug, and transfer the remaining liquid into a vial labeled "Pot Residue–Fractional".

3. Measuring Refractive Index

Using a refractometer, measure the refractive index of the compounds in each vial. Correct the refractive indices for temperature, using Equation 2.

Using the correlation curve shown in Figure 7 earlier in this module and the corrected refractive index for the solution in each collection vial, determine the percent of cyclohexane and toluene in each sample. Compare your results for simple and fractional distillation.

4. Cleaning Up

Use the labeled collection containers provided by your laboratory instructor. Clean your glassware with soap or detergent.

Caution: Wash your hands thoroughly with soap or detergent before leaving the laboratory.

Post-Laboratory Questions
1. For macroscale distillations, or for microscale distillations using glassware with elastomeric connectors, plot the data for simple distillation and for fractional distillation on one graph. Plot temperature on the vertical axis and total volume of distillate on the horizontal axis, as shown in Figure 6 earlier in this module. Draw a smooth curve through the data points for each distillation.

2. (a) At what temperatures were the first drop of distillate collected in the simple and fractional distillations?
   (b) Using Figure 1, estimate the composition of these initial samples of distillate. Based on the results, what conclusion can you draw regarding the relative efficiencies of the two separations?

3. For macroscale distillations, or for microscale distillations using glassware with elastomeric connectors, compare the plot from your simple distillation with that from your fractional distillation. In which case do the changes in temperature occur more gradually? Which method is more effective in achieving separation? Briefly explain.

4. For Hickman still or for test tube microscale distillations, compare the refractive index data for simple and fractional distillations. Do the data suggest which distillation procedure is more efficient? Briefly explain.

NAME _____   SECTION _____   DATE _____

TECH 704/Separating Cyclohexane and Toluene by Distillation

Pre-Laboratory Assignment

1. Briefly explain why you should not add boiling chips to a boiling liquid.

2. (a) Briefly explain how and why you should position the thermometer in the distillation head during a distillation.

   (b) What is the purpose of the outer jacket on a fractionating column?

   (c) How is the rate of heating adjusted when using a sand bath as a heat source?

   (d) How is the distillate collected in a test tube microscale distillation?

3. What effect does an increase in the heating rate have on the boiling temperature during a distillation?

4. As molecules move up a fractional distillation column, they condense and then revaporize. During which of these steps is the concentration of the more volatile compound of the mixture increased? Briefly explain.

5. Using Figure 2, estimate the composition of a cyclohexane–toluene distillate that is collected

at 85 °C;

at 95 °C;

at 105 °C.

ISBN 0-87540-704-8

Measuring the Melting Points of Compounds and Mixtures

Prepared by Joseph W. LeFevre, SUNY Oswego

PURPOSE OF THE EXPERIMENT

Measure the melting points of pure benzoic acid and pure mandelic acid. Determine the eutectic composition and the eutectic temperature of benzoic acid–mandelic acid mixtures. Identify an unknown compound using mixture melting points.

BACKGROUND REQUIRED

None

BACKGROUND INFORMATION

The **melting point** of a compound is the temperature at which the solid is in equilibrium with its liquid. A solid compound changes to a liquid when the molecules acquire enough energy to overcome the forces holding them together in an orderly crystalline lattice. For most organic compounds, these intermolecular forces are relatively weak.

The **melting point range** is defined as the span of temperature from the point at which the crystals first begin to liquefy to the point at which the entire sample is liquid. Most pure organic compounds melt over a narrow temperature range of 1–2 °C.

The presence of a soluble impurity almost always causes a decrease in the melting point expected for the pure compound and a broadening of the melting point range. In order to understand the effects of impurities on melting point behavior, consider the melting point–mass percent composition diagram for two different fictitious organic compounds, *X* and *Y*, shown in Figure 1. The vertical axis represents temperature and the horizontal axis represents varying mass percent compositions of *X* and *Y*.

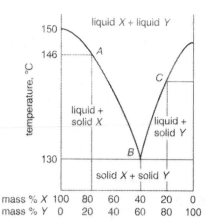

Figure 1

Melting point–mass percent composition diagram for a two-component mixture

Both compounds have sharp melting points. Compound X melts at 150 °C, as shown on the left vertical axis, and Y melts at 148 °C, as shown on the right vertical axis. As compound X is added to pure Y, the melting point of the mixture decreases along curve CB until a minimum temperature of 130 °C is reached. Point B corresponds to 40 mass percent X and 60 mass percent Y and is called the **eutectic composition** for compounds X and Y. Here, both solid X and solid Y are in equilibrium with the liquid. The **eutectic temperature** of 130 °C is the lowest possible melting point for a mixture of X and Y. At temperatures below 130 °C, mixtures of X and Y exist together only in solid form.

Consider a 100-microgram (μg) mixture composed of 20 μg of X and 80 μg of Y. In this mixture, X acts as an impurity in Y. As the mixture is heated, the temperature rises to the eutectic temperature of 130 °C. At this temperature, X and Y begin to melt together at point B, the eutectic composition of 40 mass percent X and 60 mass percent Y. The temperature remains constant at 130 °C until all 20 μg of X melts. At the eutectic temperature, X and Y will melt in the ratio of 40 parts X to 60 parts Y. If 20 μg of X melts, then 30 μg of Y (20 μg X × 60/40 ratio = 30 μg Y) also melts. At this point, the remaining 50 μg of solid Y (80 μg – 30 μg = 50 μg) is in equilibrium with a molten mixture of the eutectic composition.

As more heat is applied to the mixture, the temperature begins to rise, and the remaining Y begins to melt. Y continues to melt as the temperature increases, shown by curve BC.

Finally, at 142 °C, point C, where the liquid composition is 20 mass percent X and 80 mass percent Y, all of Y is melted. At temperatures higher than 142 °C, liquid X and liquid Y exist together with a composition of 20 mass percent X and 80 mass percent Y. Thus, the melting point at which the entire mixture liquefies is 142 °C, six degrees lower than the melting point of pure Y. Also, the melting point range 130–142 °C is quite broad.

In the previous example, X acts as an impurity in Y. Compound Y can also act as an impurity in X, as indicated in Figure 1 earlier in this experiment. For example, in a mixture composed of 80 μg of X and 20 μg of Y, the mixture begins to melt at the eutectic temperature of 130 °C. As before, at this temperature, the eutectic composition is 40 mass percent X and 60 mass percent Y. The temperature remains at 130 °C until all 20 μg of Y melts. At the eutectic temperature, X and Y will melt in the ratio of 40 parts X to 60 parts Y. Thus, if 20 µg of Y melts, 13 µg of X (20 µg $Y \times 40/60$ ratio = 13 µg X) also melts.

The remaining 67 µg of X (80 µg – 13 µg = 67 µg) melts over the range of 130 –146 °C, shown by curve BA. At 146 °C, the last traces of X melt. This melting range is larger than the range over which 20 mass percent X and 80 mass percent Y melts.

If a mixture has exactly the eutectic composition of 40 mass percent X and 60 mass percent Y, the mixture shows a sharp melting point at 130 °C. Observing this melting point could lead to the false conclusion that the mixture is a pure compound. Addition of either pure X or pure Y to the mixture causes an increase in the melting point, as indicated by curve BA or BC, respectively. Observing this melting point increase indicates that the original sample is not pure.

The initial melting that occurs at the eutectic temperature is sometimes very difficult to observe. This difficulty is especially true if only a small amount of an impurity is present, because the quantity of liquid produced at the eutectic temperature is very small. However, the temperature at which the last trace of solid melts can be accurately measured. Hence, a sample with a small amount of impurity will have an observed melting point much higher than the eutectic temperature, but lower than that of the pure compound.

Because the melting point of a compound is a physical constant, the melting point can be helpful in determining the identity of an unknown compound. A good correlation between the experimentally measured melting point of an unknown compound and the accepted melting point of a known compound suggests that the compounds may be the same. However, many different compounds have the same melting point.

A **mixture melting point** is useful in confirming the identity of an unknown compound. A small portion of a known compound, whose melting point is known from the chemical literature, is mixed with the unknown compound. If the melting point of the mixture is the same as that of the known compound, then the known and the unknown compounds are most likely identical. A decrease in the melting point of the mixture and a broadening of the melting point range indicates that the compounds are different. A flowchart for using a mixture melting point to identify an unknown compound is shown in Figure 2.

Melting points can also be used to assess compound purity. A melting point range of 5 °C or more indicates that a compound is impure. Purification of the compound causes the melting point range to narrow and the melting point to increase. Repeated purification may be necessary before the melting point range narrows to 1–2 °C and reaches its maximum value, indicating that the compound is pure.

Measuring Melting Points

In practice, measuring the melting point of a crystalline compound involves several steps. First, a finely powdered compound is packed into a melting point capillary tube to a depth of 1–2 mm. Then the capillary tube containing the sample compound is inserted into one of several devices used to measure melting points.

Figure 3(a) shows the Thiele tube apparatus, filled to the base of the neck with silicone oil or mineral oil. The capillary tube is attached to a thermometer so that the sample is located next to the middle of the

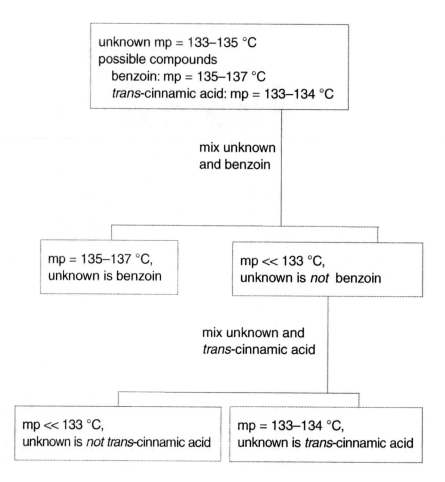

Figure 2

Flowchart for mixture melting point determination of an unknown

thermometer bulb. The thermometer is inserted into the oil and then the side arm of the Thiele tube is heated with a Bunsen burner flame.

The Thomas–Hoover Uni-Melt device, shown in Figure 3(b), contains silicone oil that is stirred and heated electrically. Silicone oil can be heated to temperatures up to 250 °C. With this device, up to seven samples can be analyzed at one time.

The Mel-Temp apparatus, shown in Figure 3(c) consists of an aluminum block that is heated electrically. The aluminum block can be heated easily to temperatures up to 400 °C, and can tolerate temperatures up to 500 °C for brief time periods. A thermometer and up to three samples can be inserted into the block at one time. A light and magnifier permit easy viewing of the sample(s).

If the melting point of the compound is unknown, it is convenient to first measure the approximate melting point of the compound, called the **orientation melting point.** The sample is heated at a rate of 10–15 °C per minute until it melts. Then the melting point apparatus is cooled to approximately 15 °C below the orientation melting point. A new sample is heated, increasing the temperature at a much slower rate of 1–2 °C per minute, to accurately measure the melting point. A slow heating rate is necessary because heating a sample too rapidly may cause the thermometer reading to differ from the actual temperature of the heat source. The

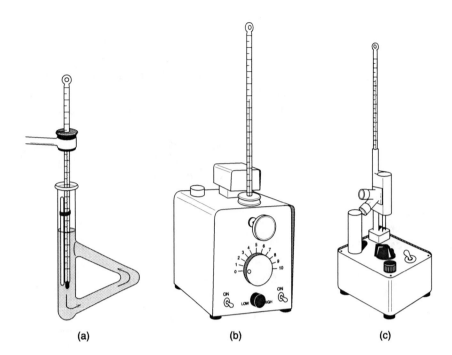

Figure 3
Different types of melting point apparatus: (a) Thiele tube; (b) Thomas–Hoover; (c) Mel-Temp

(a)   (b)   (c)

result would be an observed temperature reading that differs from the actual melting point temperature.

If the melting point of the sample is known, the sample can be quickly heated to within 10–15 °C of its melting point. Then the heating rate can be slowed to increase 1–2 °C per minute until the sample melts.

Errors in observed melting points often occur due to a poor heat transfer rate from the heat source to the compound. One cause of a poor heat transfer rate is the placement of too much sample into the capillary tube. Finely ground particles of the compound are also necessary for good heat transfer. If the particles are too coarse, they do not pack well, causing air pockets that slow heat transfer.

Sometimes slight changes, such as shrinking and sagging, occur in the crystalline structure of the sample before melting occurs. Also, traces of solvent may be present due to insufficient drying and may appear as droplets on the outside surface of the sample. This phenomenon is called **sweating** and should not be mistaken for melting. The initial melting point temperature always corresponds to the first appearance of liquid within the bulk of the sample itself.

Some compounds decompose at or near their melting points. This decomposition is usually characterized by a darkening in the color of the compound as it melts. If the decomposition and melting occur over a narrow temperature range of 1–2 °C, the melting point is used for identification and as an indication of sample purity. The melting point of such a compound is listed in the literature accompanied by *d* or *decomp.* If the sample melts over a large temperature range with decomposition, the data cannot be used for identification purposes.

Some compounds pass directly from solid to vapor without going through the liquid phase, a behavior called **sublimation.** When sublimation occurs, the sample at the bottom of the capillary tube vaporizes and recrystallizes higher up in the capillary tube. A sealed capillary tube is used to take the melting point of a compound that sublimes at or below its melting point. The literature reports the melting point for these compounds accompanied by *s, sub,* or *subl.*

In this experiment you will measure the melting points of benzoic acid, mandelic acid, and mixtures of these two compounds. Both compounds melt near 122 °C. You will use these data to construct a melting point–mass percent composition diagram. From this diagram, you will estimate the eutectic temperature and eutectic composition for benzoic acid and mandelic acid. Finally, using the mixture melting point method, you will identify an unknown compound.

Measuring the Melting Points of Compounds and Mixtures

Equipment

graph paper	metric ruler (mm)
marking pen	microspatula
melting point capillary tubes	2 watch glasses

Reagents and Properties

Substance	Quantity	Molar mass (g/mol)	mp (°C)	bp(°C)
benzoic acid	10 mg	122.12	122–123	249
mandelic acid	10 mg	152.15	120–122	

Preview

- Measure the melting point of benzoic acid
- Measure the melting point of mandelic acid
- Measure the melting point range of four mixtures containing various amounts of benzoic acid and mandelic acid
- Obtain a sample of an unknown compound
- Measure an orientation melting point and an accurate melting point of your unknown compound
- Obtain a sample of each of two substances appearing in Table 1 that have melting points similar to your unknown
- Prepare a mixture of your unknown compound and each of your selected compounds
- Measure the melting point of each mixture
- Identify your unknown compound

PROCEDURE

Wear departmentally approved safety goggles at all times while in the chemistry laboratory.

Always use caution in the laboratory. Many chemicals are potentially harmful. Prevent contact with your eyes, skin, and clothing. Avoid ingesting any of the reagents.

1. Measuring Melting Points of Benzoic Acid and Mandelic Acid

Benzoic acid is an irritant.

Place 2–3 mg of benzoic acid on a clean, dry watch glass. If the compound is not a fine powder, pulverize it using a microspatula.

Capillary tubes are fragile and easily broken.

Load a melting point capillary tube by pressing the open end of the tube into the powder. Pack the powder into the closed end of the tube by tapping the closed end against the bench top. Repeat the cycle of loading and packing until you can see 1–2 mm of benzoic acid through the tube.

NOTE: Make certain that no more than 1–2 mm of compound is placed in the capillary tube. A larger amount will give a melting point range that is too large.

To ensure good packing, drop the capillary tube with the open end up through a 1-m-long piece of glass tubing onto the bench top. Repeat several times. Place the capillary tube in the melting point apparatus provided by your laboratory instructor.

Because pure benzoic acid melts at 122–123 °C, heat the capillary tube rapidly to 110 °C. Then slow the heating rate to 1–2 °C per min. Record the temperature at which liquid first appears in the bulk of the sample and the temperature at which the entire sample becomes liquid.

NOTE: Heating the capillary tube too quickly near the melting point will result in an inaccurate melting point measurement.

The capillary tubes are hot. Allow them to cool enough to avoid burning your fingers.

When finished, remove the capillary tube. Place all used capillary tubes in the container labeled "Discarded Capillary Tubes", provided by your laboratory instructor.

Obtain 2–3 mg of mandelic acid and measure the melting point following the procedure described for benzoic acid. Pure mandelic acid melts at 120–122 °C.

2. Determining the Eutectic Temperature and Composition of a Benzoic Acid–Mandelic Acid Mixture

From your laboratory instructor, obtain four benzoic acid–mandelic acid mixtures of the following compositions:

	Percent benzoic acid	Percent mandelic acid
mixture 1	80	20
mixture 2	60	40
mixture 3	40	60
mixture 4	20	80

Using a marking pen, carefully label a capillary tube for each mixture. For example, near the top of the tube, mark the tube that will contain mixture 1 with one horizontal line. Similarly, mark the tubes for mixtures 2–4 with two, three, and four lines, respectively. Load each mixture into its capillary tube as previously described.

Place the capillaries containing mixtures 1 and 2 into the melting point apparatus. Heat the samples rapidly to 80 °C. Then slow the rate of increase to 1–2 °C per min. *Carefully* observe and record the temperature at which the crystals first begin to melt and the temperature at which the last trace of crystals melts.

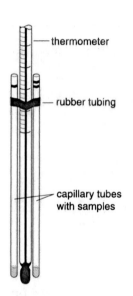

— thermometer

— rubber tubing

— capillary tubes with samples

Figure 4
Attachment of two capillary tubes to a thermometer

NOTE: If you are using a Thiele tube, place the samples to the left and right of the thermometer bulb. Secure them in place with a small ring of rubber tubing, as shown in Figure 4. Make certain the bottom of the capillary tube is positioned vertically near the midpoint of the thermometer bulb. Also, be certain the rubber tubing and pen marks are 2–3 cm above the oil surface because the oil expands when heated.

NOTE: If you are using a Mel-Temp apparatus, you will need to lift the samples a few millimeters above the base and slowly rotate the samples to see the last trace of crystals melt. Be careful not to break the capillary tubes.

Allow the apparatus to cool to 80 °C and repeat the melting point measurements, using the capillaries containing mixtures 3 and 4.

3. Identifying an Unknown Compound by Mixture Melting Point

CAUTION

Unknowns may be flammable, toxic, and irritating.

Obtain 10 mg of an unknown compound from your laboratory instructor and record its identification code. Pulverize the sample, label and load a capillary tube, and take an orientation melting point. Cool the apparatus to 15 °C below its orientation melting point. Prepare a new sample, and accurately measure the melting point.

From Table 1 (on the next page), identify the two compounds that have melting points closest to the melting point of your unknown compound. Obtain a few milligrams of each of these compounds. Place one known compound on a clean, dry, labeled watch glass. Add an approximately equal amount of your unknown compound.

Table 1 *Melting points of compounds used as unknowns*

Compound	mp (°C)	Compound	mp(°C)
benzhydrol	65–67	*trans*-cinnamic acid	133–134
biphenyl	69–72	benzoin	135–137
phenanthrene	99–101	benzilic acid	150–153
o-toluic acid	103–105	adipic acid	152–154
acetanilide	113–115	benzanilide	164–166
fluorene	114–116	4-bromoacetanilide	167–169
(*R,S*)-mandelic acid	120–122	4-hydroxybenzoic acid	215–217
benzoic acid	122–123	anthracene	216–218

Similarly, place the other known compound on a second watch glass and add an approximately equal amount of your unknown. Pulverize and mix each sample thoroughly, using a clean microspatula each time. Load the samples into separate, labeled capillary tubes. Also, load two capillary tubes with pure unknown.

Take the melting point of one of the mixtures and the pure unknown *simultaneously*. Quickly heat the samples to within 30 °C of the pure compound's melting point. Then slow the heating rate increase to 1–2 °C per min.

Repeat the procedure using the other mixture. Compare your data and identify your unknown.

4. Cleaning Up

Use the labeled collection containers provided by your laboratory instructor. Wash your glassware with soap or detergent.

CAUTION

Wash your hands thoroughly with soap or detergent before leaving the laboratory.

name   _section_   _date_

Post-Laboratory Questions

1. Using the data from Parts 1 and 2 of the Procedure, plot on graph paper the *upper temperatures* of the melting point ranges for benzoic acid and mandelic acid on the left and right vertical axes, respectively, as was done in Figure 1 for compounds *X* and *Y*. Plot the *upper temperatures* of the melting point ranges of the four mixtures on the same graph, using the proper mass percent of each compound on the horizontal axis. Use a temperature range of 80–130 °C on the vertical axis. From the graph, determine the approximate eutectic temperature and eutectic composition of a benzoic acid–mandelic acid mixture.

NOTE: Draw straight lines through the points, one straight line through the points for benzoic acid, mixture 1, and mixture 2; another straight line through the points for mandelic acid, mixture 3, and mixture 4. Do not attempt to curve lines as shown in Figure 1.

---

2. Using the melting point–mass percent composition diagram you drew for Question 1, identify the approximate melting point ranges for benzoic acid–mandelic acid mixtures of the following compositions.

   (a) 90:10

   (b) 70:30

   (c) 30:70

   (d) 10:90

3. Describe in detail the melting point behavior of the 80:20 benzoic acid–mandelic acid mixture.

4. Devise a flowchart similar to the one in Figure 2 to show how you identified your unknown.

5. Using your textbook or another appropriate resource, find the structural formula for your unknown. Make a drawing of the formula.

6. Briefly explain why you were told to simultaneously measure the melting points of the mixtures and of the pure unknown in Part 3 of the Procedure.

_____   _____   _____

Pre-Laboratory Assignment

1. Briefly identify or explain

(a) two useful functions served by knowing the melting point of an organic compound.

(b) why a finely powdered sample should be used in a melting point measurement.

(c) why it is important to heat a sample slowly to obtain an accurate melting point.

(d) two reasons why it is sometimes difficult to measure the temperature at which the crystals first begin to liquefy.

(e) what two effects a soluble impurity usually has on the melting point of a compound.

(f) what occurred when crystals began to disappear from the bottom of the capillary tube rather than turning to a liquid.

2. A sample has an experimental melting point of 100–101 °C. Can you conclude that the sample is pure? Briefly explain your reasoning.

3. Using Figure 1, explain in detail the melting point behavior of a mixture composed of 60 mass percent X and 40 mass percent Y.

4. An unknown compound melted at 131–133 °C. It is thought to be one of the following compounds (mp, °C): *trans*-cinnamic acid (133–134); benzamide (128–130); DL-malic acid (131–133); or benzoin (135–137). The mixture melting points of the unknown compound with each of the test compounds are listed below. What is the unknown compound? Briefly explain your reasoning.

Unknown plus	mp range (°C)
trans-cinnamic acid	110–120
benzamide	130–132
DL-malic acid	114–124
benzoin	108–116

5. Using your textbook or another appropriate resource, find the structural formula for benzoic acid and mandelic acid. Draw the structural formulas of these compounds.

Purifying Acetanilide by Recrystallization

Prepared by Carl Wigal, Lebanon Valley College

PURPOSE OF THE EXPERIMENT

Select an appropriate recrystallizing solvent. Separate and purify acetanilide from a mixture by recrystallization. Compare the melting points of impure and recrystallized acetanilide.

BACKGROUND REQUIRED

You should know how to measure mass, in milligrams, and volume, in milliliters. You should know how to measure melting points.

BACKGROUND INFORMATION

Impurities often contaminate organic compounds that have been synthesized in the laboratory or isolated from natural sources. **Recrystallization** is a purification process used to remove impurities from organic compounds that are solid at room temperature. This process is based on the premise that the solubility of a compound in a solvent increases with temperature. Conversely, the solubility of the compound decreases as the solution cools, and crystals form.

Very pure compounds can be produced by recrystallization. As a heated solution of the desired compound cools, a small, pure seed crystal of the compound forms in the solution. Layer by layer, additional molecules attach to this crystal, forming a growing crystal lattice, as shown in Figure 1. The molecules in the crystal have a greater affinity for other molecules of the same kind than they do for any impurities present in the solution. In effect, the process of crystal formation removes one kind of molecule from the solution.

Choosing a Recrystallizing Solvent

Selecting an appropriate recrystallizing solvent to use is probably the most difficult step of recrystallization. The primary consideration when choosing a recrystallizing solvent is the extent to which the compound and impurities

Figure 1

(a) Identical molecules attach to one another, forming a crystal lattice; (b) impurities have different shapes or sizes and do not layer

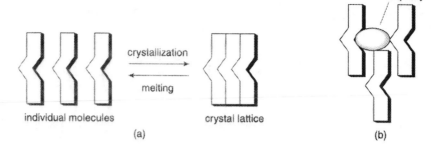

Figure 2

Ideal solubility patterns of a compound, line A, and accompanying impurities, lines B and C, at varying temperatures

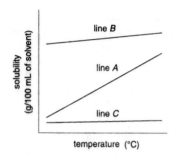

are soluble in the solvent at high and low temperatures. The graph in Figure 2 shows three possible scenarios for how the solubilities of the compound and the impurities depend on temperature.

Ideally, the compound to be recrystallized should be very soluble in the chosen solvent at elevated temperatures, but almost insoluble in the cold solvent, as shown by line A. Impurities should be soluble in the chosen solvent at all temperatures so that impurities stay in solution, as shown by line B. Alternatively, impurities should be insoluble at all temperatures so they can be filtered from the hot solution, as shown by line C.

Experimentation is needed to select an appropriate recrystallizing solvent. Typically, several solvents are used to test the extent of solubility of the compound. A small amount of the compound is mixed with a few milliliters of each solvent. The compound's solubility is observed at room temperature and near the solvent's boiling point. If the compound is soluble in a solvent at room temperature, the solvent is not suitable. If the compound is insoluble at room temperature and soluble near the solvent's boiling point, the solvent is a suitable candidate.

"Insoluble" is a relative term. All compounds are soluble to some extent in every solvent. For example, benzoic acid in water has a solubility of 6.80 grams per 100 milliliters at 100 °C. However, benzoic acid has a solubility of only 0.34 gram per 100 milliliters in water at 25 °C. Benzoic acid is typically listed as insoluble in 25 °C water.

When considering the solubility of an organic compound, a general rule is *like dissolves like*. Polar organic molecules contain functional groups that can hydrogen bond, such as $-OH$, $-NH_2$, and $-CO_2H$. Polar molecules are generally most soluble in polar solvents. Many organic molecules are nonpolar. Nonpolar molecules are most soluble in nonpolar solvents. A list of commonly used recrystallization solvents is shown in Table 1.

The boiling point of the recrystallization solvent should be lower than the melting point of the compound to be recrystallized. If the solvent's boiling point is higher than the compound's melting point, the compound will oil out. **Oiling out** occurs when a compound is insoluble in a solution at a temperature above the compound's melting point. As a result, the compound is deposited as an oil, and not as crystals.

Another important criterion for selecting a recrystallizing solvent relates to recovery of the compound. An abundant quantity of crystals must be produced as the solution cools to room temperature or below.

The four major criteria for selecting a recrystallizing solvent are summarized in Table 2.

Table 1 *Commonly used recrystallization solvents, in order of decreasing polarity*

Solvent	bp(°C)	Solvent	bp(°C)
Water	100	Ethyl ether	35
Methanol	65	Dichloromethane	40
Ethanol (95%)	78	Toluene	111
Acetone	56	Petroleum ether	35–60
Ethyl acetate	77		

Table 2 *Criteria for selecting a recrystallizing solvent*

(1) Compound being purified must be insoluble in solvent at room temperature

(2) Compound must be soluble in boiling solvent

(3) Solvent's boiling point must be lower than the compound's melting point

(4) An abundant quantity of crystals must be recoverable from the cool solvent

Often, the requirements necessary for successful recrystallization are not met by a single solvent. In these cases, a mixture of two solvents, called a **solvent pair,** is used. Two solvents are selected that are miscible with each other, but have opposite abilities to dissolve the compound. The compound to be recrystallized should be soluble in one solvent (*A*) of the pair and should be relatively insoluble in the second solvent (*B*).

To determine the proper combinations of the two solvents, the compound is dissolved in a minimum volume of solvent *A* near the boiling temperature of this solvent. Next, solvent *B* is added to the boiling mixture until the mixture becomes cloudy, indicating that the compound is precipitating from solution. A few drops of solvent *A* are added to redissolve the precipitate, producing a clear solution. Then the solvent pair is treated just like a single recrystallization solvent. Common solvent pairs are ethanol and water, acetone and ether, and acetic acid and water.

Dissolving the Compound

Once a suitable solvent is found, the recrystallization process is continued by dissolving the compound in a minimum volume of boiling solvent. Then a five percent excess of the solvent is added to the saturated solution to prevent premature crystallization. For example, if 10 mL of a boiling solvent is required to *just* dissolve a compound, five percent of 10 mL or 0.5 mL would be added to bring the total volume to 10.5 mL.

Decolorizing the Solution

Occasionally, a sample may contain a soluble impurity that produces a colored solution, and that solution colors crystals that would otherwise be colorless. In that case, activated carbon, or decolorizing carbon, is used to remove these colored impurities from solution. Activated carbon has a

Figure 3
A gravity filtration apparatus used to filter undissolved impurities

Recrystallizing Pure Compound

Collecting, Washing, and Drying the Crystals

surface area that adsorbs dissolved organic substances. Adding an excess of carbon must be avoided, because carbon can also adsorb the compound that is being recrystallized, reducing the percent recovery.

The hot solution is filtered by gravity filtration through a funnel containing a fluted filter paper to remove any insoluble compound, including the carbon. If no undissolved impurities are present, or if carbon has not been added, the filtration step is omitted. A typical gravity filtration apparatus is shown in Figure 3. The funnel, filter paper, and collection flask are heated with boiling solvent prior to filtering the solution to prevent premature crystal formation.

Using a *fluted* filter paper increases surface area inside the funnel and speeds the filtering process. Figure 4 on the next page shows how to produce a fluted filter paper.

After the compound is dissolved in a minimal amount of boiling solvent and the solution is filtered, as necessary, the solution is allowed to slowly cool to room temperature. If crystal formation occurs too rapidly, impurities may become trapped in the crystals. Then the filtered solution is cooled in an ice-water bath for a few minutes to maximize crystal formation. Crystals usually form as the solution temperature decreases.

Sometimes, crystals do not form in the cooled solution. In this case, two methods can be used to induce crystallization. One method involves scratching the inside of the flask with a glass stirring rod. The freshly scratched glass supplies sites for seed crystal formation. Alternatively, a seed crystal of the pure compound can be placed into the solution to promote crystal growth.

Vacuum filtration is the best method for separating the crystals from the **mother liquor,** or remaining solvent. A typical vacuum filtration apparatus is shown in Figure 5 on the next page.

In vacuum filtration, a receiver flask with a sidearm, called a **filter flask,** is connected by heavy-walled vacuum tubing to a vacuum source. A Büchner funnel is fitted to the filter flask with a rubber stopper or filter adapter.

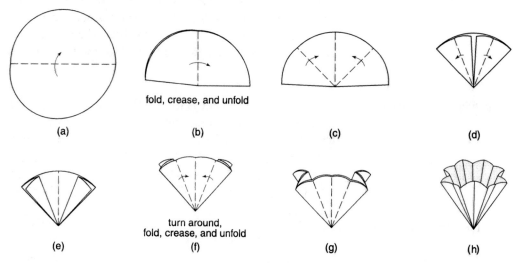

Figure 4
Folding a fluted filter paper

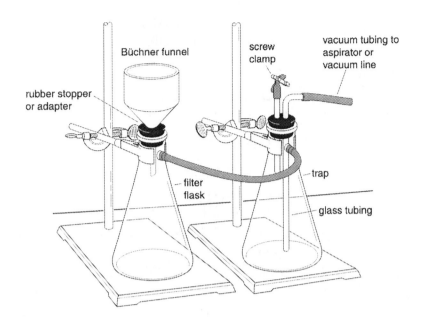

Figure 5
A typical vacuum filtration apparatus

The most common source of vacuum is a **water aspirator.** In a water aspirator, water moves past a small hole leading into a sidearm that can be attached to a trap. A partial vacuum is created because of the reduced pressure at the point where the rapidly moving water passes the hole. At that point, air is pulled into the aspirator sidearm. This phenomenon is called the **Bernoulli effect.**

A **trap** can be used in tandem with a water aspirator to prevent contamination of the solution in the filter flask with water. Sudden drops in water pressure can cause water to be drawn into the filter flask. Fitting a trap between the filter flask and the aspirator prevents any reverse water flow from reaching the filter flask.

To recover the pure crystals, the perforated Büchner funnel plate is covered with a filter paper disk, which is moistened with recrystallization solvent. With vacuum applied, the solution containing the suspended crystals is poured onto the filter paper so that a uniform thickness of crystals collects on the paper. After the mother liquor has been pulled through the filter, the crystals are washed with small portions of cold solvent. Then the crystals are dried and their mass is measured.

Calculating Percent Recovery

Percent recovery is calculated by dividing the mass of the recrystallized compound by the mass of the crude compound before recrystallization, as shown in Equation 1.

$$\% \text{ recovery} = \left(\frac{\text{mass of recrystallized compound, g}}{\text{mass of crude compound, g}} \right)(100\%) \quad \text{(Eq. 1)}$$

Assessing Purity

Purity of a recrystallized compound is assessed by observing its color and by measuring its melting point range. If a compound is described in the chemical literature as having white crystals, the recrystallized compound should appear white. If the compound has an off-white color, the compound should again be recrystallized using activated carbon.

A pure compound melts over a narrow range of 1–3 °C near its reported melting point. If a *dry* recrystallized compound has a melting point range of four degrees or more, it should be recrystallized again.

PURIFYING ACETANILIDE BY RECRYSTALLIZATION

Equipment

2 beakers, 100-mL	Microspatula
250-mL beaker[†]	Pasteur pipet, with latex bulb
Büchner funnel, with filter paper	Sand bath[*]
2 graduated Erlenmeyer flasks, 25-mL	Screw clamp
	Stirring rod, glass
11-cm fluted filter paper	2 support stands
125-mL filter flask, with 1-hole stopper	5 test tubes, 13 × 100-mm
	2 utility clamps
Short-stem filter funnel	Vacuum trap
10-mL graduated cylinder	250-mL filter flask
25-mL graduated cylinder	2-hole stopper
Hot plate	2 pieces glass or plastic tubing
Labels	Vacuum tubing

[*]or crystallizing dish on electric hot plate or electric heating well with heat controller
[†]for ice bath

Reagents and Properties

Substance	Quantity	Molar mass (g/mol)	mp (°C)	bp(°C)
Acetanilide	1 g	135.17	113–115	
Acetone	2 mL	58.08		56
Carbon, activated	60 mg			
Ethanol	2 mL	46.07		78
Petroleum ether	2 mL	*		35–60

[*]mixture of hydrocarbons

Preview

- Check solubility of acetanilide in four solvents
- Choose a recrystallizing solvent
- Weigh the acetanilide
- Dissolve the acetanilide in the hot recrystallizing solvent
- Add activated carbon to remove dissolved impurities and filter the hot solution

- Recrystallize the pure acetanilide
- Collect the crystals of acetanilide
- Wash, dry, and weigh the crystals
- Measure the melting points of crude and recrystallized acetanilide

PROCEDURE

CAUTION

Wear departmentally approved safety goggles at all times while in the chemistry laboratory.

Always use caution in the laboratory. Many chemicals are potentially harmful. Prevent contact with your eyes, skin, and clothing. Avoid ingesting any of the reagents.

1. Choosing a Recrystallizing Solvent

CAUTION

Acetanilide is toxic and irritating. Acetone and ethanol are flammable and irritating. Petroleum ether is flammable and toxic. Use these compounds in a *fume hood*.

Label four 13 × 100-mm test tubes "acetone", "water", "ethanol", and "petroleum ether". Place approximately 100 mg of acetanilide into each test tube. Use a microspatula to pulverize the acetanilide. Place 2.0 mL of the appropriate solvent into each test tube. Thoroughly stir each mixture. Record whether the acetanilide is soluble or insoluble in each solvent at room temperature.

NOTE: Lumps of acetanilide may be slow to dissolve, interfering with the correct solvent selection.

CAUTION

Heated test tubes containing solvent boil over easily. Be careful to avoid burns from the hot solvent.

Select the test tube(s) containing the solvent(s) in which acetanilide did not dissolve at room temperature. Using a sand bath, heat the mixture(s) to boiling. Record whether acetanilide is soluble or insoluble in each hot solvent.

Allow the heated solvent(s) to cool slowly to room temperature. Prepare an ice–water bath by half filling a 250-mL beaker with equal volumes of ice and water. Place the tube(s) into the bath for 5 min, and observe whether recrystallization occurs. Record your observations.

Based on your observations, choose an appropriate solvent from which to recrystallize acetanilide. Consult your laboratory instructor concerning your solvent choice before proceeding to Part 2. Place the solvents in the test tubes into appropriate containers labeled "Recovered Acetone", "Recovered Ethanol", "Recovered Water", and "Recovered Petroleum Ether", provided by your laboratory instructor.

2. Dissolving the Compound

Weigh 500 mg of acetanilide and place it into a 25-mL Erlenmeyer flask. Place 15 mL of the appropriate recrystallizing solvent into a second 25-mL Erlenmeyer flask. Add a boiling chip. Using a hot plate, heat the solvent to boiling.

Using beaker tongs, pick up the hot flask containing the boiling solvent. Use a Pasteur pipet to add 0.5–1 mL of boiling solvent to the flask containing the acetanilide. Swirl the flask with each addition. Keep the solvent in both flasks at boiling by placing the flasks on the hot plate. Continue the solvent additions until the acetanilide *just* dissolves.

Using beaker tongs, remove the flasks from the hot plate. Allow the acetanilide solution to cool below the solvent boiling point. Observe the solution color. Record your observations. Measure and record your solvent volume.

Calculate the additional solvent volume needed to have a 5% excess. Measure and add that solvent volume to the acetanilide flask.

3. Decolorizing the Solution

CAUTION

Activated carbon is an irritant. Prevent eye, skin, and clothing contact. Avoid inhaling dust and ingesting the carbon. *Do not add carbon to a boiling solution.* This addition will cause the solution to boil over and burn your skin. Also, do not boil a solution containing carbon too vigorously, or the solution may boil over.

Assemble a gravity filtration apparatus, as shown in Figure 3 earlier in this module. Weigh 60 mg of activated carbon. *Conduct the Procedure in Parts A and B simultaneously.*

NOTE: So that crystals will not form in the funnel, plan to filter the boiling solution from Part *B* using the filter apparatus from Part *A* while the filter apparatus is still hot.

A. Heating the Gravity Filtration Apparatus

Place 20 mL of the recrystallizing solvent into a 100-mL beaker. Add a boiling chip. Heat the solvent to boiling on a hot plate. Using beaker tongs, pick up the hot beaker containing the boiling solvent. Preheat the filtration apparatus by pouring the solvent through the funnel containing a fluted filter paper. Do not allow the boiling chip to go into the funnel. Collect the solvent in another beaker. Place the gravity filtration apparatus on the hot plate to keep the solvent hot.

B. Adding the Activated Carbon

At the same time, add the 60 mg of activated carbon to the Erlenmeyer flask with the acetanilide solution. Reheat the solution to boiling.

When you have completed Parts *A* and *B*, pour the boiling solvent from the filtration apparatus beaker into the other 100-mL beaker. *While the gravity filtration apparatus is still hot from the recrystallizing solvent,* filter the boiling solution containing the carbon through the gravity filtration apparatus. Collect the liquid in the 25-mL receiving flask. Observe the color of the filtered solution. Record your observations.

4. Recrystallizing Pure Acetanilide

Allow the decolorized solution containing the acetanilide to cool to room temperature. When the solution has reached room temperature, place the Erlenmeyer flask into an ice–water bath for 5 min to complete the crystallization.

5. Collecting, Washing, and Drying the Crystals

While the solvent and solution are cooling in the ice bath, assemble a vacuum filtration apparatus as shown in Figure 5 earlier in this module, using a 125-mL filter flask. Also prepare a washing solvent by placing 5 mL of the recrystallizing solvent into a test tube. Cool the tube and its contents in the ice-water bath.

Weigh a filter paper and record its mass. Once crystallization is complete, turn on the water to the aspirator, and moisten the filter paper with a few drops of recrystallizing solvent. Swirl the flask containing the acetanilide, and pour the crystals and mother liquor into the Büchner funnel, using a glass rod to direct the crystals to the middle of the filter paper.

After the mother liquor has been pulled into the filter flask, release the vacuum by loosening the screw clamp on the trap. Remove the Büchner funnel from the filter flask and pour the mother liquor into a beaker. Tighten the screw clamp and reattach the Büchner funnel.

Use 4–5 mL portions of the mother liquor to rinse the remaining crystals of acetanilide from the Erlenmeyer flask. Pour the rinses into the Büchner funnel.

Wash the crystals in the Büchner funnel with the cold recrystallizing solvent. Allow the crystals to dry by pulling air through the funnel for 10 min. Then disconnect the vacuum tubing and turn off the aspirator. Remove the filter paper and crystals. Disassemble the filtration apparatus.

Weigh your dried crystals and filter paper, and record the mass. Observe the color and shape of the crystals and record your observations.

Measure and record the melting point ranges of both crude and recrystallized acetanilide. If your laboratory instructor directs you to do so, place your crystals into a labeled sample vial to turn in.

6. Cleaning Up

Use the labeled collection containers provided by your laboratory instructor. Clean your glassware with soap or detergent.

⚠️

CAUTION

Wash your hands thoroughly with soap or detergent before leaving the laboratory.

_____   _____   _____
name   *section*   *date*

Post-Laboratory Questions

1. The solubility of benzoic acid in water is 6.80 g per 100 mL at 100 °C and 0.34 g per 100 mL at 25 °C.

   (a) Calculate the minimum volume of water needed to dissolve 1.00 g of benzoic acid at 100 °C.

   (b) Calculate the maximum theoretical percent recovery from the recrystallization of 1.00 g of benzoic acid from 15 mL of water, assuming the solution is filtered at 25 °C.

2. The solubility of acetanilide in your recrystallizing solvent is 5.0 mg per mL at 10 °C.

   (a) Calculate the maximum percent recovery in this experiment, assuming a 15.0-mL recrystallizing solution is filtered at 10 °C.

   (b) Calculate the percent recovery of the acetanilide produced in your experiment.

   (c) How do your results compare to the maximum percent recovery? Briefly explain.

3. A student rushed through this experiment. Describe the effect that the following procedural changes would have on the percent recovery of acetanilide. Briefly explain the basis of each answer.

   (a) Rather than adding 0.5-mL portions of boiling solvent to the acetanilide, the student added 5-mL portions of boiling solvent.

   (b) The student did not pre-heat the gravity filtration apparatus in Part 3.

   (c) The student forgot to cool 5 mL of solvent in Part 5 and washed the crystals with room-temperature solvent.

_____   _____   _____
name   section   date

Pre-Laboratory Assignment

1. Briefly explain why

    (a) you should not heat organic solvents over a Bunsen burner flame.

    (b) you should add activated carbon to a cool solution and then heat the mixture to boiling rather than add the carbon to a boiling solution.

2. Indicate a procedure to solve the following recrystallization problems.

    (a) oiling out

    (b) lack of crystal formation

    (c) presence of colored impurities

    (d) premature recrystallization in the funnel stem during gravity filtration

3. Compound *A*, a white crystalline solid with a melting point of 75 °C, has the solubility profile shown in the following table. Which of the solvents listed would be a good recrystallizing solvent for Compound *A*? Briefly explain. The boiling points for these solvents are shown in Table 1 earlier in this module.

Compound A solubility profile

Solvent	Solubility at 25 °C	Solubility at boiling point
Water	I	S
Methanol	I	S
Acetone	S	S
Ethyl ether	S	S

4. A student purified a 500-mg sample of phthalic acid by recrystallization from water. The published solubility of phthalic acid in 100 mL of water is 0.54 g at 14 °C and 18 g at 99 °C.

(a) What is the smallest volume of boiling water the student could use to dissolve 500 mg of phthalic acid?

Dissolution of phthalic acid in boiling water produced a dark-colored solution. The student allowed the solution to cool, added several spatulas full of activated carbon, and heated the mixture to boiling. After gravity filtration, the clear and colorless solution was allowed to cool to room temperature. Crystals formed, and the student isolated 380 mg of phthalic acid.

(b) Calculate the percent recovery of phthalic acid in this experiment.

(c) Suggest one or more procedural errors the student made that could be responsible for some loss of phthalic acid.

Isolating Clove Oil from Cloves Using Steam Distillation

Prepared by Joseph W. LeFevre, SUNY Oswego

PURPOSE OF THE EXPERIMENT

Isolate clove oil from cloves by steam distillation and extraction. Use reactions with bromine, potassium permanganate, and iron(III) chloride to characterize the product. Analyze the product purity by thin-layer chromatography.

EXPERIMENTAL OPTIONS

Semi-Microscale Steam Distillation
Microscale Steam Distillation
  Using Glassware with Elastomeric Connectors
  Using the Hickman Still
Characterizing the Product

BACKGROUND REQUIRED

You should be familiar with distillation, extraction, drying organic solvents, speeding evaporation of organic solvents, thin-layer chromatography, and general microscale techniques.

BACKGROUND INFORMATION

Simple and fractional distillations are carried out on miscible mixtures. Ideal mixtures follow **Raoult's law:** The total vapor pressure of the system is determined by adding together the products of the vapor pressure and the respective mole fraction of each compound. For a two-compound system, this relationship is shown in Equation 1, where P_T is the total vapor pressure, P_1^0 and P_2^0 are the vapor pressures of pure compounds 1 and 2, and X_1 and X_2 are the respective mole fractions.

$$P_T = P_1^0 X_1 + P_2^0 X_2 \qquad \text{(Eq. 1)}$$

Distillation can also be performed on mixtures in which the two compounds are *not* miscible. This process is called **codistillation**. When one of the compounds is water, the process is called **steam distillation**.

When two immiscible liquids are distilled, the total vapor pressure P_T above the liquid is equal to the sum of the vapor pressures of each compound. This relationship, known as **Dalton's law**, is shown in Equation 2.

$$P_T = P_1^0 + P_2^0 \qquad \text{(Eq. 2)}$$

The respective mole fractions are *not* included in this equation because, in an ideal situation, each liquid vaporizes independently of the other. When P_T is equal to atmospheric pressure of 760 torr, compounds 1 and 2 begin to codistill, with each compound contributing to P_T.

Consider water as compound 1. The vapor pressure of pure water at its boiling point of 100 °C is 760 torr. Because compound 2 also contributes to P_T, the mixture will distill at a temperature less than 100 °C. The actual distillation temperature will depend on the vapor pressure of compound 2. Steam distillation offers an advantage in that volatile compounds that are unstable or have high boiling points can codistill with water at relatively low temperatures. This process avoids decomposition that might occur at the normal boiling point of the compound of interest. For example, eugenol, the major compound of clove oil, boils at a relatively high temperature of 254 °C. Steam distillation avoids this high temperature and results in the distillation of eugenol at a temperature slightly less than 100 °C.

In practice, steam distillation is usually carried out by one of two methods. In the first method, an excess of water is added to the compound of interest in a distilling flask. The mixture is then heated to the boiling point. The resulting vapor is condensed and collected in a receiving flask. The compound of interest is then separated from the water, often by extraction. In the second method, steam is bubbled into the compound of interest to effect the distillation. In this experiment, you will use the first method because it is easier to set up.

Clove oil belongs to a large class of natural products called the **essential oils**. Many of these compounds are used as flavorings and perfumes and, in the past, were considered to be the "essence" of the plant from which they were derived.

Cloves are the dried flower buds of the clove tree, *Eugenia caryophyllata*, found in India and other locations in the Far East. Steam distillation of freshly ground cloves results in clove oil, which consists of several compounds. Eugenol is the major compound, comprising 85–90 percent. Eugenol acetate comprises 9–10 percent. These structures are shown in Figure 1.

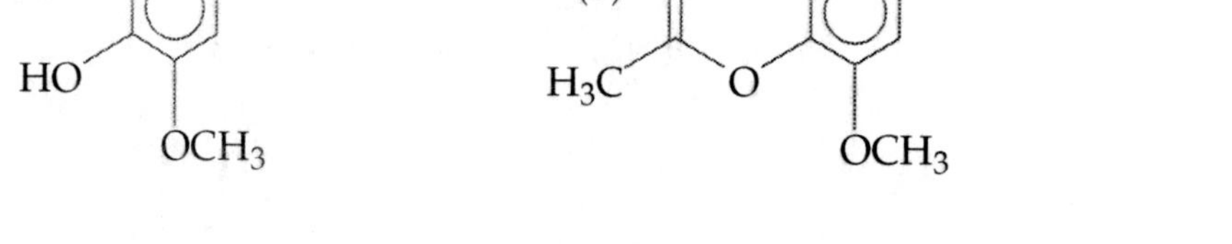

Figure 1
Structures for (a) eugenol and (b) eugenol acetate

Qualitative Tests

Eugenol contains a carbon–carbon double bond and an aromatic hydroxyl group called a phenol. These functional groups provide the basis for simple chemical tests used to characterize the clove oil. A solution of bromine (Br_2) in dichloromethane decolorizes as Br_2 reacts with the double bond to form a colorless compound, as shown in Equation 3. A positive test is the disappearance of the red Br_2 color.

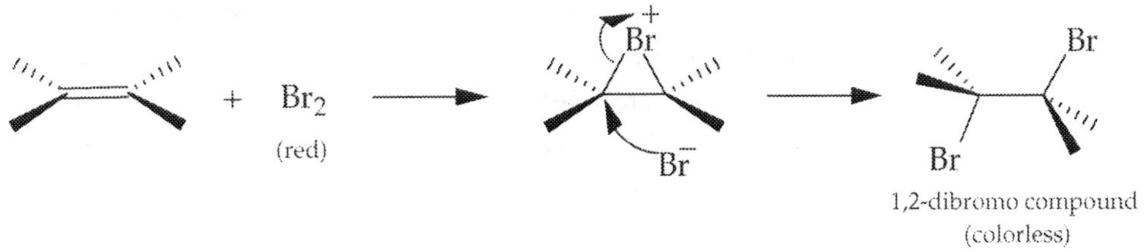

(Eq. 3)

1,2-dibromo compound
(colorless)

A potassium permanganate ($KMnO_4$) solution can oxidize a double bond at room temperature to form a 1,2-diol with the simultaneous reduction of Mn^{7+} in $KMnO_4$ to Mn^{4+} in manganese dioxide (MnO_2), as shown in Equation 4. A positive test is the disappearance of the purple $KMnO_4$ and the appearance of MnO_2 as a muddy brown precipitate.

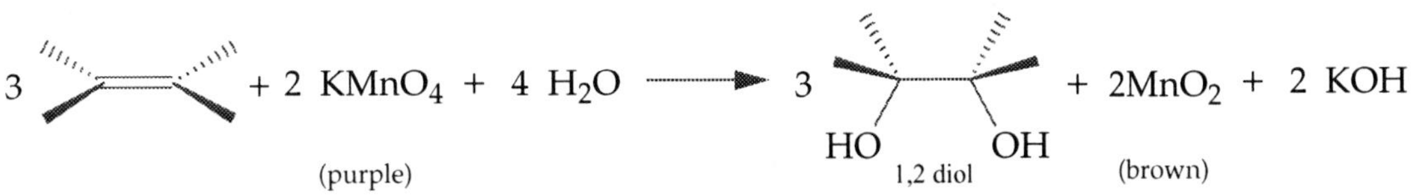

(Eq. 4)

Phenols (Ar–OH) react with the Fe^{3+} ion in iron(III) chloride ($FeCl_3$) to give complexes that are blue, green, red, or purple, as shown in Equation 5. The color may last for only a few seconds or for many hours, depending on the stability of the complex.

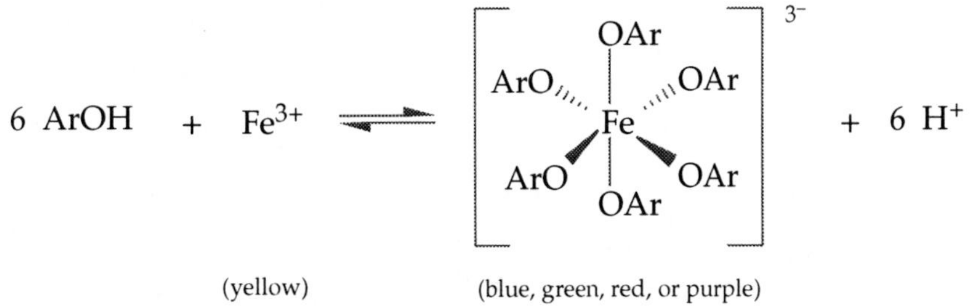

(Eq. 5)

In this experiment, you will steam distill clove oil from freshly ground cloves. Following the distillation, clove oil and water will be present in the receiving flask. Because clove oil will be a minor fraction of the distillate, the clove oil must be extracted from the water into an organic solvent such as dichloromethane. Removing the dichloromethane layer leaves clove oil as the product.

Semi-Microscale Steam Distillation

Equipment

boiling chips	sand bath[†‡]
Bunsen burner	125-mL separatory funnel[§]
cotton[*]	standard-taper glassware
electric flask heater	Claisen connecting tube
50-mL Erlenmeyer flask,	condenser,
with stopper	with adapter and tubing
glass stirring rod	distilling head
10-mL graduated cylinder	100-mL round-bottom flask
50-mL graduated cylinder	2 round-bottom flasks, 50-mL
marking pen	thermometer, −10 to 260 °C,
microspatula	with adapter
mortar and pestle	support ring
3 Pasteur pipets, with latex bulb	2 support stands
powder funnel	3 utility clamps

[*] for Pasteur filter pipet
[†] or hot-water bath
[‡] sand in crystallizing dish on electric hot plate or sand in electric heating well with heat controller
[§] also use as addition funnel

Reagents and Properties

Substance	Quantity	Molar mass (g/mol)	bp (°C)
cloves	5 g		
dichloromethane	21 mL	84.93	40
eugenol[*]		164.20	254
methanol	10 mL	32.04	64.7
sodium chloride, sat. solution	10 mL	58.44	
sodium sulfate, anhydrous	0.5 g	142.04	

[*]product

Preview

- Grind the cloves with a mortar and pestle
- Place the ground cloves and water in the distilling flask
- Assemble the steam distillation apparatus
- Distill the mixture
- Extract the clove oil into dichloromethane
- Dry the dichloromethane layer with anhydrous Na_2SO_4
- Remove the dichloromethane from the clove oil by distillation
- Weigh the clove oil

PROCEDURE

Chemical Alert

dichloromethane—*toxic and irritant*
eugenol—*irritant*
methanol—*flammable and toxic*
anhydrous sodium sulfate—*irritant and hygroscopic*

CAUTION

Wear departmentally approved safety goggles at all times while in the chemistry laboratory.

1. Conducting Steam Distillation

Weigh 5 g of whole cloves. Grind them to a coarse powder, using a mortar and pestle. Reweigh the powder and record the mass.

Use a powder funnel to transfer the ground cloves to a 100-mL round-bottom flask. Add 40 mL of deionized or distilled water and a boiling chip to the flask. Mix well with a glass stirring rod. Mark the level of the mixture on the side of the flask.

Add 30 mL of water to a 50-mL round-bottom flask. Mark the level of the water on the side of the flask. Then discard the water from the flask.

Assemble the steam distillation apparatus shown in Figure 2. Use the 100-mL round-bottom flask as the pot. Use the 50-mL round-bottom flask as the receiver. If a vacuum adapter is not used, *make certain there is an opening to the atmosphere.* Pour 100 mL of water into the addition funnel. Start the flow of water through the condenser.

Adjust a Bunsen burner flame to lessen the hot central cone. Heat the pot by waving the flame back and forth under the pot. Maintain a distillation rate of approximately one drop every 3–5 s.

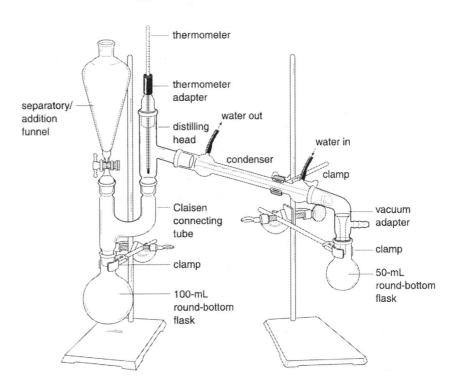

Figure 2
Semi-microscale steam distillation apparatus

© 1998 Cengage Learning

NOTE: Do not heat the mixture too rapidly. The clove mixture tends to foam when rapidly heated. The burner flame can easily be added and withdrawn to control the heating rate.

Add water to the pot at 10-min intervals to keep the water level at the mark. Stop the distillation when approximately 30 mL of distillate has been collected.

2. Extracting the Clove Oil

CAUTION

Dichloromethane is toxic and irritating. Use a *fume hood*. Clove oil (eugenol) is irritating. Prevent eye, skin, and clothing contact.

Allow the receiver to cool to room temperature. Carefully pour the distillate from the receiver into a 125-mL separatory funnel. Add 10 mL of saturated NaCl solution.

Using a Pasteur pipet, carefully rinse the condenser and the inside neck of the receiving flask with 5 mL of dichloromethane. Swirl the flask gently to dissolve the remaining clove oil. Add this dichloromethane to the distillate in the separatory funnel.

NOTE: Significant amounts of clove oil will adhere to the condenser and the sides and neck of the receiving flask.

Cap the separatory funnel and gently swirl the contents for several seconds. *Vent the separatory funnel frequently.* After the pressure has been vented, shake the contents vigorously to thoroughly mix the two layers.

Swirl the separatory funnel. At the same time, gently tap the outside of the separatory funnel with your index finger to force into the bottom layer any droplets of dichloromethane that are adhering to the sides of the funnel.

Allow the layers to separate. Drain the lower dichloromethane layer into a 50-mL Erlenmeyer flask, making certain that none of the aqueous layer is transferred to the flask.

Rinse the condenser and the receiver with a second 5-mL portion of dichloromethane. Transfer the rinsing to the separatory funnel. Repeat the extraction of the aqueous layer.

Drain the second dichloromethane extract from the separatory funnel and combine it with the first one in the 50-mL Erlenmeyer flask. Repeat the rinsing and extraction process with a third 5-mL portion of dichloromethane. Combine the third extract in the same 50-mL Erlenmeyer flask.

CAUTION

Anhydrous sodium sulfate (Na_2SO_4) is irritating and hygroscopic. Do not inhale and ingest this compound.

Add approximately 0.5 g of anhydrous Na_2SO_4 to the flask containing the dichloromethane extracts. Stopper the flask. Allow the extracts to dry for 5 min.

Weigh a clean, dry 50-mL round-bottom flask to the nearest 0.001 g and record the mass. Using a Pasteur filter pipet, transfer the dried dichloromethane into the flask, making certain that no Na_2SO_4 is transferred with the solution. Use three additional 2-mL portions of dichloromethane to rinse the Na₂SO₄ and ensure complete transfer of the clove oil to the beaker.

Assemble a simple distillation apparatus using the 50-mL round-bottom flask as the pot. Add a boiling chip. Use a 40 °C sand bath or a hot-water bath to distill the dichloromethane away from the product.

When all of the dichloromethane has been distilled, cool the flask. Weigh it to the nearest 0.001 g and record the mass. Subtract the mass of the empty flask to obtain the mass of the clove oil.

CAUTION

Methanol is flammable and toxic. Keep away from flames or other heat sources. Prevent eye, skin, and clothing contact. Use a *fume hood*.

Dissolve the clove oil in 10 mL of methanol. Proceed to the Characterizing the Product Section later in this module.

3. Cleaning Up

Place your recovered materials in the appropriate labeled collection containers as directed by your laboratory instructor. Clean your glassware with soap or detergent.

CAUTION

Wash your hands thoroughly with soap or detergent before leaving the laboratory.

MICROSCALE STEAM DISTILLATION

Using Glassware with Elastomeric Connectors

Equipment

25-mL beaker	10-mL graduated cylinder
boiling chip	marking pen
15-mL centrifuge tube, with cap	microburner
copper metal sponge	microspatula
cotton*	mortar and pestle
10-mL Erlenmeyer flask, with stopper	3 Pasteur pipets, with latex bulb
	1.0-mL pipet
125-mL Erlenmeyer flask	sand bath†
glass stirring rod	support ring
glassware,	support stand
with elastomeric connectors	thermometer, −10 to 260 °C, with adapter
distilling head/air condenser	
distilling tube, with syringe port	2 utility clamps
10-mL round-bottom flask	wire gauze
1-mL syringe	

* for Pasteur filter pipet
† sand in crystallizing dish on electric hot plate or sand in electric heating well with heat controller

Reagents and Properties

Substance	Quantity	Molar mass (g/mol)	bp (°C)
cloves	0.5 g		
dichloromethane	4mL	84.93	40
eugenol*		164.20	254
ice			
methanol	1 mL	32.04	64.7
sodium chloride, sat. solution	1 mL	58.44	
sodium sulfate, anhydrous	50 mg	142.04	

*product

Preview

- Grind the cloves with a mortar and pestle
- Place the ground cloves and water in the distilling flask
- Assemble the steam distillation apparatus
- Distill the mixture
- Extract the clove oil into dichloromethane
- Dry the dichloromethane layer with anhydrous Na$_2$SO$_4$
- Remove the dichloromethane from the clove oil
- Weigh the clove oil

PROCEDURE

Chemical Alert

dichloromethane—*toxic and irritant*

eugenol—*irritant*

methanol—*flammable and toxic*

anhydrous sodium sulfate—*irritant and hygroscopic*

CAUTION

Wear departmentally approved safety goggles at all times while in the chemistry laboratory.

---

1. Conducting Steam Distillation

Grind 10 whole cloves to a coarse powder, using a small mortar and pestle. Weigh 0.400–0.500 g of the powder and record the mass to the nearest 0.001 g.

Use a microspatula to carefully transfer the ground cloves to a 10-mL round-bottom flask. Add a boiling chip and 4 mL of deionized or distilled water. Mix well with a glass stirring rod. Mark the level of the mixture on the side of the flask.

Add 3 mL of water to a 15-mL centrifuge tube. Mark the level of the water on the side of the tube. Then discard the water from the tube.

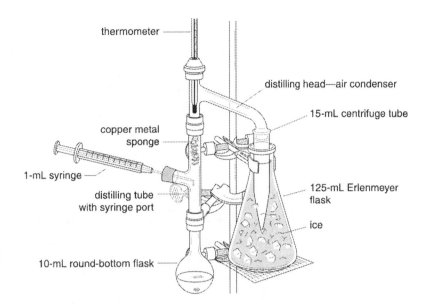

thermometer

distilling head—air condenser

15-mL centrifuge tube

copper metal sponge

1-mL syringe

distilling tube with syringe port

125-mL Erlenmeyer flask

ice

Figure 3

Microscale steam distillation apparatus using elastomeric connectors

10-mL round-bottom flask

Place a small plug of copper metal sponge in the distillation head to help prevent the mixture from foaming over into the centrifuge tube when the distilling flask is heated.

Fill a 125-mL Erlenmeyer flask three-quarters full with crushed ice. Place the centrifuge tube in the flask. Assemble the remainder of the distilling apparatus, as shown in Figure 3. Start the flow of water through the condenser.

Adjust a microburner flame to lessen the hot central cone. Heat the pot by waving the flame back and forth under the pot. Heat the mixture to maintain a distillation rate of approximately one drop every 5 s.

NOTE: Do not heat the mixture too quickly. Rapid heating may cause the mixture to foam violently. A microburner flame can easily be added and withdrawn to control the heating rate.

Draw 1.0 mL of water into the syringe. Add water dropwise to the pot every 5 min to keep the water level to the mark. Refill the syringe with water as needed. Add more ice, as needed, to the Erlenmeyer flask containing the centrifuge tube. Stop the distillation when 3 mL of distillate has been collected in the centrifuge tube.

2. Extracting the Clove Oil

CAUTION

Dichloromethane is toxic and irritating. Use a *fume hood*. Clove oil (eugenol) is irritating. Prevent eye, skin, and clothing contact.

Remove the centrifuge tube from the flask. Add 1 mL of saturated NaCl solution.

Add 1 mL of dichloromethane to the centrifuge tube. Cap the tube and gently mix the layers, being careful to *vent the tube frequently*. After the initial pressure build-up has subsided, shake the centrifuge tube vigorously to mix the layers efficiently.

Swirl the tube. At the same time, gently tap the outside of the centrifuge tube with your index finger to force into the bottom layer any droplets of dichloromethane that are adhering to the sides of the tube.

Using a Pasteur pipet, remove the lower dichloromethane layer containing the clove oil into a 10-mL Erlenmeyer flask. Make certain that no water is transferred to the flask.

Repeat the extraction process two more times using 1-mL portions of dichloromethane. Combine all three dichloromethane extracts in the same 10-mL Erlenmeyer flask.

CAUTION

Anhydrous sodium sulfate (Na$_2$SO$_4$) is irritating and hygroscopic. Do not inhale and ingest this compound.

Add approximately 50 mg of anhydrous Na$_2$SO$_4$ to the flask containing the dichloromethane extracts. Stopper the flask. Allow the extracts to dry for 5 min.

Weigh a clean, dry 25-mL beaker to the nearest 0.001 g and record the mass. Using a Pasteur filter pipet, transfer the dried dichloromethane into the beaker, making certain that no Na$_2$SO$_4$ is transferred with the solution. Use two additional 0.5-mL portions of dichloromethane to rinse the Na$_2$SO$_4$ and ensure complete transfer of the clove oil to the beaker.

In a *fume hood*, place the beaker on the *surface* of a 40 °C sand bath to evaporate the dichloromethane. Use a gentle stream of air or nitrogen to speed the evaporation.

NOTE: When evaporating the dichloromethane, use a *gentle* stream of air or nitrogen, one you *barely* feel against your hand. A strong stream of air or nitrogen may blow the solution out of the beaker and product will be lost.

When all of the dichloromethane has been evaporated, weigh the beaker to the nearest 0.001 g and record the mass. Subtract the mass of the empty beaker to obtain the mass of the clove oil.

CAUTION

Methanol is flammable and toxic. Keep away from flames or other heat sources. Prevent eye, skin, and clothing contact. Use a *fume hood*.

Dissolve the clove oil in 1 mL of methanol. Proceed to the Characterizing the Product Section later in this module.

3. Cleaning Up

Place your recovered materials in the appropriate labeled collection containers as directed by your laboratory instructor. Clean your glassware with soap or detergent.

CAUTION

Wash your hands thoroughly with soap or detergent before leaving the laboratory.

MICROSCALE STEAM DISTILLATION

Using the Hickman Still

Equipment

25-mL beaker	marking pen
boiling chip	microburner
5 mL conical vial, with screw cap	microspatula
	mortar and pestle
condenser, with tubing	1-mL pipet[†]
copper metal sponge	4 Pasteur pipets, with latex bulb
cotton[*]	10-mL round-bottom flask
10-mL Erlenmeyer flask, with stopper	sand bath[‡]
	support ring
glass stirring rod	support stand
10-mL graduated cylinder	2 utility clamps
Hickman still	wire gauze

[*] for Pasteur filter pipet

[†] or adjustable micropipet

[‡] sand in crystallizing dish on electric hot plate or sand in electric heating well with heat controller

Reagents and Properties

Substance	Quantity	Molar mass (g/mol)	bp (°C)
cloves	0.5 g		
dichloromethane	4 mL	84.93	40
eugenol[*]		164.20	254
methanol	1 mL	32.04	64.7
sodium chloride, sat. solution	0.5 mL	58.44	
sodium sulfate, anhydrous	50 mg	142.04	

[*]product

Preview

- Grind the cloves with a mortar and pestle
- Place the ground cloves and water in the distilling flask
- Assemble the steam distillation apparatus
- Distill the mixture
- Extract the clove oil into dichloromethane
- Dry the dichloromethane layer with anhydrous Na_2SO_4
- Remove the dichloromethane from the clove oil
- Weigh the clove oil

PROCEDURE

Chemical Alert

dichloromethane—*toxic and irritant*

eugenol—*irritant*

methanol—*flammable and toxic*

anhydrous sodium sulfate—*irritant and hygroscopic*

CAUTION

Wear departmentally approved safety goggles at all times while in the chemistry laboratory.

1. Conducting Steam Distillation

Grind 10 whole cloves to a coarse powder, using a small mortar and pestle. Weigh 0.400–0.500 g of the powder and record the mass to the nearest 0.001 g.

Use a microspatula to carefully transfer the ground cloves to a 10-mL round-bottom flask. Add a boiling chip and 4 mL of deionized or distilled water. Mix well with a glass stirring rod. Mark the level of the mixture on the side of the flask.

Place a small plug of copper metal sponge in the neck of the Hickman still to help prevent the mixture from foaming over as it is heated.

Attach the Hickman still to the round-bottom flask. Assemble the remainder of the apparatus, as shown in Figure 4. Start the flow of water through the condenser.

Adjust a microburner flame to lessen the hot central cone. Heat the pot by waving the flame back and forth under the pot. Heat the mixture to maintain a distillation rate of approximately one drop every 5 s.

NOTE: Do not heat the mixture too rapidly. The clove mixture tends to foam when rapidly heated. The microburner flame can easily be added and withdrawn to control the heating rate.

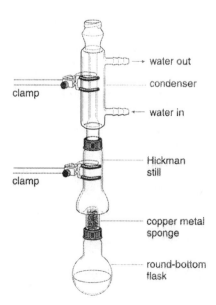

Figure 4

Microscale steam distillation apparatus using a hickman still

When the bottom portion of the Hickman still is full of distillate, remove the flame. Using a bent-tip Pasteur pipet, carefully remove the distillate from the Hickman still. Place the distillate in a 5-mL conical vial. Cap the vial to avoid spillage.

NOTE: A standard Pasteur pipet can be used in a Hickman still model that has a built-in side port.

Using a clean Pasteur pipet, add water through the top of the condenser to keep the water level at the mark on the round-bottom flask. Again use the flame to distill the mixture. Continue the distillation until 3 mL of distillate has been collected in the 5-mL conical vial.

2. Extracting the Clove Oil

CAUTION

Dichloromethane is toxic and irritating. Use a *fume hood*. Clove oil (eugenol) is irritating. Prevent eye, skin, and clothing contact.

Add 0.5 mL of saturated NaCl solution to the vial. Using a bent-tip Pasteur pipet and a 0.5-mL portion of dichloromethane, carefully wash down the inside walls of the Hickman still to remove residual clove oil that adhered to the glass. Transfer the dichloromethane to the 5-mL conical vial containing the distillate.

Repeat the rinsing with a second 0.5-mL portion of dichloromethane. Transfer the second portion of dichloromethane to the 5-mL conical vial.

Cap the vial tightly and gently mix the layers, being careful to *vent the vial frequently*. After the initial pressure build-up has subsided, shake the vial vigorously to thoroughly mix the layers.

Swirl the vial. At the same time, gently tap the outside of the vial with your index finger to force into the bottom layer any droplets of dichloromethane that are adhering to the sides of the vial.

Using a Pasteur pipet, transfer the lower dichloromethane layer containing the clove oil into a 10-mL Erlenmeyer flask. Make certain that no water is transferred to the flask.

Repeat the extraction process two more times, using 1-mL portions of dichloromethane. Combine all three dichloromethane extracts in the same 10-mL Erlenmeyer flask.

CAUTION

Anhydrous sodium sulfate (Na$_2$SO$_4$) is irritating and hygroscopic. Do not inhale and ingest this compound.

Add approximately 50 mg of anhydrous Na$_2$SO$_4$ to the flask containing the dichloromethane extracts. Allow it to dry for 5 min.

Weigh a clean, dry 25-mL beaker to the nearest 0.001 g and record the mass. Using a Pasteur filter pipet, transfer the dried dichloromethane into the beaker, making certain that no Na$_2$SO$_4$ is transferred with the solution. Use two additional 0.5-mL portions of dichloromethane to rinse the Na$_2$SO$_4$ and ensure complete transfer of the clove oil to the beaker.

In a *fume hood*, place the beaker on the *surface* of a 40 °C sand bath to evaporate the dichloromethane. Use a gentle stream of air or nitrogen to speed the evaporation.

NOTE: When evaporating the dichloromethane, use a *gentle* stream of air or nitrogen, one you *barely* feel against your hand. A strong stream of air or nitrogen may blow the solution out of the beaker and product will be lost.

When all of the dichloromethane has been evaporated, weigh the beaker to the nearest 0.001 g and record the mass. Subtract the mass of the empty beaker to obtain the mass of the clove oil.

CAUTION

Methanol is flammable and toxic. Keep away from flames or other heat sources. Prevent eye, skin, and clothing contact. Use a *fume hood*.

Dissolve the clove oil in 1 mL of methanol. Proceed to the Characterizing the Product Section below.

3. Cleaning Up

Place your recovered materials in the appropriate labeled collection containers as directed by your laboratory instructor. Clean your glassware with soap or detergent.

CAUTION

Wash your hands thoroughly with soap or detergent before leaving the laboratory.

Characterizing the Product

Equipment

Bunsen burner	4 Pasteur pipets, with latex bulb
developing chamber*	pencil
10-mL graduated cylinder	6 test tubes, 13 × 100-mm
marking pen	3 × 7-cm TLC plate, silica gel,
2 melting point capillary tubes†	with fluorescent indicator
metric ruler	

*4-oz jar with lid or 250-mL beaker covered with aluminum foil
†for TLC micropipets

Reagents and Properties

Compound	Quantity	Molar mass (g/mol)	bp (°C)
acetone	0.5 mL	58.08	56
bromine, 1% in dichloromethane	<1 mL		
n-hexane	4.5 mL	86.18	69
iron(III) chloride, 1% aq.	<1 mL	162.21	
methanol	6 mL	32.04	64.7
potassium permanganate, 0.05M	<1 mL	158.04	

PROCEDURE

Chemical Alert

acetone—*flammable and irritant*
bromine—*toxic and oxidizer*
dichloromethane—*toxic and irritant*
eugenol—*irritant*
n-hexane—*flammable and irritant*
iodine—*toxic and corrosive*
iron(III) chloride—*toxic and corrosive*
methanol—*flammable and toxic*
potassium permanganate—*corrosive and oxidizer*

1. Analyzing Clove Oil by Chemical Tests

CAUTION

Clove oil (eugenol) is irritating. Methanol is flammable and toxic. Keep away from flames or other heat sources. Prevent eye, skin, and clothing contact. Do not inhale and ingest these compounds. Use a *fume hood*.

Obtain six test tubes and label them 1–6. Label tubes 2, 4, and 6 "control". Add 1 mL of methanol to each of the six tubes.

Using a Pasteur pipet, add 5 drops of the methanol-clove oil solution to test tubes 1 and 3. Add 10 drops of the methanol-clove oil solution to test tube 5. Gently swirl each tube.

Testing with Bromine in Dichloromethane

CAUTION

Bromine (Br$_2$) is toxic and oxidizing. Dichloromethane is toxic and irritating. Prevent eye, skin, and clothing contact. Do not inhale and ingest these compounds. Use a *fume hood*.

Using a Pasteur pipet, add a 1% Br$_2$ in dichloromethane solution dropwise to test tube 1. Record your observations after each drop is added. Note how many drops of the dichloromethane-Br$_2$ solution are needed until pale yellow coloration remains. Repeat this procedure using test tube 2.

NOTE: When all of the clove oil has reacted with Br$_2$, a pale yellow color will remain.

Testing with Potassium Permanganate

CAUTION

Potassium permanganate (KMnO$_4$) is corrosive and oxidizing. Prevent eye, skin, and clothing contact. Do not inhale or ingest KMnO$_4$.

Using a Pasteur pipet, add three drops of 0.05*M* KMnO$_4$ to test tube 3 and record your observations. Repeat this procedure using test tube 4.

Testing with Iron(III) Chloride

CAUTION

Iron(III) chloride (FeCl₃) is toxic and corrosive. Prevent eye, skin, and clothing contact. Do not inhale or ingest FeCl₃.

Using a Pasteur pipet, add one drop of 1% $FeCl_3$ solution to test tube 5 and one drop to test tube 6. Record your observations.

2. Analyzing Clove Oil by Thin-Layer Chromatography

CAUTION

Acetone and *n*-hexane are flammable and irritating. Keep away from flames or other heat sources. Prevent eye, skin, and clothing contact. Do not inhale and ingest these compounds. Use a *fume hood*.

CAUTION

Clove oil (eugenol) is irritating. Methanol is flammable and toxic. Keep away from flames or other heat sources. Prevent eye, skin, and clothing contact. Do not inhale and ingest these compounds. Use a *fume hood*.

Obtain a 3 × 7-cm silica gel TLC plate from your laboratory instructor. Draw a *very faint* pencil line 1 cm from the bottom to mark the origin. Make two vertical marks that intersect the pencil line 0.5 cm from each edge of the plate and a third mark 1.5 cm from one edge.

Prepare micropipets for spotting the TLC plates by drawing out melting point capillary tubing. Using a micropipet, spot a standard sample of eugenol once on the middle mark, keeping the spot as small as possible. Using a new micropipet, spot your methanol-clove oil sample once on the left-hand mark. Using the same micropipet, spot your sample twice on the right hand mark, allowing the solvent to evaporate between spottings.

Prepare a developing chamber by pouring 4.5 mL of *n*-hexane and 0.5 mL of acetone into a 4-oz jar. Place the TLC plate into the chamber and attach the lid. Allow the eluent to develop the plate.

NOTE: Do not put filter paper or paper towel in the developing chamber. In this case, a better separation occurs without chamber saturation.

CAUTION

Ultraviolet radiation can cause severe eye damage. Wear goggles. Do not look directly into the UV lamp.

Iodine (I₂) is toxic and corrosive. Prevent eye, skin, and clothing contact. Do not inhale and ingest I₂. Use a *fume hood*.

After developing the plate, *immediately* mark the eluent front. Dry the plate in a *fume hood*. Visualize the chromatogram under short-wave UV light or in an I_2 chamber, as directed by your laboratory instructor. Use a pencil to circle the spots on your plate.

Measure the distance from the origin to the eluent front. Measure the distance from the origin to the center of each spot. Record your observations.

NOTE: Eugenol acetate should appear as a minor spot at a higher R_f than that of eugenol.

---

3. Cleaning Up

Place your recovered materials in the appropriate labeled collection containers as directed by your laboratory instructor. Clean your glassware with soap or detergent.

CAUTION

Wash your hands thoroughly with soap or detergent before leaving the laboratory.

name _section_ _date_

Post-Laboratory Questions

1. Calculate the percent yield of clove oil based upon the initial mass of the ground cloves.

2. Give your test results for the reaction of your eugenol product with each of the test reagents.

3. Complete the following reactions, giving the correct structure for each organic product.

    (a) eugenol + Br_2 →

    (b) eugenol acetate + $KMnO_4$ →

    (c) eugenol + $FeCl_3$ →

    (d) eugenol acetate + $FeCl_3$ →

4. Complete the following table after performing the TLC analysis on your clove oil sample. Indicate by a yes or no answer whether the spots are visible under UV light or I_2 vapors.

Compound	R_f	UV	I_2
eugenol			
eugenol acetate			
other			

5. Using your R_fs, list the compounds in your clove oil in order of increasing polarity. Briefly explain your answer.

_____   _____ _____
name   section   date

Pre-Laboratory Assignment

1. What precautions must be taken when mixing reagents in a separatory funnel or centrifuge tube?

2. Briefly define the following terms:
  (a) codistillation

  (b) steam distillation

  (c) Raoult's law

  (d) Dalton's law

  (e) essential oil

3. Why is steam distillation preferable to simple distillation for isolating high-boiling natural products?

12

EXPERIMENT 3

Extraction

Extraction
Critical thinking application

Extraction is one of the most important techniques for isolating and purifying organic substances. In this method, a solution is mixed thoroughly with a second solvent that is **immiscible** with the first solvent. (Remember that immiscible liquids do not mix; they form two phases or layers.) The solute is extracted from one solvent into the other because it is more soluble in the second solvent than in the first.

The theory of extraction is described in detail in Technique 12, Sections 12.1–12.2, pp. 698–702. You should read these sections before continuing this experiment. Because solubility is the underlying principle of extraction, you may also wish to reread Technique 10.

Extraction is a technique used by organic chemists, but it is also used to produce common products with which you are familiar. For example, vanilla extract, the popular flavoring agent, was originally extracted from vanilla beans using alcohol as the organic solvent. Decaffeinated coffee is made from coffee beans that have been decaffeinated by an extraction technique (see essay "Caffeine," p. 78). This process is similar to the procedure in Part A of this experiment, in which you will extract caffeine from an aqueous solution.

The purpose of this experiment is to introduce the macroscale technique for performing extractions and allow you to practice this technique. This experiment also demonstrates how extraction is used in organic experiments.

Required Reading

Review:	Technique 10	Solubility
New:	Technique 12	Extraction
	Essay	Caffeine (p. 78)

Special Instructions

Be careful when handling methylene chloride. It is a toxic solvent, and you should not breathe its fumes excessively or spill it on yourself.

In Part B, it is advisable to pool the data for the distribution coefficients and calculate class averages. This will compensate for differences in the values due to experimental error.

Suggested Waste Disposal

You must dispose of all methylene chloride in a waste container marked for the disposal of halogenated organic wastes. Place all other organic wastes into the nonhalogenated organic waste container. The aqueous solutions obtained after the extraction steps must be disposed of in the container designated for aqueous waste.

PART A. EXTRACTION OF CAFFEINE

One of the most common extraction procedures involves using an organic solvent (nonpolar or slightly polar) to extract an organic compound from an aqueous solution. Because water is highly polar, the mixture will separate into two layers or phases: an aqueous layer and an organic (nonpolar) layer.

In this experiment, you will extract caffeine from an aqueous solution using methylene chloride. You will perform the extraction step three times using three separate portions of methylene chloride. Because methylene chloride is more dense than water, the organic layer (methylene chloride) will be on the bottom. After each extraction, you will remove the organic layer. The organic layers from all three extractions will be combined and dried over anhydrous sodium sulfate. After transferring the dried solution to a preweighed container, you will evaporate the methylene chloride and determine the weight of caffeine extracted from the aqueous solution. This extraction procedure succeeds because caffeine is much more soluble in methylene chloride than in water.

Prelab Calculation

In this experiment, 0.170 g of caffeine is dissolved in 10.0 mL of water. The caffeine is extracted from the aqueous solution three times with 5.0-mL portions of methylene chloride. Calculate the total amount of caffeine that can be extracted into the three portions of methylene chloride (see Technique 12, Section 12.2, p. 700). Caffeine has a distribution coefficient of 4.6 between methylene chloride and water.

Procedure

Preparation. Add exactly 0.170 g of caffeine and 10.0 mL of water to a screw-cap centrifuge tube. Cap the tube and shake it vigorously for several minutes until the caffeine dissolves completely. It may be helpful to heat the mixture slightly to dissolve all the caffeine.

Extraction. Using a Pasteur pipet, transfer the caffeine solution to a 125-mL separatory funnel. (Don't forget to close the stopcock!) Using a 10-mL graduated cylinder, obtain 5.0 mL of methylene chloride and add to the separatory funnel. Stopper the funnel and hold it as shown in Figure 12.6, page 705. Hold the stopper in place *firmly* and invert the separatory funnel. While the funnel is inverted, release the pressure by slowly opening the stopcock. Continue inverting and venting until the "whoosh" is no longer audible. The two layers must now be mixed thoroughly so that as much caffeine as possible is transferred from the aqueous layer to the methylene chloride layer. However, if the mixture is mixed too vigorously, it may form an emulsion. Emulsions look like a third frothy layer between the other two layers, and they can make it difficult for the layers to separate. Follow these instructions carefully to prevent the formation of an emulsion. Shake the mixture gently by inverting the funnel repeatedly in a rocking motion. Initially, a good rate of shaking is about one rock per two seconds. When it is clear that an emulsion is not forming, you may shake the mixture more vigorously, perhaps one time per second. (Note that it is usually not prudent to shake the heck out of it!) Shake the mixture for at least one minute. When you have finished mixing the liquids, place the separatory funnel in the iron ring and let it stand until the layers separate completely.[1] Place a 50-mL Erlenmeyer flask under the separatory funnel and remove the top stopper on the funnel. Allow the bottom (organic) layer to drain slowly by partially opening the stopcock. When the interface between the upper and lower phases just begins to enter the bore of the stopcock, close the stopcock immediately.

Repeat this extraction two more times using 5.0 mL of fresh methylene chloride each time. Combine the organic layer from each of these extractions with the methylene chloride solution from the first extraction.

Drying the Organic Layers.   If there are any visible signs of water in the flask containing the combined organic layers, *you must make another transfer before adding the drying agent.* Otherwise, you will need to use an excessive amount of drying agent, which may result in losing some caffeine.[2] Visible signs of water include drops of water on the sides of the container or in the methylene chloride or a layer of water on the surface.

To make this additional transfer, use a clean, dry Pasteur pipet to transfer the methylene chloride solution without any of the visible water to another clean, dry Erlenmeyer flask. Place the two Erlenmeyer flasks right next to each other to minimize loss due to spillage while making this transfer. Add about 3 g of granular anhydrous sodium sulfate to dry the organic layer. If all the sodium sulfate clumps together when the mixture is stirred with a spatula, add some additional drying agent. Stopper the flask and allow the mixture to stand for 10–15 minutes. Stir occasionally by swirling the flask. The solution should be completely clear at this point. If it is not, add some additional anhydrous sodium sulfate, swirl the flask, and allow it to stand for another 10–15 minutes.

Evaporation of Solvent.   Transfer the dried methylene chloride solution with a clean, dry Pasteur pipet to a dry, preweighed 50-mL Erlenmeyer flask, while leaving the drying agent behind. Evaporate the methylene chloride by heating the flask in a hot water bath at about 45°C.[3] This should be done in a hood and can be accomplished more rapidly if a stream of dry air or nitrogen gas is directed at the surface of

---

[1] If an emulsion has formed, the two layers may not separate on standing. If they do not separate after about 1–2 minutes, first try swirling the separatory funnel to break the emulsion. If this does not work, try method 5 on page 716.

[2] Loss of product occurs because some of the solution containing caffeine will adhere to the surface of the drying agent.

[3] A more environmentally friendly procedure is to use a rotary evaporator (see Technique 7, Section 7.11, p. 643). With this method, the methylene chloride is recovered and can be reused.

the liquid (see Technique 7, Section 7.10, p. 639). When the solvent has evaporated, remove the flask from the bath and dry the outside of the flask. Do not leave the flask in the water bath for a long time after the solvent has evaporated because the caffeine may sublime. When the flask has cooled to room temperature, weigh it to determine the amount of caffeine that was in the methylene chloride solution. Compare this weight with the amount of caffeine calculated in the Prelab Calculation.

PART B. DISTRIBUTION OF A SOLUTE BETWEEN TWO IMMISCIBLE SOLVENTS

In this experiment, you will investigate how several different organic solids distribute themselves between water and methylene chloride. A solid compound is mixed with the two solvents until equilibrium is reached. The organic layer is removed, dried over anhydrous sodium sulfate, and transferred to a tared container. After evaporating the methylene chloride, you will determine the weight of the organic solid that was in the organic layer. By finding the difference, you can also determine the amount of solute in the aqueous layer. The distribution coefficient of the solid between the two layers can then be calculated and related to the polarity of the solid and the polarities of the two liquids.

Three different compounds will be used: benzoic acid, succinic acid, and sodium benzoate. Their structures are given below. You should perform this experiment on one of the solids and share your data with two other students who worked with the other two solids. Alternatively, data from the entire class may be pooled and averaged.

Benzoic acid   Succinic acid   Sodium benzoate

Procedure

Place 0.075 g of one of the solids (benzoic acid, succinic acid, or sodium benzoate) into a screw-cap centrifuge tube. Add 3.0 mL of methylene chloride and 3.0 mL of water to the tube. Cap the tube and shake it for about 1 minute. The correct way to shake is to invert the tube and right it in a rocking motion. A good rate of shaking is about one rock per second. When it is clear that an emulsion is not forming, you may shake it more vigorously, perhaps two to three times per second. Check for undissolved solid. Continue shaking the tube until all the solid is dissolved.

Allow the centrifuge tube to sit until the layers have separated. Using a Pasteur pipet, you should now transfer the organic (bottom) layer into a test tube.

Ideally, the goal is to remove all of the organic layer without transferring any of the aqueous layer. However, this is difficult to do. Try to squeeze the bulb so that when it is released completely, you will draw up the amount of liquid that you desire. If you have to hold the bulb in a partially depressed position while making a transfer, it is likely that you will spill some liquid. It is also necessary to transfer the liquid in two or three steps. First, depress the bulb completely so that as much of the bottom layer as possible will be drawn into the pipet. Place the tip of the pipet squarely in the **V** at the bottom of the centrifuge tube and release the bulb slowly. When making the transfer, it is essential that the centrifuge tube and the test tube are held next to each other. A good technique for this is illustrated in Figure 12.8, page 709. After transferring the first portion, repeat this process until all of the bottom layer has been transferred to the test tube. Each time, depress the bulb only as much as is necessary and place the tip of the pipet in the bottom of the tube.

If there are any visible signs of water in the test tube containing the combined organic layers, *you must make another transfer before adding the drying agent.* Visible signs of water include drops of water on the sides of the container or in the methylene chloride or a layer of water on the surface.

To make this additional transfer, use a clean, dry Pasteur pipet to transfer the methylene chloride solution without any of the visible water to another clean, dry test tube. Add about 0.5 g of granular anhydrous sodium sulfate to dry the organic layer. If all the sodium sulfate clumps together when the mixture is stirred with a spatula, add some additional drying agent. Stopper the tube and allow the mixture to stand for 10–15 minutes. Shake the tube occasionally or stir with a spatula.

Transfer the dried methylene chloride solution with a clean, dry Pasteur pipet to a dry, preweighed test tube, leaving the drying agent behind. Evaporate the methylene chloride by heating the test tube in a warm water bath while directing a stream of dry air or nitrogen gas at the surface of the liquid. When the solvent has evaporated, remove the test tube from the bath and dry the outside of the tube. When the test tube has cooled to room temperature, weigh the test tube to determine the amount of solid solute that was in the methylene chloride layer. Determine by difference the amount of the solid that was dissolved in the aqueous layer. Calculate the distribution coefficient for the solid between methylene chloride and water. Because the volume of methylene chloride and water was the same, the distribution coefficient can be calculated by dividing the weight of solute in methylene chloride by the weight of solute in water.

Optional Exercise.   Repeat the preceding procedure using 0.075 g of caffeine, 3.0 mL of methylene chloride, and 3.0 mL of water. Determine the distribution coefficient for caffeine between methylene chloride and water. Compare this to the literature value of 4.6.

PART C. HOW DO YOU DETERMINE WHICH ONE IS THE ORGANIC LAYER?

A common problem that you might encounter during an extraction procedure is not knowing for sure which layer is organic and which is aqueous. Although the procedures in this textbook often indicate the expected relative positions of the two layers, not all procedures will give this information, and you should be prepared for surprises. Sometimes, knowing the densities of the two solvents is not sufficient, because dissolved substances can significantly increase the density of a solution. It is very important to know the location of the two layers, because usually one layer contains the desired product and the other layer is discarded. A mistake at this point in an experiment would be disastrous!

The purpose of this experiment is to give you some practice in determining which layer is aqueous and which layer is organic (see Technique 12, Section 12.8, p. 712). As described in Section 12.8, one effective technique is to add a few drops of water to each layer after they have been separated. If the layer is water, then the drops of added water will dissolve in the aqueous layer and increase its volume. If the added water forms droplets or a new layer, then it is the organic layer.

Procedure

Obtain three test tubes, each containing two layers.[4] For each tube, you will be told the identity of the two layers, but you will not be told their relative positions. Determine experimentally which layer is organic and which layer is aqueous. Dispose of all these mixtures into the waste container designated for halogenated organic wastes. After determining the layers experimentally, look up the densities of the various liquids in a handbook to see if there is a correlation between the densities and your results.

PART D. USE OF EXTRACTION TO ISOLATE A NEUTRAL COMPOUND FROM A MIXTURE CONTAINING AN ACID OR BASE IMPURITY

In this experiment, you will be given a solid sample containing an unknown neutral compound and an acid or base impurity. The goal is to remove the acid or base by extraction and isolate the neutral compound. By taking the melting point of the neutral compound, you will identify it from a list of possible compounds. There are many organic reactions in which the desired product, a neutral compound, is contaminated by an acid or

---

[4]The three mixtures will likely be (1) water and *n*-butyl chloride, (2) water and *n*-butyl bromide, and (3) *n*-butyl bromide and saturated aqueous sodium bromide.

base impurity. This experiment illustrates how extraction is used to isolate the product in this situation.

In Technique 10, "Solubility," you learned that organic acids and bases can become ions in acid–base reactions (see "Solutions in Which the Solute Ionizes and Dissociates," p. 673). Before reading on, review this material if necessary. Using this principle, you can separate an acid or base impurity from a neutral compound. The following scheme, which shows how both an acid and a base impurity are removed from the desired product, illustrates how this is accomplished:

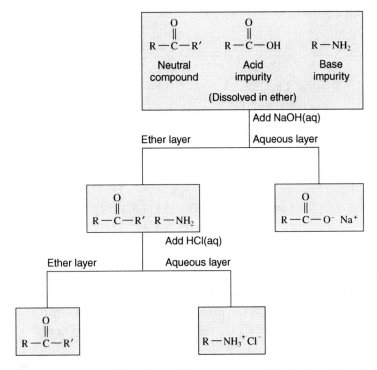

Flowchart showing how acid and base impurities are removed from the desired product.

The neutral compound can now be isolated by removing the water dissolved in the ether and evaporating the ether. Because ether dissolves a relatively large quantity of water (1.5%), the water must be removed in two steps. In the first step, the ether solution is mixed with a saturated aqueous NaCl solution. Most of the water in the ether layer will be transferred to the aqueous layer in this step (see Technique 12, Section 12.9, p. 715). Finally, the remainder of the water is removed by drying the ether layer over anhydrous sodium sulfate. The neutral compound can then be isolated by evaporating the ether. In most organic experiments that use a separation scheme such as this, it would be necessary to perform a crystallization step to purify the neutral compound. However, in this experiment the neutral compound should be sufficiently pure at this point to identify it by melting point.

The organic solvent used in this experiment is ether. Recall that the full name for ether is diethyl ether. Because ether is less dense than water, this experiment will give you practice in performing extractions where the nonpolar solvent is less dense than water.

The following procedure details removing an acid impurity from a neutral compound and isolating the neutral compound. It contains an additional step that is not normally part of this kind of separation scheme: The aqueous layers from each extraction are segregated and acidified with aqueous HCl. The purpose of this step is to verify that the acid impurity has been removed completely from the ether layer. In the Optional Exercise, the sample contains a neutral compound with a base impurity; however, a detailed procedure is not given. If you are assigned this exercise, you must create a procedure by using the principles discussed in this introduction and by studying the following procedure for isolating the neutral compound from an acid impurity.

Procedure

Isolating a Neutral Compound from a Mixture Containing an Acid Impurity. Add 0.36 g of an unknown mixture to a screw-cap centrifuge tube.[5] Add 10.0 mL of ether to the tube and cap it. Shake the tube until all the solid dissolves completely. Transfer this solution to a 125-mL separatory funnel.

Add 5.0 mL of 1.0 M NaOH to the separatory funnel and shake for 30 seconds, using the same procedure described in Part A. Let the layers separate. Remove the bottom (aqueous) layer and place this in an Erlenmeyer flask labeled "1st NaOH extract." Add another 5.0-mL portion of 1.0 M NaOH to the funnel and shake for 30 seconds. When the layers have separated, remove the aqueous layer and put this in an Erlenmeyer flask labeled "2nd NaOH extract."

With stirring, add 6 M HCl dropwise to each of the two test flasks containing the NaOH extracts until the mixture is acidic. Test the mixture with litmus or pH paper to determine when it is acidic. Observe the amount of precipitate that forms. What is the precipitate? Does the amount of precipitate in each flask indicate that all the acid impurity has been removed from the ether layer containing the unknown neutral compound?

To the ether layer in the separatory funnel, add 5.0 mL of saturated aqueous sodium chloride. Shake for 30 seconds and let the layers separate. Remove and discard the aqueous layer. Pour the ether layer (without any water) from the *top* of the separatory funnel into a clean, dry Erlenmeyer flask. Add about 1 g of anhydrous sodium sulfate to dry the ether layer. If all the sodium sulfate clumps together when the mixture is stirred with a spatula, add some additional drying agent. Stopper the flask and allow the mixture to stand for 10–15 minutes. Stir occasionally by swirling the flask.

Transfer the dried ether solution with a clean, dry Pasteur pipet to a dry, pre-weighed Erlenmeyer flask, leaving the drying agent behind. Evaporate the ether by heating the flask in a warm water bath. This should be done in a hood and can be accomplished more rapidly if a stream of dry air or nitrogen gas is directed at the surface of the liquid (see Technique 7, Section 7.10, p. 639).[6] When the solvent has evaporated, remove the flask from the bath and dry the outside of the flask. Once the flask

---

[5] The mixture contains 0.24 g of one of the neutral compounds given in the list on page 34 and 0.12 g of benzoic acid, the acid impurity.

[6] See footnote 3, p. 29.

has cooled to room temperature, weigh it to determine the amount of solid solute that was in the ether layer. Obtain the melting point of the solid and identify it from the following table:

	Melting Point (°C)
Fluorenone	82–85
Fluorene	116–117
1,2,4,5-Tetrachlorobenzene	139–142
Triphenylmethanol	162–164

Optional Exercise: Isolating a Neutral Compound from a Mixture Containing a Base Impurity. Obtain 0.36 g of an unknown mixture containing a neutral compound and a base impurity.[7] Develop a procedure for isolating the neutral compound, using the preceding procedure as a model. After isolating the neutral compound, obtain the melting point and identify it from the list of compounds given above.

PART E. CRITICAL THINKING APPLICATION

Procedure

1. Add 4 mL of water and 2 mL of methylene chloride to a screw-cap centrifuge tube.
2. Add 4 drops of solution A to the centrifuge tube. Solution A is a dilute aqueous solution of sodium hydroxide containing an organic compound.[8] Shake the mixture for about 30 seconds, using a rapid rocking motion. Describe the color of each layer (see the following table).
3. Add 2 drops of 1 M HCl. Let the solution sit for 1 minute and note the color change. Then shake for about 1 minute, using a rapid rocking motion. Describe the color of each layer.
4. Add 4 drops of 1 M NaOH and shake again for about 1 minute. Describe the color of each layer.

---

[7] The mixture contains 0.24 g of one of the neutral compounds given in the list on this page and 0.12 g of ethyl 4-aminobenzoate, the base impurity.

[8] Solution A: Mix 25 mg of 2,6-dichloroindophenol (sodium salt) with 50 mL of water and 1 mL of 1 M NaOH. This solution should be prepared the same day it is used.

Color

Step 2	Aqueous	
	Methylene chloride	
Step 3	Aqueous	
	Methylene chloride	
Step 4	Aqueous	
	Methylene chloride	

REPORT

Part A

1. Show your calculations for the amount of caffeine that should be extracted by the three 5.0-mL portions of methylene chloride (see Prelab Calculation).
2. Report the amount of caffeine isolated. Compare this weight with the amount of caffeine calculated in the Prelab Calculation. Comment on the similarity or difference.

Part B

1. Report in table form the distribution coefficients for the three solids: benzoic acid, succinic acid, and sodium benzoate.
2. Is there a correlation between the values of the distribution coefficients and the polarities of the three compounds? Explain.
3. If you completed the Optional Exercise, compare the distribution coefficient you obtained for caffeine with the corresponding literature value. Comment on the similarity or difference.

Part C

1. For each of the three mixtures, report which layer was on the bottom and which one was on the top. Explain how you determined this for each mixture.
2. Record the densities for the liquids given in a handbook.
3. Was there a correlation between the densities and your results? Explain.

Part D

1. Answer the following questions about the first and second NaOH extracts.
   a. Comment on the amount of precipitate for both extracts when HCl is added.
   b. What is the precipitate formed when HCl is added?

   c. Does the amount of precipitate in each tube indicate that all the acid impurity has been removed from the ether layer containing the unknown neutral compound?

2. Report the melting point and weight of the neutral compound you isolated.

3. Based on the melting point, what is the identity of this compound?

4. Calculate the percent recovery for the neutral compound. List possible sources of loss.

If you completed the Optional Exercise, complete steps 1–4 for Part D.

Part E

Describe fully what occurred in steps 2, 3, and 4. For each step, include (1) the nature (cation, anion, or neutral species) of the organic compound, (2) an explanation for all the color changes, and (3) an explanation for why each layer is colored as it is. Your explanation for (3) should be based on solubility principles and the polarities of the two solvents. (*Hint:* It may be helpful to review the sections in your general chemistry textbook that deal with acids, bases, and acid–base indicators.)

REFERENCE

Kelly, T. R. "A Simple, Colorful Demonstration of Solubility and Acid/Base Extraction." *Journal of Chemical Education, 70* (1993): 848.

QUESTION

1. Caffeine has a distribution coefficient of 4.6 between methylene chloride and water. If 52 mg of caffeine are added to a conical vial containing 2 mL of water and 2 mL of methylene chloride, how much caffeine would be in each layer after the mixture had been mixed thoroughly?

13

Chromatography

Oh, oh, you forgot to put the cap on your ballpoint pen, so you now have a major league inkspot on the pocket of your best L. L. Bean sports shirt as a reward for your negligence. You dab it with a wet cloth, only to see the spot grow even bigger. And lo and behold, new colors seems to be appearing as the spot widens. Congratulations! You have just performed a form of chromatography in which you have crudely separated some of the dyes that comprise the ink. In this chapter, we'll be learning some of the basic chromatographic techniques that are used to separate mixtures, by taking advantage of the differential distribution of the individual compounds between two immiscible phases that, in the case of your shirt, were its fibers and the water you used in an effort to remove the stain. These techniques are now so powerful and sophisticated that even enantiomers (Sec. 7.1) may be separated efficiently by such means.

6.1 INTRODUCTION

We described the common laboratory techniques of recrystallization, distillation, and extraction for purifying organic compounds in Chapters 3 through 5. In many cases, however, the mixtures of products obtained from chemical reactions do not lend themselves to ready separation by any of these techniques because the physical properties of the individual components are too similar. Fortunately there are a number of chromatographic procedures available that we can use to effect the desired purification, and some of them are described in this chapter.

The word **chromatography** was first used to describe the colored bands observed when a solution containing plant pigments is passed through a glass column containing an adsorbent packing material. From that origin, the term now encompasses a variety of separation techniques that are widely used for analytical and preparative purposes. All methods of chromatography operate on the principle that the components of a mixture will distribute unequally between two immiscible phases, which is also the basis for separations by extraction (Chap. 5). The **mobile phase** is generally a liquid or a gas that flows continuously over the fixed **stationary phase,** which may be a solid or a liquid. The individual components of the mixture have different affinities for the mobile and stationary phases so a dynamic equilibrium is established in which each component is selectively, but temporarily, removed from the mobile phase by binding to the stationary phase. When the equilibrium concentration of that substance in the mobile phase decreases, it is released from the stationary phase and the process continues. Since each component partitions between the two phases with a different equilibrium

See more on
Chromatography

See Chromatography/
Nobel Prize

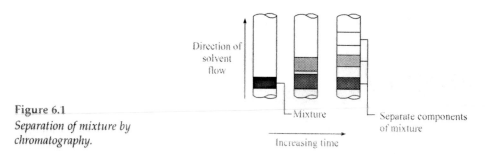

Figure 6.1
Separation of mixture by chromatography.

constant or **partition coefficient,** the components separate into separate regions termed **migratory bands** (Fig. 6.1). *The component that interacts with or binds more strongly to the stationary phase moves more slowly in the direction of the flow of the mobile phase.* The attractive forces that are involved in this selective adsorption are the same forces that cause attractive interactions between any two molecules: electrostatic and dipole–dipole interactions, hydrogen bonding, complexation, and van der Waals forces.

See more on *HPLC*

The chromatographic methods used by modern chemists to identify and/or purify components of a mixture are characterized by the nature of the mobile and stationary phases. For example, the techniques of **thin-layer** (TLC), **column,** and **high-performance** (or **high-pressure**) **liquid chromatography** (HPLC) each involve *liquid-solid* phase interactions. **Gas-liquid partition chromatography** (GLC), also known as **gas chromatography** (GC), involves distributions between a mobile *gas* phase and a stationary *liquid* phase coated on a solid support. These important techniques can be used as tools to analyze and identify the components in a mixture as well as to separate the mixture into its pure components for preparative purposes. Although there are other chromatographic techniques, such as ion exchange and paper chromatography, a review of those methods is beyond the scope of this discussion.

6.2 THIN-LAYER CHROMATOGRAPHY

See more on *TLC*

Thin-layer chromatography (TLC) is a form of **solid-liquid adsorption** chromatography and is an important technique in organic chemistry for rapid analysis of small quantities of samples, sometimes as little as 10^{-9} g. Thus, TLC is frequently used to monitor the progress of reactions and of preparative column chromatographic separations as well as to determine the optimal combinations of solvent and adsorbent for such separations (Sec. 6.3). An important limitation to this technique, and that of column chromatography as well, is that it cannot be used on volatile compounds having boiling points below about 150 °C (760 torr).

To execute a TLC analysis, a *small* amount of the sample to be analyzed, or a solution of it, is first applied to a solid **adsorbent** bound to a rectangular glass or plastic plate (Fig. 6.2a). The adsorbent serves as the stationary phase. Next, the plate, with its spotted end down, is placed in a closed jar, called a **developing chamber** (Fig. 6.3). The chamber contains a *saturated atmosphere* of a suitable **eluant** or **eluting solvent,** which is the mobile phase and may be comprised of either a single solvent or mixture of two or more. A folded filter paper is often used to help maintain solvent equilibration in the chamber. It is important that the level of

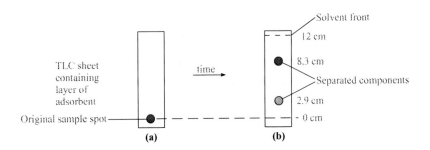

Figure 6.2
*Thin-layer chromatography.
(a) Original plate loaded with
sample. (b) Developed
chromatogram.*

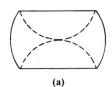

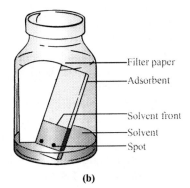

Figure 6.3
*TLC chamber. (a) Folded filter
paper to be placed in developing
chamber for solvent equilibration.
(b) Developing chamber with filter
paper and TLC plate.*

solvent in the chamber be *below* the location of the spot on the TLC plate. Other-wise, the sample would be removed from the plate by dissolution in the bulk sol-vent, thereby ruining the analysis.

When the plate is placed in the chamber, the solvent begins to ascend the plate. The individual components of the sample, which initially were at the bottom, or "origin," are carried up the plate along with the eluting solvent at a rate that is dependent on their relative affinities for the solid adsorbent: More weakly adsorbed compounds move up the plate faster than do those that are more strongly adsorbed. Ideally, when the solvent front has nearly reached the top of the TLC plate, which normally takes only a few minutes, each component of the original sample will appear as a separate spot on the plate (Fig. 6.2b). This completes the development of the chromatogram, and the plate is then removed from the developing chamber for analysis.

Adsorbents

The solid adsorbent in TLC is usually alumina (Al_2O_3) or silica gel (silicic acid, $SiO_2 \times H_2O$), both of which are polar. Alumina is the more polar of the two and is commercially available in three forms: neutral, acidic, and basic. Acidic and basic alumina are sometimes used to separate basic and acidic compounds, respectively, but neutral alumina is the most common form of this adsorbent for TLC. Silica gel, which is slightly acidic, is the adsorbent used in the experimental procedures described in this section.

As you might imagine, consideration of the acidic or basic character of the solid adsorbent used for a TLC experiment can be particularly important if the substances to be analyzed contain functional groups that are sensitive to acids or bases. In a worst-case scenario, the adsorbent may function as a catalyst to destroy the functionality by chemical reaction during the course of the analysis; this greatly complicates the interpretation of the TLC results.

Although TLC plates may be prepared in the laboratory, their ready commercial availability generally makes this unnecessary. The plates are produced by mixing the adsorbent with a small quantity of a **binder** such as starch or calcium sulfate and spreading the mixture as a layer approximately 250 μ thick on the supporting plate. The binder is needed for proper adhesion of the thin layer of adsorbent to the plate. TLC plates should be dried in an oven for an hour or more at 110 °C prior to use, to remove any atmospheric moisture adsorbed on them. This is necessary because the activity of the adsorbent and its effectiveness in separating the components of a mixture are decreased because water occupies binding sites on the surface of the solid.

The strength of adsorption of organic compounds to the stationary phase of the TLC plate depends on the polarity and nature of the adsorbent and the type of functional groups present in the compounds. Substances containing carboxyl groups and other polar functional groups are more strongly adsorbed than are those containing less polar moieties, such as those present in alkenes and alkyl halides, as the **elutropic series** shown in Figure 6.4 indicates. When a sample contains compounds having highly polar functionalities, more polar eluants may be required to effect a TLC analysis, as discussed next.

Eluant

Selecting the eluant or the mobile liquid phase is an important decision that must be made in planning a TLC analysis. The best solvent or combination of solvents is determined by trial and error so several TLC plates may need to be prepared and developed using different eluants to determine the optimal conditions.

Certain criteria guide the selection of the eluant. For example, an effective eluting solvent must readily dissolve the solute but not compete with it for binding sites on the stationary phase. If the mixture to be separated is not soluble in the solvent, the individual components may remain adsorbed at the origin. Another criterion is that a solvent should not be too polar because it may bind strongly to the adsorbent and force the solute to remain in the mobile phase. In such circumstances, the components will move rapidly up the TLC plate, offering little opportunity to establish the solid-liquid equilibria required for separation. Consequently, the eluting solvent must be significantly *less* polar than various components of the mixture to obtain an effective separation. As a rule, the relative ability of different solvents to move a given substance up a TLC plate is termed **eluting power** and is generally found to follow the order shown in Figure 6.5.

Increasing adsorption on
polar stationary phases

Figure 6.4
Elutropic series for polar stationary phases.

$RCO_2H > ROH > RNH_2 > R^1R^2C{=}O > R^1CO_2R_2 > OCH_3 > RR^1R^2C{=}CR^3R^4 > RHal$

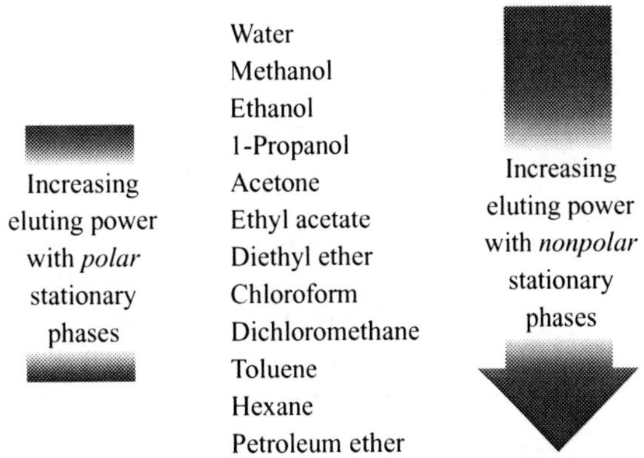

Water
Methanol
Ethanol
1-Propanol
Acetone
Ethyl acetate
Diethyl ether
Chloroform
Dichloromethane
Toluene
Hexane
Petroleum ether

Increasing eluting power with *polar* stationary phases

Increasing eluting power with *nonpolar* stationary phases

Figure 6.5
Eluting power of solvents as function of polarity of stationary phases.

Experimental Technique

The general protocol for preparing and developing a TLC plate was described earlier. We have not yet discussed the means for detecting or "visualizing" the separated components of a mixture in a TLC analysis. There are several ways of doing this. The easiest situation is that in which the compounds being separated are colored, so visual detection is easy, a "no-brainer," so to speak. Many organic compounds are colorless, however, and a variety of methods have been developed to detect their presence on the plate:

1. Compounds that **fluoresce** may be located by placing the plate under an ultraviolet light. Since the spots disappear when the light is removed, it is necessary to circle the spots with a pencil in order to have a permanent record of the chromatogram. There are also commercially available plates that contain a fluorescent material as part of their coating; compounds that do not fluoresce but do absorb ultraviolet light then appear as dark spots under ultraviolet light.

2. The chromatographic plate may be sprayed with a variety of reagents such as sulfuric acid, potassium permanganate, phosphomolybdic acid, and ninhydrin; these reagents react with the individual components to produce colored or dark spots.

3. The chromatographic plate may be exposed to iodine vapor by placing it in a closed chamber containing several crystals of iodine. As the iodine forms complexes with the various organic compounds, the spots become brown. Since the process is reversible and the spots fade, it is necessary to circle the spots with a pencil in order to have a permanent record of the chromatogram.

Once the separation of the components of the mixture is complete and the individual spots have been detected, the **retention factor** (R_f) of each compound may be calculated as shown below for the chromatogram pictured in Figure 6.2b:

$$R_f = \frac{\text{distance traveled by substance}}{\text{distance traveled by solvent}}$$

$$R_f(\text{compound 1}) = \frac{2.9 \text{ cm}}{12 \text{ cm}} = 0.24$$

$$R_f(\text{compound 2}) = \frac{8.3 \text{ cm}}{12 \text{ cm}} = 0.69$$

The R_f-value for a compound is a physical constant for a given set of chromatographic conditions, so the adsorbent and the eluting solvent should be recorded along with the experimentally determined R_f-values.

There are many important applications of TLC in modern organic chemistry. For example, TLC is commonly used to identify components of an unknown mixture by running chromatograms of the unknown sample side by side with known standards. Multiple aliquots of samples collected from chromatographic columns (Sec. 6.3) may be analyzed by TLC to follow the chromatographic separation. Alternatively, it is possible to follow the progress of a reaction by TLC by monitoring the disappearance of starting material or the appearance of product. Samples are simply withdrawn from a reaction mixture and subjected to TLC analysis.

Applications

Two experiments are presented here to demonstrate the TLC technique. The first involves the separation of the pigments present in spinach leaves. A variety of other sources including crushed tomato pulp or carrot scrapings as well as leaves from grasses, shrubs, and trees may be substituted; however, *waxy* leaves are not acceptable.

In the second experiment, the **diastereomers** (geometric isomers) (Sec. 7.1) *syn*-azobenzene (**1**) and *anti*-azobenzene (**2**) are separated. Commercially available azobenzene consists predominantly of the more stable *anti*- form, but this isomer may be isomerized to the less stable *syn*- isomer by irradiation with ultraviolet light or sunlight. Since the colors of the two isomers differ, they may be detected visually. The course of the reaction and the effectiveness of the irradiation is followed by placing spots of irradiated and nonirradiated samples side by side on the TLC strip.

1

Syn-azobenzene

2

Anti-azobenzene

EXPERIMENTAL PROCEDURES

Separation of Spinach Pigments by TLC

Discovery Experiment   **Purpose** To identify solvent mixtures that will separate the colored components in spinach leaves using thin-layer chromatography.

SAFETY ALERT

Petroleum ether, ethanol, and acetone are highly volatile and flammable solvents. Be certain there are *no flames* in the vicinity during this experiment.

Procedure

**See Pre-Lab
Exercises and
MSDSs**

Preparation Answer the Pre-Lab Exercises on page PL. 29. Read the MSDSs for chemicals used in this procedure. Read or review Section 2.21.

Apparatus A wide-mouth bottle with a screw-top cap, small mortar and pestle, 2-cm × 10-cm silica gel TLC plates, and capillary pipets.

Setting Up Prepare a developing chamber by placing a folded filter paper lengthwise in a wide-mouth bottle (Fig. 6.3). As directed by your instructor or by working in teams, prepare several mixtures of eluants that contain different ratios of varying pairs of the following solvents: petroleum ether, bp 60–80 °C (760 torr), chloroform, acetone, and ethanol. For example, prepare 10 mL of a 70:30 mixture of petroleum ether and acetone to use as one eluant. Add an amount of the eluant to the developing chamber so that it forms a 1-cm layer on the bottom of the container. Screw the cap onto the bottle *tightly,* and *shake* the container *well* to saturate the atmosphere of the chamber with vapors of the solvent.

Preparing the Sample Using a small mortar and pestle, thoroughly grind a spinach leaf in a mixture of 4 mL of petroleum ether and 2 mL of ethanol. Transfer the liquid extract to a test tube using a Pasteur pipet and *swirl* the extract gently with an equal volume of water. Do not shake the test tube, because emulsions (Sec. 2.21) are easily formed, and these can be a source of great frustration to you. Remove and discard the aqueous layer; if you do not know which layer is the aqueous one, perform the necessary test (Sec. 2.21). Wash the organic layer with water two more times to remove the ethanol and any water-soluble materials that are present in the leaves. Transfer the petroleum ether extract to the Erlenmeyer flask and add several spatula-tips full of anhydrous sodium sulfate. After 5–10 min, decant the solution from the drying agent. If the solution is not deeply colored, concentrate it using a gentle stream of air or nitrogen to remove some of the solvent.

Preparing and Developing a Plate Obtain a 2-cm × 10-cm strip of silica gel chromatogram sheet *without* a fluorescent indicator. Handle the strip *only* by the sides to avoid contaminating the plate with oils from your hands. Place a pencil dot in the middle of the sheet about 1 cm from one end. Using a capillary pipet, apply a spot of pigment solution over the pencil dot by *lightly* and *briefly* applying the tip of the pipet to the surface of the plate; you may blow gently on the plate as the sample is applied. Do not allow the spot to diffuse to a diameter of more than 1–2 mm during application of the sample. Perform the spotting process an additional four or five times, allowing the solvent of each drop to evaporate before adding the next. When the spot has thoroughly dried, place the strip in the developing chamber containing the first eluant; be careful not to splash solvent onto the plate. The spot *must be above* the solvent level. Allow the solvent front to move to within 2–3 mm of the top of the strip and then remove the strip. Mark the position of the solvent front with a pencil, and allow the plate to air-dry. Repeat this process with other eluants as directed by your instructor.

Analysis A good separation will reveal as many as eight colored spots. These are the carotenes (orange), chlorophyll *a* (blue-green), the xanthophylls (yellow), and chlorophyll *b* (green). Calculate the R_f-values of all spots on the plate(s) you developed. Compile these data, together with those of others if you worked as a team, and determine which solvent mixture provided the best and which the worst separations. Draw a picture to scale of the plates you developed that showed the best and worst separations and include them in your notebook as a permanent record.

Discovery Experiment *Effect of Solvent Polarity on Efficiency of Separation*

Explore the possible consequences of using only petroleum ether, a nonpolar solvent, for extracting the pigments from spinach leaves. For comparative purposes, use the same solvent mixture for developing the TLC plate as you did in the original procedure.

Analysis of Plant Pigments from Various Sources

Investigate the distribution of pigments obtained from other sources of green leaves such as beets, chard, trees, and shrubs. Avoid the use of waxy leaves, as their coating makes extraction and isolation of the pigments more difficult.

WRAPPING IT UP

Put the unused eluants containing only *petroleum ether, acetone,* and *ethanol* in the container for nonhalogenated organic liquids and any unused eluants containing *chloroform* in the container for halogenated organic liquids. Discard the dry chromatographic plates in the nonhazardous solid waste container.

EXPERIMENTAL PROCEDURES

Separation of Syn- and Anti-Azobenzenes by TLC

Discovery Experiment **Purpose** To identify solvent mixtures that will separate *syn-* and *anti-*azobenzenes using thin-layer chromatography.

SAFETY ALERT

1. **Petroleum ether, ethanol, and acetone are highly volatile and flammable solvents. Be certain there are *no flames* in the vicinity during this experiment.**

2. **Since azobenzene is a suspected carcinogen, avoid contacting it with your skin or ingesting it.**

Procedure

See Pre-Lab Exercises and MSDSs

Preparation Answer the Pre-Lab Exercises on page PL. 31. Read the MSDSs for chemicals used in this procedure.

Apparatus A wide-mouth bottle with a screw-top cap, 3-cm × 10-cm silica gel TLC plates, and a capillary pipet.

Setting Up Prepare a developing chamber by placing a folded filter paper lengthwise in a wide-mouth bottle (Fig. 6.3). As directed by your instructor, prepare three or four mixtures of eluants that contain different ratios of varying pairs of the following solvents: petroleum ether, bp 60–80 °C (760 torr), chloroform, acetone, and ethanol. For example, prepare 10 mL of a 90:10 mixture of petroleum ether and chloroform to use as one eluant. Add an amount of the eluant to the developing chamber so that it forms a 1-cm layer on the bottom of the container. Screw the cap onto the bottle *tightly,* and *shake* the container *well* to saturate the atmosphere of the chamber with vapors of the solvent.

Preparing and Developing a Plate Obtain three or four 3-cm × 10-cm strips of silica gel chromatogram sheets *without* a fluorescent indicator. Handle the strip *only* by the sides in order to avoid contaminating the plate with oils from your hands. Place one pencil dot about 1 cm from the left side and about 1 cm from one end of one sheet and another about 1 cm from the right side the same distance from the bottom as the first. Using a capillary pipet, carefully apply a *small* spot of a 10% solution of commercial azobenzene in toluene, which you should obtain from your instructor, over one of the pencil dots. Do not allow the spot to diffuse to a diameter of more than 1–2 mm during application of the sample. Repeat this process for each strip. Allow the spots to dry and then expose the plates to sunlight for one to two hours (or a sunlamp for about 20 min).

When the irradiation is complete, apply another spot of the *original* solution on the plate over the second pencil dot in the same manner as just described and allow each strip to dry. Place a strip in the developing chamber, being careful not to splash solvent onto the plate. Both spots *must be above* the solvent level. Allow the solvent to move to within approximately 2–3 mm of the top of the strip and then remove the strip. Repeat this process for each additional strip using a different eluting solvent as directed by your instructor. Mark the position of the solvent front with a pencil, and allow the plate to air-dry.

Analysis Note the number of spots arising from each of the two original spots. Pay particular attention to the relative intensities of the two spots nearest the starting point in each of the samples; these are *syn*-azobenzenes. Calculate the R_f-values of each of the spots on your developed plate. In your notebook include a picture of the developed plate drawn to scale as a permanent record. Identify the solvent mixture that gave the best separation of *syn*- and *anti*-azobenzene.

Discovery Experiment

Analysis of Analgesics by TLC

Design and execute an experimental procedure for testing over-the-counter analgesics such as Excedrin™ and Tylenol™ and Advil™ for the presence of caffeine (**3**) and/or acetaminophen (**4**). A 50:50 (v:v) mixture of ethanol and dichloromethane can be used to extract the active ingredients.

See more on
Acetaminophen

See more on
Caffeine

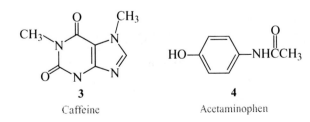

3
Caffeine

4
Acetaminophen

WRAPPING IT UP

Put the *unused eluants* containing mixtures of only *petroleum ether, acetone,* and *ethanol* in the container for nonhalogenated organic liquids and any unused mixtures containing *chloroform* in the container for halogenated organic liquids. Put the dry chromatographic plates in the hazardous solid waste container, since they contain small amounts of azobenzene.

EXERCISES

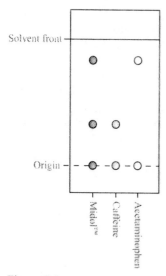

Figure 6.6
TLC analysis of mixture.

1. What may occur if a mixture containing a component that is very sensitive to acidic conditions is subjected to TLC analysis in which silica gel serves as the stationary phase?

2. In a TLC experiment, why should the spot not be immersed in the solvent in the developing chamber?

3. Explain why the solvent must not be allowed to evaporate from the plate during development.

4. Explain why the diameter of the spot should be as small as possible.

5. Which of the two diastereomers of azobenzene would you expect to be more thermodynamically stable? Why?

6. From the results of the TLC experiment with the azobenzenes, describe the role of sunlight.

7. A student obtained the silica gel TLC plate shown in Figure 6.6 by spotting samples of Midol™, caffeine, and acetaminophen on the plate and eluting with petroleum ether:chloroform (9:1 v/v).

   a. What are the R_f-values of acetaminophen and of caffeine, respectively?

   b. Based on this TLC analysis, what are the ingredients in a tablet of Midol™?

   c. What are the mobile and stationary phases, respectively, in this TLC experiment?

   d. No spots were observed visually when the TLC plate was removed from the developing chamber. How might the student effect visualization of the spots?

   e. Another student accidentally used Midol PM™ in her experiment and observed only one spot. Speculate as to which spot was absent and offer a possible explanation for the difference in this student's result.

6.3 COLUMN CHROMATOGRAPHY

**See more on
Column
Chromatography**

Column chromatography is another form of **solid-liquid adsorption** chromatography and depends on the same fundamental principles as does thin-layer chromatography (TLC, Sec. 6.2), as you will see from the discussion that follows. It has an advantage over TLC in that multigram amounts of mixtures can be separated but has the disadvantage that this technique requires considerably more time to perform. The

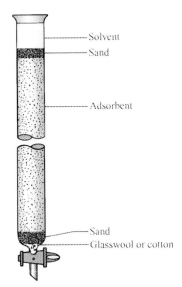

Figure 6.7
Chromatography column.

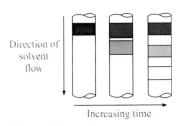

Figure 6.8
Separation of mixture by column chromatography.

Adsorbents

larger scale of separations using this technique make it valuable for purifying components of a reaction mixture so that one of them may be purified and used in a subsequent chemical reaction.

In column chromatography, a multicomponent mixture is typically dissolved in a small amount of an appropriate solvent and applied to the top of a packed column containing a finely divided, active solid **adsorbent** that serves as the stationary phase (Fig. 6.7). Next an **eluant** or **eluting solvent,** which is the mobile phase, is passed down the column. The individual components of the mixture, which were initially adsorbed on the stationary phase at the top of the column, begin to move downward with the eluting solvent (Fig. 6.8). These components travel at different rates depending on their relative affinities for the packing material; a more weakly adsorbed compound is eluted faster from the column than is a more strongly adsorbed compound. The individual components are collected in separate containers as they exit from the bottom of the column in bands. The solvent is then removed from each fraction by evaporation to provide the pure components, which are characterized and identified by determining their physical constants (Chaps. 3 and 4) and spectral properties (Chap. 8).

As with TLC (Sec. 6.2), the chromatographically separated bands are easily observed when all of the components of a mixture are colored. Many organic compounds are colorless, however, and other methods are required for detecting the banks as they elute from the column. For those organic compounds that absorb ultraviolet or visible light (Sec. 8.4), **electronic detectors** that measure differences in the absorption of light as the solvent exits the column are used to locate the bands of the individual components. Detectors that measure differences in the **refractive index** of the **eluate** are also used to identify the different bands; such detectors do not rely on absorption of light by the organic components.

If a detector is not available, the progress of the chromatographic separation can be conveniently followed using TLC to analyze the eluate at regular intervals. Another method, albeit more laborious, involves collecting small, equal fractions of the eluate from the column in a series of flasks. The solvent in each flask is then evaporated, and the presence or absence of a solute in the residue then provides a means of locating the bands of each component. If there is adequate separation of the different bands, a given flask will often contain only one constituent of the original mixture. That component will normally appear in a number of consecutive fractions, however.

Alumina and silica gel are the most commonly used adsorbents for column chromatography, just as they are for TLC. The quality of these adsorbents is high, in that they have *uniform particle size* and *high specific area.* The higher the specific area, the faster the equilibrium of the solute between the mobile and solid phases is established and the narrower the bands. High specific areas on the order of several hundred m^2/g are common for good grades of alumina and silica gel.

As noted in the discussion of TLC, the strength of the adsorption of an organic compound to the solid support depends on the polarity and nature of the adsorbent as well as on the nature of the functional groups present in the molecule. When **normal-phase column chromatography** is performed, a polar stationary phase such as alumina or silica gel is used in combination with organic solvents as the mobile phase or eluant. Under these conditions, the **elutropic series** described for TLC in Section 6.2 applies.

In **reverse-phase column chromatography,** the packing material for the stationary phase consists of glass beads coated with a nonpolar, hydrocarbon film,

$$RCO_2H < ROH < RNH_2 < R^1R^2C{=}O < R^1CO_2R^2 < ROCH_3 < R^1R^2C{=}CR^3R^4 < RHal$$

Figure 6.9

Elutropic series for nonpolar stationary phases.

Increasing adsorption on nonpolar stationary phases

and mixtures of water and organic solvents are generally used as the eluting solvents. Under these conditions, nonpolar organic molecules are more strongly attracted to the nonpolar stationary phase, whereas polar solutes are more strongly attracted to the mobile phase. The order of elution is then the *reverse* of that shown earlier, with the more polar components of a mixture eluting more rapidly than the less polar ones. The elutropic series then becomes the reverse (Figure 6.9). Reverse-phase chromatography may sometimes be used to separate mixtures that are inseparable by normal-phase chromatography.

Eluant

The most efficient method for determining the optimal solvent system(s) for a specific column chromatographic separation often is to perform a series of trial separations using TLC. These trials can be run quickly and the amount of material needed is small.

The same criteria for selecting an eluant for TLC apply to normal-phase column chromatography. For example, if the mixture to be separated is not soluble or only slightly soluble in the eluant being used, the components will remain permanently adsorbed to the stationary phase near the top of the column. Conversely, if the components are too readily displaced from the adsorbent by the eluant, they will move down the column too rapidly to allow the needed equilibration between the stationary and mobile phases and will not be separated from one another. To allow equilibration in normal-phase column chromatography, the eluting solvent must be *less* polar than the components of the mixture. Although the relative eluting power of solvents for normal-phase column chromatography is the same as that for TLC when alumina or silica gel is used as an adsorbent, that for reverse-phase chromatography is the reverse (Fig. 6.10).

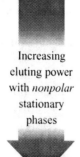

Increasing eluting power with *nonpolar* stationary phases

Water
Methanol
Ethanol
1-Propanol
Acetone
Ethyl acetate
Diethyl ether
Chloroform
Dichloromethane
Toluene
Hexane
Petroleum ether

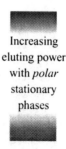

Increasing eluting power with *polar* stationary phases

Figure 6.10

Eluting power of solvents as function of polarity of stationary phases.

Experimental Technique

With this general discussion as background, we can now discuss some of the experimental aspects of performing column chromatography. The optimal adsorbent and eluting solvent(s) typically are first determined using TLC, and then the column is packed with the adsorbent. The amount of adsorbent used to prepare the column varies according to the differences in partition coefficients and polarities of the individual components in the chromatographic system. For simple separations, it is possible to use as little as 10 g of adsorbent for each 1 g of the mixture, but when the components of the mixture have similar polarities, this ratio must be increased to as much as 100–200:1; a ratio of about 25:1 is a convenient starting point. As a general rule of thumb, the ratio of height-to-diameter for the packed column should be about 8:1.

The column is made of glass and is fitted with a stopcock or a segment of polyethylene tubing with a screw clamp to control the flow of solvent through the column. The column is prepared by first inserting a plug of cotton or glasswool into the small end of the column using a long glass rod or a piece of wire; this prevents the adsorbent from washing out of the bottom. A layer of white sand, approximately 1 cm deep, is then added to provide an even bed for the adsorbent (Fig. 6.7).

Proper packing of the column is vital to the success of column chromatography because this step ultimately determines the efficiency of separation. Two general protocols are followed for this operation. The first of these, the **dry-pack** method, involves pouring the dry adsorbent slowly into a vertical glass column half-filled with the solvent that will serve as the eluant. The other technique is the **wet-pack** method, in which a slurry of the adsorbent in the eluting solvent is added to the column; this is the preferred procedure when silica gel is the adsorbent. With both methods, the column must be constantly tapped as the solid settles through the liquid to ensure even and firm packing of the adsorbent and to remove any entrapped air bubbles. Some solvent may be drained from the column during this operation, but the liquid level in the column should *never* be allowed to fall below the top of the adsorbent. If this occurs, the air bubbles that form in the column will allow *channeling*, which results in poor separations because the components are eluted as ragged rather than sharp bands. *Uniform packing of the adsorbent is essential* so the solvent will move down the column with a horizontal front.

To complete packing the column, a layer of sand is normally placed on top of adsorbent, as shown in Figure 6.7. The purpose of the sand is twofold: (1) It allows the sample to flow evenly onto the surface of the adsorbent, and (2) it prevents disruption of the packing material as eluting solvent is added.

Mixtures of solids are typically dissolved in a *minimal* volume of a solvent before being transferred to the top of the column; a liquid mixture may be transferred directly to the column. It is important to distribute the sample evenly on the surface of the adsorbent and to use as little solvent as possible in loading the column. This procedure ensures that the bands that form during development of the chromatogram will be narrow, thereby providing the best possible separation. If too much solvent is used to dissolve the sample, the initial band will be broad, and poor resolution of the mixture may result.

Once the sample has been loaded onto the column, there are several different techniques that may be used to elute its components. In a **simple elution** experiment, a *single* solvent is passed through the column during the entire course of the separation. This procedure works well for the separation of mixtures containing only two or three compounds having similar polarities. However, the more common chromatographic procedure is **stepwise** or **fractional elution.** In this technique, a series of increasingly more polar solvents is used to elute the mixture from the column. A nonpolar solvent such as petroleum ether or hexane is first used to move the least polar component of the mixture down the column, while the others remain at or near the top of the column. After elution of the first band, the polarity of the eluant is increased using either pure solvents or combinations of mixed solvents so that the bands are individually eluted from the column. Systematic and gradual increases in solvent polarity are sometimes essential so that individual bands remaining on the column separate and do not co-elute. As the polarity of the solvent system increases, those components of the mixture that are more tightly adsorbed on the column will begin to move. As a rule of thumb, a volume of solvent approximately equal to three times the column volume is passed through the column prior to switching to a solvent of higher polarity.

The separation is monitored using one of a variety of methods. Unfortunately, many organic compounds are not highly colored, as we noted above, and sophisticated devices for their detection are rarely available in the undergraduate laboratory. The most effective technique for following the separation is to collect fractions of equal volume in tared flasks, to concentrate the solvent, and to reweigh the flasks. The fractions containing the different bands may then be easily identified by the relative amounts of solute in each flask. One may also use TLC to monitor the separation.

In the experiment that follows, column chromatography will be used to separate fluorene (5) from an oxidation product, 9-fluorenone (6). One of these compounds is white, the other is yellow. Consequently, the progress of the chromatography may be followed by evaporation of the solvent at periodic intervals as well as by observing the slower-moving yellow band.

5
Fluorene
White
                    6
9-Fluorenone
Yellow

Column Chromatography

Purpose To separate fluorene and 9-fluorenone by column chromatography.

SAFETY ALERT

Petroleum ether is a highly volatile and flammable mixture of low-boiling hydrocarbons. During the preparation and development of the chromatographic column, be certain that there are *no flames* in the vicinity.

Procedure

See Pre-Lab
Exercises and
MSDSs

Preparation Answer the Pre-Lab Exercises on page PL. 33. Read the MSDSs for chemicals used in this procedure. Read or review Sections 2.13 and 2.29.

Apparatus A *dry* 50-ml glass buret or chromatography column about 1 cm in diameter and 25 cm long and fitted with either a Teflon stopcock or a short piece of polyethylene tubing and a screw clamp, three 25- or 50-mL Erlenmeyer flasks, watchglass, Pasteur pipet, and apparatus for simple distillation. Consult with your instructor regarding whether the glassware, sand, and alumina require oven-drying prior to use.

Setting Up Clamp the glass buret or chromatography column in a vertical position with its *ungreased* stopcock, preferably Teflon, *closed.* Using a piece of glass tubing, insert a small plug of cotton or glasswool loosely into the bottom of the column. Cover the cotton or glasswool plug with enough clean *dry* sand to form a layer about 1 cm thick, and add approximately 25 mL of petroleum ether, bp 30–60 °C (760 torr). Place a funnel on top of the column, and *slowly* add 5 g of *dry* neutral alumina to the column while constantly tapping the buret. A rubber "tapping mallet" may be made by placing a pencil in a one-hole rubber stopper. When this process has been completed, wash the inner walls of the column with additional petroleum ether to remove any alumina that may adhere to the sides. Cover the alumina with a 1-cm layer of clean sand, and open the stopcock to allow the solvent to drain into an Erlenmeyer flask until the solvent level reaches just to the *top of the alumina.* The column is now ready for the addition of the sample mixture (Fig. 6.11).

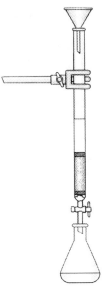

Figure 6.11
Set-up for column chromatography.

Separation Obtain a sample of an approximately 1:1 mixture of fluorene (**5**) and 9-fluorenone (**6**) and accurately determine its melting-point range. In a small test tube, suspend about 0.1 g of this mixture in 0.5 mL of petroleum ether and slowly add just enough dichloromethane with a Pasteur pipet to effect solution. Using a Pasteur or filter-tip pipet, carefully transfer this solution directly to the top of the column. Open the stopcock until the liquid level is at the top of the alumina. *Do not allow the solvent to drain below the level of the alumina,* as air bubbles and channels might develop in the solid support. Add approximately 1–2 mL of fresh petroleum ether to the top of the column, and again allow the liquid to drain to the top of the alumina.

Fill the buret with approximately 20 mL of fresh petroleum ether, open the stopcock, and collect the eluant in an Erlenmeyer flask. Follow the progress of the chromatography by collecting a drop or two of eluant on a watchglass with every 5 mL that elutes from the column. When the solvent evaporates, any white solid present will be visible on the watchglass. You can determine when all of the white solid has been eluted using this visualization technique. Your instructor might also direct you to follow the chromatography by TLC using 15% dichloromethane in petroleum ether as the developing solvent (Sec. 6.2). Most of the white solid should elute in a volume of 15–20 mL of petroleum ether, and slow movement of a yellow band down the column should occur. Wash any of the white solid from the tip of the column into your collection flask with fresh petroleum ether.

When all of the white solid has eluted from the column, change the collection flask to another clean Erlenmeyer flask. Elute the column with about 5 mL of petroleum ether, and then change the eluant to dichloromethane, a more polar solvent. Watch the progress of the yellow band as it now proceeds rapidly down the column. When this yellow band just reaches the bottom of the column, change to a third clean Erlenmeyer flask. The intermediate fraction should not contain significant amounts of solid; verify this by evaporating a few drops on a watchglass.

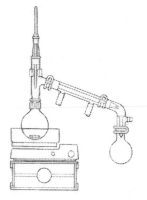

Continue eluting the column with dichloromethane until the eluant is colorless; approximately 10 mL will be required.

Isolation The first and third fractions should contain pure samples of fluorene and 9-fluorenone. Most of the solvent in these fractions may be removed by simple distillation (Sec. 2.13) or by one of the techniques outlined in Section 2.29. Attach the flask to a water aspirator or house vacuum to remove the last traces of solvent under reduced pressure.

Analysis When the crystals of each of the purified compounds are completely dry, determine their melting points and weights. Use your experimentally determined melting points to identify the order of elution of fluorene and fluorenone from the column and record your observations and conclusions in your notebook. Based upon the weight of the mixture used, calculate the percent recovery of fluorene and 9-fluorenone.

 Discovery Experiment *Column Chromatographic Separation of Benzyl Alcohol and Methyl Benzoate*

Design and execute an experimental procedure for separating benzyl alcohol (**7**) from methyl benzoate (**8**) by normal-phase column chromatography.

$$\text{—CH}_2\text{OH} \qquad \text{—COCH}_3$$

7
Benzyl alcohol

8
Methyl benzoate

WRAPPING IT UP

Place recovered *petroleum ether* in the container for nonhalogenated organic liquids, but pour the recovered *dichloromethane* into a container for halogenated organic liquids. Spread out the *alumina adsorbent*, which is wet with organic solvent, in a hood to dry and then place it in the nonhazardous solid waste container.

EXERCISES

1. Define the following terms.
   a. eluate
   b. eluant
   c. adsorbent
   d. reverse-phase chromatography
2. In normal-phase column chromatography, which solvent has more eluting power, petroleum ether or dichloromethane? In what way is the eluting power of a solvent related to its polarity?
3. In reverse-phase column chromatography, which phase is the more polar: the stationary phase or the mobile phase?
4. How does the principle of "like dissolves like" explain the affinity of a compound for the mobile phase relative to the stationary phase?

5. When separating a mixture by normal-phase column chromatography, why is it better to change from a less-polar solvent to a more-polar solvent rather than the opposite?

6. If the polarity of the eluant is to be increased during column chromatography, the increase is normally made gradually. However, in this procedure *pure* dichloromethane rather than intermediate mixtures of petroleum ether and dichloromethane was added to the column. Why is this variation from the usual technique acceptable in this case?

7. State two major differences between TLC and column chromatography.

8. If you had 5.0 g of material that needed to be purified, would you opt for using TLC or column chromatography to purify your material? Explain your answer.

9. Why is it preferable to use a Teflon or an ungreased stopcock rather than a greased stopcock on a column used for column chromatography?

10. Why should care be exercised in the preparation of the column to prevent air bubbles from being trapped in the adsorbent?

11. Why is a layer of sand placed above the cotton plug prior to the addition of the column packing material?

12. Does fluorene or 9-fluorenone move faster down the column when petroleum ether is used as the eluant? Why?

13. Consider the structures of fluorene (**5**) and 9-fluorenone (**6**).

    a. Other than the aromatic rings, specify what functional group, if any, is present in **6**.

    b. Predict which compound is more polar and explain why.

    c. Which compound would you expect to elute from a normal-phase column first and why?

14. In the separation of fluorene and fluorenone by column chromatography, what is the stationary phase? The mobile phase?

15. The observed melting point of the 1:1 mixture of fluorene and 9-fluorenone should be relatively sharp, although lower than the melting point of either of the pure compounds. On the other hand, a 3:1 mixture has a broad melting-point range of about 60–90 °C. Explain these observations. (*Hint:* See Sec. 3.3.)

16. A mixture containing compounds **9–11** was separated by normal-phase column chromatography, using neutral alumina as the stationary phase and petroleum ether as the eluant. Predict the order in which **9–11** will elute from the column.

17. Most peptides (polymers of amides constructed from amino acids) are very polar molecules; therefore, they are most successfully purified by reverse-phase chromatography.

a. In this type of column chromatography, is the mobile or stationary phase more polar?

b. Provide an explanation for why reverse-phase chromatography is more appropriate in this application than normal-phase chromatography.

18. A typical eluting solvent for reverse-phase column chromatography is acetonitrile (CH_3CN), water, and a buffer. In what way is this mobile phase different from the one you used to separate fluorene (**5**) from 9-fluorenone (**6**)?

6.4 GAS-LIQUID CHROMATOGRAPHY

See more on *GC*

Gas-liquid chromatography (GLC), which is also called **gas chromatography** (GC), is a technique that may be used to separate mixtures of volatile compounds whose boiling points may differ by less than 0.5 °C. It can also be applied as an analytical tool to identify the components of a mixture or in preparative applications when quantities of the pure components are desired.

Basic Principles of Gas-Liquid Chromatography

Gas-liquid chromatography operates on the principle of partitioning the components of a mixture between a mobile gaseous phase and a stationary liquid phase. In practice, a sample is injected into a heated chamber where it is immediately vaporized and carried through a column by a flowing inert gas such as helium or nitrogen, which is called the **carrier gas.** This gaseous mixture is the **mobile phase.** The column is packed with a finely divided solid support that has been coated with a viscous, high-boiling liquid, which serves as the **stationary phase.** As the mobile phase moves through the column, its components are continuously partitioned between the two phases. Those components that show a higher affinity for the mobile phase move through the column more quickly, whereas those with a stronger attraction to the stationary phase migrate more slowly, and separation occurs. As with a fractional distillation column (Sec. 4.4), a GLC column may be characterized by the number of theoretical plates it provides. GLC columns typically have many more theoretical plates, however, so they can effect separations that would be impossible using fractional distillation.

The **retention time** of a component is the elapsed time required for the compound to pass from the point of injection to the detector and may be used for purposes of identification. The retention time of a component is *independent* of the presence or absence of other components in the sample mixture. There are four experimental factors that influence retention time of a compound: (1) the *nature* of the stationary phase, (2) the *length* of the column, (3) the *temperature* of the column, and (4) the *flowrate* of the inert carrier gas. Thus, for a particular column, temperature, and flowrate, the retention time will be the same for a specific compound.

Although a large number of **stationary liquid phases** are available, only a few are widely used (Table 6.1). Each liquid phase has a maximum temperature limit above which it cannot be used. This temperature depends upon the stability and volatility of the liquid phase; at higher temperatures the liquid phase will vaporize and "bleed" from the column with the mobile phase.

The differences in the *partition coefficients* (Secs. 5.2 and 5.3) of the individual components of a mixture in GLC depend primarily upon the differences in solubility of each of the components in the liquid phase. Two important factors determining the solubility of a gas in a liquid are its vapor pressure at the **ambient temperature,** which is the temperature of the column, and the magnitude of its

Table 6.1 *Common Stationary Phases for Gas-Liquid Chromatography*

Liquid Phase	Type	Property	Maximum Temperature Limit, °C
Carbowax 20M	Hydrocarbon wax	Polar	250
OV-17	Methylphenyl silicone	Intermediate polarity	300
QF-1	Fluorosilicone	Intermediate polarity	250
SE-30	Silicone gum rubber	Nonpolar	375

interactions with the liquid phase. Regarding the first factor, the solubility of a gas in a liquid decreases as its vapor pressure increases. This means the more volatile components of a gaseous mixture tend to pass through the column more rapidly and elute before the less volatile ones. The impact of the second factor is understandable from the principle that *like dissolves like* (Sec. 3.2). Polar samples are most effectively separated by using a polar liquid phase, whereas nonpolar compounds are best separated using a nonpolar liquid phase.

The stationary liquid phase is normally coated as a thin film on an inert solid support. The support is composed of small, uniformly meshed granules, so that a large surface area of the liquid phase is available for contact with the vapor phase to ensure efficient separation. Some common types of solid supports include Chromosorb P and Chromosorb W, which are composed of diatomaceous earth. The surface areas of these supports varies from 1 to 6 m^2/g. Columns are now commercially available with a wide variety of liquid phases on different solid supports. An alternative method of supporting the liquid phase is used in capillary columns. In these columns, the liquid is coated directly onto the inner walls of the tubing. These columns are highly efficient but relatively expensive.

In general, the efficiency, or **resolution,** of a column increases with increasing length and decreasing diameter. Increasing the pathlength increases the difference in retention times between bands, whereas decreasing the diameter of the column gives rise to narrower bands. With a small band separation, as measured from the band centers, wide bands are more likely to overlap (Fig. 6.12a) than narrow bands (Fig. 6.12b).

The two other experimental factors that may be varied to alter the degree of separation of the bands are the *temperature* at which the column is maintained and the *flowrate* of the carrier gas. Increasing the temperature results in shorter retention times, because the solubility of gases in liquids decreases with increasing temperature. The partition coefficients are affected, and the bands move through the column at a faster rate. Higher flowrates also cause retention times to decrease. In spite of the decreased resolution and band separation obtained at higher temperatures and flowrates, these conditions are sometimes necessary for substances that would otherwise have very long retention times.

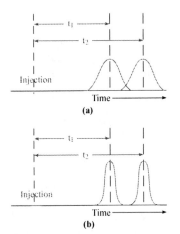

Figure 6.12
Effect of bandwidth on resolution. (a) Wide bands. (b) Narrow bands.

Instrumentation

All commercially available gas-liquid chromatographs (GLCs) have a number of basic features in common. These are illustrated schematically in Figure 6.13. Parts 1–5 are associated with supplying the dry **carrier gas,** usually helium or nitrogen, and allowing an operator to control its flow. The mixture to be separated is injected using a gastight syringe through a septum into the **injection block** (6), an

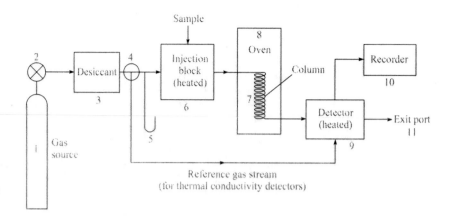

Figure 6.13
Schematic diagram of apparatus for GLC.

See more on *GC Sequence*

See more on *FID Detectors*

individually heated chamber in which the sample is immediately vaporized. The sample then enters the flowing stream of carrier gas and is swept into and through the **column (7)**, which is located in an **oven (8)** and consists of coiled aluminum, stainless steel, or glass tubing containing an appropriate stationary phase. In the column, the individual components separate into bands that ultimately pass through a **detector (9)**, producing a signal whose voltage is proportional to the amount of material other than carrier gas present in the mobile phase. One type of detector that is commonly used is the **thermal conductivity detector** (TCD), which operates on the basis of differences in the thermal conductivity of the mobile phase as a function of its composition. A **flame ionization detector** (FID) is much more sensitive and operates by detecting the number of ions produced by passing the mobile phase through a hydrogen flame. The **recorder (10)** plots the changes in voltage measured by the detector as a function of time to give the **gas chromatogram.** The vapors then pass from the detector into either the atmosphere or a collection device at the **exit port (11)**.

The GLCs available in the introductory organic laboratory often can only be operated at a constant oven temperature, the so-called **isothermal** mode of operation. Some GLCs, however, have a temperature-programming option, which allows the temperature of the oven, and consequently that of the column, to be varied over a range of temperatures. This is particularly useful when the sample being analyzed contains components having widely varying boiling points. Thus, the oven temperature may be held at a constant temperature for a specified period of time at the beginning of an analysis but then may be increased to higher temperatures as a function of time. For example, the temperature program illustrated in Figure 6.14 involved an initial temperature of 100 °C. After 5 minutes, the temperature was ramped up to 125 °C at a rate of 5 °C/min, held at that temperature for 5 additional minutes, and then further ramped up at a rate of 10 °C/min to a final temperature of 175 °C for completing the analysis. The programming option allows the higher-boiling components of the mixture to elute in a reasonable period of time because rates of elution increase with increasing temperatures. If the analysis had been performed at the higher temperature, the lower-boiling components might have eluted too quickly to be separated from each other.

Another modification of a GLC involves its direct connection to a mass spectrometer (MS) to produce a hybrid instrument commonly called a **GC-MS.** This combination provides a powerful analytical technique because the GC-MS combines the separating power of GLC with the ability of mass spectrometry (Sec. 8.5)

See more on *GC-MS*

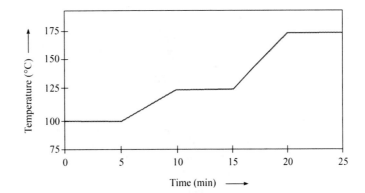

Figure 6.14
Example of temperature vs. time program for a GLC analysis.

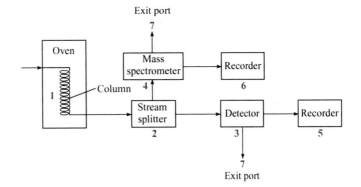

Figure 6.15
Partial schematic diagram of a GC-MS.

to determine molar masses using very small amounts of material (see the Historical Highlights at the end of this chapter). Thus, a GC-MS allows the mass spectrum of each component of a mixture of volatile compounds to be obtained as each individual component emerges from the GLC. If the components of a mixture are known, as they would be if you were analyzing a fraction obtained by normal-phase column chromatography of a mixture of benzyl alcohol (**7**) and methyl benzoate (**8**) (Optional Discovery Experiment, Sec. 6.3), you could use the information provided by the mass spectrum, as discussed below, to confirm the identity and order of elution from the chromatographic column of each of these colorless compounds. If the components are unknown, on the other hand, knowledge of the molar mass of each compound, coupled with information about the origin of the mixture being analyzed, may allow assignment of structures to the unknown substances. Other spectral data (Chap. 8) are generally required before structural assignments can be made, however.

A partial schematic of a GC-MS is shown in Figure 6.15; the elements of the GLC that precede the column have been omitted but are the same as those shown in Figure 6.13. By comparing Figures 6.13 and 6.15, you see that a GC-MS has the outlet of the column (**1**) leading to a **stream splitter** (**2**), which sends part of eluant to a **detector** (**3**), usually an FID, and part of it to a **mass spectrometer** (**4**); **recorders** (**5, 6**) provide the necessary records of when components are eluting from the GLC and what their mass spectra are. Both the GLC and the MS units are vented to the atmosphere (**7**).

Experimental Techniques

Qualitative Analysis. The *retention time* of a pure compound is constant under a specified set of experimental conditions, including the column, temperature, and flowrate. Consequently this property may be used as a *first* step to identify an unknown compound or the individual components in a mixture. In a typical experiment, an unknown compound or mixture is injected into the injection port of a GLC, and the retention time(s) of the component(s) is (are) measured. A series of known samples are then injected under the same conditions. Comparison of the retention times of the standard samples with those of the unknown allows a preliminary identification of the component(s) of the unknown. A convenient way of confirming that the retention times of a standard and the unknown are the same involves injecting a sample prepared by combining equal amounts of the two. If a *single* peak is observed in the chromatogram, the *retention times* of the standard and the unknown are identical. However, observation of the same retention time for a known and an unknown substance is a *necessary but not sufficient* condition to establish identity, because it *is* possible for two different compounds to have the same retention time. Independent confirmation of the identity of the unknown by spectral (Chap. 8) or other means is imperative.

An example of the use of GLC as a qualitative, analytical tool is illustrated in Figure 6.16. These sets of peaks represent a gas chromatographic separation of the distillation fractions of a mixture of cyclohexane and toluene similar to those obtained in the distillation experiment described in Section 4.3. The notations *A, B,*

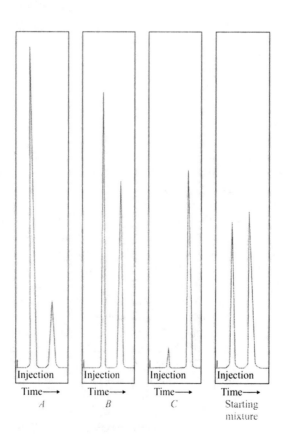

Figure 6.16
GLC analysis of the distillation fractions from the distillation experiment in Section 4.3.

and *C* refer to the three fractions taken in that experiment. The individual peaks in the mixture may be identified by comparing their retention times with those of pure cyclohexane and pure toluene; the peak with the shorter retention time in the mixture is cyclohexane, whereas the peak with the longer retention time is toluene.

The GC-MS analysis of a mixture of benzyl alcohol (**7**, bp 215.3 °C, 760 torr) and methyl benzoate (**8**, bp 199.6 °C, 760 torr) is provided in Figure 6.17. Figure 6.17a is the GLC trace of the mixture. Because the GLC column being used separates mixtures on the basis of the relative basis of the boiling points of its components, Peak A, which emerges first, should be **8**, whereas Peak B should be **7**. This could be confirmed with a GLC if the retention times of **7** and **8** were determined separately. Such additional analyses would not be necessary with GC-MS, however, because the masses of the two compounds are different, that of **7** being 108.14 atomic mass units (amu), and that of **8** is 136.15 amu. Figures 6.17b and 6.17c are the mass spectra corresponding to Peaks A and B, respectively. In Figure 6.17b we see that the molecular ion is at m/z 108, whereas it is at m/z 136 in Figure 6.17c. This proves that Peaks A and B are benzyl alcohol and methyl benzoate, respectively; our expectation of the reverse order of elution, based on considering boiling points, has been proven wrong. The stationary phase of the column must interact more strongly than expected with **8**. In any case, the GC-MS analysis has provided unambiguous identification of the two peaks through a *single* analysis of the mixture. Moreover, integration of the peaks in the GLC tract would provide a quantitative measure of their relative proportions in the mixture being analyzed.

A feature that may complicate the interpretation of the mass spectrum from a GC-MS analysis may be seen in Figure 6.17c. This feature is a small peak at m/z 146, a value that is not associated with either of the components contained in our known mixture of **7** and **8**. Although the substance that is the source of the peak could be an impurity in our sample, it is not. Rather, it is a peak produced from the "stationary" phase of the GLC column being used; the temperature at which the GLC was operating caused a small amount of the high-boiling material comprising this phase to "bleed" from the column into the MS, which results in minor peaks appearing in the spectrum. Such peaks can be confusing if you are not prepared for their possible presence.

A second example illustrating the power of an analysis by GC-MS rather than GLC alone is that of a mixture of methyl benzoate (**8**) and diethyl malonate (**12**), as seen in Figure 6.18. The boiling point of **12** (199.3 °C, 760 torr) is essentially identical to that of **8** (see above), and considering the differing polarities expected for these two esters, predicting their order of elution from a GLC column (Fig. 6.18a) is problematical. However, the mass spectra associated with the two peaks eluting at 150 and 164 seconds in the GLC trace show that Peak A must be diethyl malonate (Fig. 6.18b), whereas Peak B is methyl benzoate (Fig. 6.18c). You may be perplexed by the fact that the molecular ion from **12** appears to have m/z 161 rather than the expected value of 160.17. This could be the result of poor calibration of the instrument, so that the m/z values are inaccurate; proper calibration of the instrument is critical for proper interpretation of GC-MS data. However, the explanation in this case is that diethyl malonate apparently has a propensity to be protonated under the conditions of the mass spectrometric analysis, so it is this ion rather than the molecular ion that is being detected; this is yet another phenomenon that can make interpretation of GC-MS data difficult for a beginner. In any event, a single GC-MS analysis of the mixture of **8** and **12** allows unambiguous determination of the order

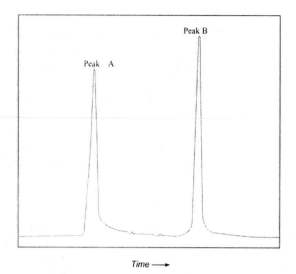

(a)   Time ⟶

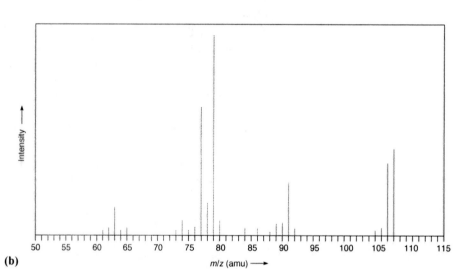

(b)   m/z (amu) ⟶

Figure 6.17
*GC-MS analysis of a mixture of
benzyl alcohol and methyl benzoate. (a) GLC trace. Column
and conditions: 0.5-mm × 15-m,
0.25-μ film of BPX5 (DB-5);
initial column temperature: 50 °C
(2.0 min); ramp rate: 15 °C/min;
final column temperature: 260 °C
(30 min); flowrate: 1.5 mL/min.
(b) MS spectrum of Peak A.
(c) MS spectrum of Peak B.*

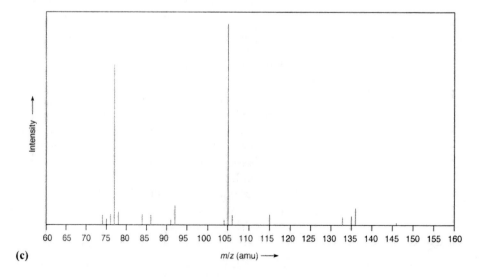

(c)   m/z (amu) ⟶

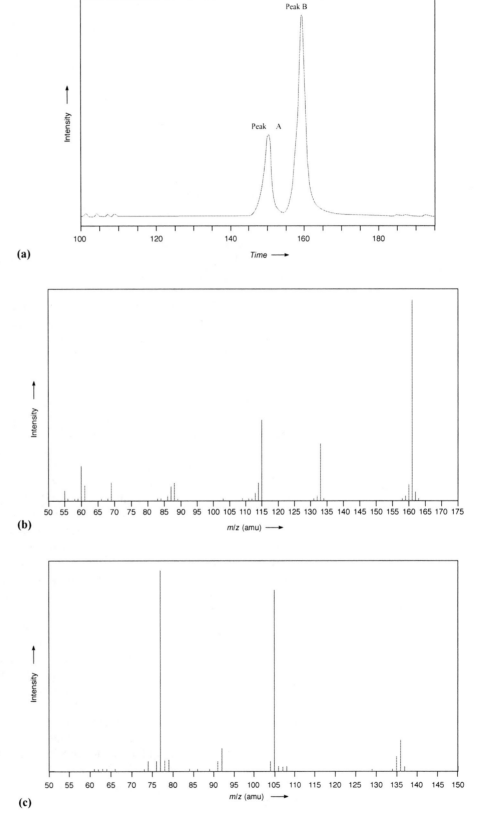

Figure 6.18
GC-MS analysis of a mixture of methyl benzoate and diethyl malonate. (a) GLC trace. Column and conditions: 0.5-mm × 15-m, 0.25-μ film of BPX5 (DB-5); initial column temperature: 50 °C (2.0 min); ramp rate: 15 °C/min; final column temperature: 260 °C (30 min); flowrate: 1.5 mL/min. (b) MS spectrum of Peak A. (c) MS spectrum of Peak B.

of elution from the GLC column of these esters, just as we saw in the analysis of the mixture of **7** and **8**.

$$CH_3CH_2O-\underset{\underset{O}{\|}}{C}-CH_2-\underset{\underset{O}{\|}}{C}-OCH_2CH_3$$

12

Diethyl malonate

Quantitative Analysis. The voltage output of the detector is related to the mole fraction of the material being detected in the vapor, so there is a correlation between the *relative areas* under the peaks in the chromatogram and the *relative amounts* of each of the components in the mixture. The quantitative evaluation of the chromatogram thus requires reliable methods for determining these peak areas.

An **electronic integrator,** which measures the intensity of detector output as a function of time, is the most accurate method for determining peak areas. However, these devices are expensive, so they are usually found only in research laboratories. Since the thickness and density of chart paper are reasonably uniform, another means of determining the relative areas involves carefully cutting the peaks out with scissors; the peak areas are then assumed to be proportional to their weight, as measured on an analytical balance. The original chromatogram should be saved as a permanent record, so the peaks should be cut from a photocopy of the chromatogram.

If the peaks are symmetrical, as are those shown in Figure 6.16, the areas may be approximated by assuming them to be equilateral triangles. The area of a symmetrical peak is then determined by multiplying the width of the peak at its half-height times its height. The percentage of each component in the mixture may be computed as the area of the peak corresponding to that component, expressed as a percentage of the sum of the areas of all peaks in the chromatogram. A sample calculation of this type is shown in Figure 6.19.

Although the peak areas are related to the mole fraction of the component in the mobile phase, they are not *quantitatively* related because the response of the detector varies with the class of the compound. Not all compounds have the same thermal conductivity (TCD), nor do they ionize in a hydrogen flame to form the same types or number of ions (FID). Thus, it is necessary to *correct* the measured areas in the chromatogram using the appropriate **response factor** to obtain an accurate quantitative analysis of the mixture. Although response factors for different compounds may be determined experimentally, approximate values are published in monographs on gas chromatography. The response factors for thermal conductivity and flame ionization detectors for compounds that you may encounter in this experiment are given in Table 6.2. Notice that the correction factors vary more widely for flame ionization detectors than for thermal conductivity detectors. In the experimental section, you have the opportunity to calculate the response factor for an unknown compound.

To analyze a mixture of substances quantitatively when **weight factors** are known, the peak area for each component is simply *multiplied* by the weight factor for that particular compound. The resulting *corrected* areas are used to calculate the percentage composition of the mixture according to the procedure outlined in Figure 6.19. Note that using these factors provides the composition on a *weight percentage* basis.

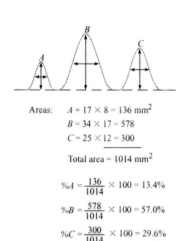

Areas: $A = 17 \times 8 = 136$ mm^2
         $B = 34 \times 17 = 578$
         $C = 25 \times 12 = 300$
         ―――――――――――
         Total area $= 1014$ mm^2

$\%A = \dfrac{136}{1014} \times 100 = 13.4\%$

$\%B = \dfrac{578}{1014} \times 100 = 57.0\%$

$\%C = \dfrac{300}{1014} \times 100 = 29.6\%$

―――――――――――
                                   100%

Figure 6.19
Determination of percentage composition of a mixture by GLC.

Table 6.2 *Weight (W_f) and Mol (M_f) Correction Factors for Some Representative Substances**

Substance	Thermal Conductivity		Flame Ionization	
	W_f	M_f	W_f	M_f
Benzene	1.00	1.00	1.00	1.00
Toluene	1.02	0.86	1.01	0.86
Ethylbenzene	1.05	0.77	1.02	0.75
Isopropylbenzene	1.09	0.71	1.03	0.67
Ethyl acetate	1.01	0.89	1.69	1.50
n-Butyl acetate	1.10	0.74	1.48	0.99
Heptane	0.90	0.70	1.10	0.86
o-Xylene	1.08	0.79	1.02	0.75
m-Xylene	1.04	0.76	1.02	0.75
p-Xylene	1.04	0.76	1.02	0.75
Ethanol	0.82	1.39	1.77	3.00
Water	0.71	3.08	—	—

*McNair, H.M.; Bonelli, E.J. *Basic Gas Chromatography*, 5th ed., Varian Aerograph, Walnut Creek, CA, 1969.

Calculation of the composition of a mixture on a mole percentage basis requires the use of **mole factors,** M_f. These are obtained by dividing the weight factors by the molar masses of each component of the standard solution and normalizing the resulting numbers. A sample calculation utilizing mole correction factors is provided below in the analysis of a mixture of ethanol, heptane, benzene, and ethyl acetate with a GLC equipped with a thermal conductivity detector. The last column shows the percentage composition calculated directly from the measured peak areas, without correction for detector response. The dramatic differences in the calculated composition with and without this correction, as noted in the last two columns, underscore the importance of this correction for quantitative analysis.

Compound	Area (A) (mm^2)	Uncorrected % ($A/207.1 \times 100$)	M_f	$A \times M_f$	Mol % ($A \times M_f/194 \times 100$)
Ethanol	44.0	21.2	1.39	61.2	31.5
Heptane	78.0	37.7	0.70	54.6	28.1
Benzene	23.2	11.2	1.00	23.2	11.9
Ethyl acetate	61.9	29.9	0.89	55.4	28.5
Total	207.1	100		194.4	100

Use of Syringes. Liquid samples are injected into the heated injection port of a gas chromatograph using a gas-tight syringe with a capacity of 1–10 µL. The sample is either injected neat or dissolved in a volatile liquid such as diethyl ether or pentane. The sample should not contain nonvolatile substances that may eventually clog the injection port or contaminate the stationary phase of the column.

Gas-tight syringes are precision-made and expensive. You should handle them carefully and adhere to the following procedure when using them. To fill the syringe, draw slightly more than the desired volume of the sample into the barrel by withdrawing the plunger as needed, point the syringe needle-up, push out the excess liquid, and then wipe the tip of the needle with a tissue. To inject the sample, insert the needle *straight* into the septum as far as it will go, *push the plunger all the way in with one quick motion*, and remove the syringe from the septum while holding the plunger in place. If the sample is injected slowly, it will produce a wider band on the column and the peaks will be broadened. Be careful to *avoid bending the needle or the plunger* during the injection. It is important to *clean the syringe immediately after use.* Rinse it with a volatile solvent such as acetone and dry it by drawing a stream of air through it.

EXPERIMENTAL PROCEDURES

A ▪ QUALITATIVE AND QUANTITATIVE ANALYSES OF A MIXTURE OF COMPOUNDS BY GLC

Purpose To identify individual components of a mixture and to quantify the relative amounts of each by gas-liquid chromatography.

SAFETY ALERT

The solvents and other liquids used in sample mixtures for GLC analysis are flammable and volatile. There should be *no open flames* used in the vicinity of these liquids.

Procedure

See Pre-Lab Exercises and MSDSs

Preparation Answer the Pre-Lab Exercises on page PL. 35. Read the MSDSs for chemicals used in this procedure. Read or review Section 2.5.

Apparatus Gas chromatograph and a gas-tight syringe.

Setting Up Since there is considerable variation in the operating procedures of different commercial gas chromatographs, consult your instructor for specific directions for using the instrument. Obtain a mixture of liquid compounds from your instructor. A suitable mixture would be one containing varying amounts of some or all of the following compounds: ethanol, ethyl acetate, toluene, *n*-butyl acetate, ethylbenzene, and isopropylbenzene.

Injection Following the directions of your instructor, use the syringe to inject a 1–5-μL sample of your mixture into the gas-liquid chromatograph to obtain a gas chromatogram. In the same way, obtain a chromatogram of pure samples of ethanol, ethyl acetate, toluene, *n*-butyl acetate, ethylbenzene, and isopropylbenzene under the same instrumental conditions used for the mixture.

Qualitative Analysis Identify each of the components in your mixture as follows: (1) Compare the retention time of each of the components of the mixture with the retention times of the authentic samples of pure compounds. (2) Verify your assignments for one or more components of the mixture by preparing a series of new sample mixtures, each of which will contain one volume of the pure known compound with two volumes of the original mixture. Prepare a gas chromatogram of this new mixture. The peak of the mixture that has been amplified in the new chromatogram corresponds to the pure compound that has been added.

Quantitative Analysis Use the quantitative method recommended by your instructor to determine the relative areas under the peaks in your chromatogram of the mixture. Correct these values by multiplying the measured area by the appropriate weight or molar correction factors for the type of detector in the GLC. These factors may be found in Table 6.2 or will be provided by your instructor. Determine the relative amounts, in weight and mole percentages, of each of the components of the mixture.

 Discovery Experiment *Analysis of Factors Affecting Retention Times*

Design and execute experiments that explore how factors such as flowrate and temperature influence the GLC retention times of a standard mixture of compounds.

Effect of Stationary Phase on Separation of a Mixture

Design and execute experiments that explore how the nature of the stationary phase of a GLC column influences the separation of a mixture of volatile compounds having a range of polarities. Consult with your instructor regarding the variety of GLC columns that would be available for your investigation.

WRAPPING IT UP

Pour any unused *volatile organic compounds* into the appropriate container for non-halogenated liquids or halogenated hydrocarbons; put any mixture that contains a halogenated hydrocarbon in the container for halogenated hydrocarbons.

B ▪ DETERMINING GLC RESPONSE FACTORS

 Discovery Experiment   **Purpose** To determine the weight and mole correction factors for compounds using flame ionization or thermal conductivity detectors.

SAFETY ALERT

The solvents and other liquids that are used in sample mixtures for GLC analysis are flammable and volatile. *No flames* should be used in the vicinity of these liquids.

Procedure

See Pre-Lab Exercises and MSDSs

Preparation Answer the Pre-Lab Exercises on page PL. 37. Read the MSDSs for chemicals used in this procedure. Read or review Section 2.5.

Apparatus Gas chromatograph, 1-mL syringe, and a gas-tight syringe.

Setting Up Since there is considerable variation in the operating procedures of different commercial gas chromatographs, consult your instructor for specific directions to use the instrument in your laboratory. Look up the densities of the compound whose weight and mole response factors are to be determined and the standard substance whose response factors are known. For example, the standard sample may be any of the compounds in Table 6.2. Prepare a test solution by combining 0.5 mL of the compound whose response factors are to be determined and 0.5 mL of the standard in a small vial or test tube and swirl the solution to mix the two components *completely.* Assuming the volumes of the two liquids are additive, calculate the weight fraction and mole fraction composition of the mixture.

Injection Following the directions of your instructor, use a gas-tight syringe to inject a 1–5-μL sample of the test mixture into the GLC to obtain a chromatogram. Repeat this process for each of the compounds for which you are to obtain weight and mole response factors.

Analysis Use the quantitative method recommended by your instructor to determine the areas under the two peaks in your gas chromatogram of the test mixture. Divide the weight fraction and mole fraction of each of the two components by the area under the peak for that component. Normalize the value for the weight and mole factors for the unknown by the corresponding weight and mole factors for the standard and record these values in your notebook.

Discovery Experiment   *Molar Response Factors of Isomers*

Using the protocol of this experimental procedure, determine whether the molar response factors, M_f, for either a pair of acyclic or a pair of cyclic isomers are identical.

Molar Response Factors of Nonisomeric Compounds

Using the protocol of this experimental procedure, determine whether the molar response factors, M_f, for a pair of nonisomeric compounds, one of which is a hydrocarbon and the other of which contains a heteroatom, have the same molecular weight. Possible examples might be (a) cyclohexane and cyclopentanone and (b) hexane and 2- or 3-pentanone.

WRAPPING IT UP

Pour any unused *volatile organic compounds* into the appropriate container for non-halogenated liquids or halogenated hydrocarbons; put any mixture that contains a halogenated hydrocarbon in the container for halogenated hydrocarbons.

EXERCISES

1. Define the following terms.
   a.   stationary phase
   b.   mobile phase
   c.   carrier gas

    d. retention time

    e. solid support

    f. thermal conductivity

2. Refer to the GLC traces given in Figure 6.16. These are analyses of the various fractions collected during the fractional distillation of the mixture of cyclohexane and toluene. The weight and mole correction factors (flame ionization detector) for cyclohexane are 0.84 and 0.78, respectively, and those for toluene are given in Table 6.2. Accurately determine both the weight percent and the mole percent compositions of the distillation fractions *A, B,* and *C.*

3. Benzene (1 g, 12.5 mmol) is allowed to react with 1-chloropropane (1 g, 12.5 mmol) and $AlCl_3$. The product (1.2 g) is subjected to analysis on a GLC equipped with a thermal conductivity detector. The chromatogram shows two product peaks identified as *n*-propylbenzene (area = 65 mm^2; W_f = 1.06) and isopropylbenzene (area = 113 mm^2; W_f = 1.09). Calculate the percent yield of each of the two isomeric products obtained in this reaction. Note that since each of the products has the same molar mass of 120, the use of weight factors gives both weight and mole percent composition.

4. A gas chromatogram of the organic components of a sample of beer using a column that separates compounds on the basis of their relative boiling points provides a GLC trace with several peaks. Two of the smaller peaks, with retention times of 9.56 and 16.23 minutes, are believed to be ethyl acetate and ethyl butyrate, respectively.

    a. From the above information, which component of the sample, ethyl acetate or ethyl butyrate, elutes faster? What are the reported boiling points of these two substances?

    b. What GLC experiment(s) could you perform to confirm the identity of the peaks at 9.56 and 16.23 minutes?

    c. The major component of the sample elutes first. What organic compound present in beer do you suspect is responsible for this peak? Is your speculation consistent with the reported boiling point of the compound you are proposing? Explain.

    d. Suggest two ways in which you could adjust the conditions of the experiment so as to reduce the retention time for all components in the sample.

5. In the Olympics and other major athletic competitions, a GC-MS is used to screen athletes for their use of banned substances such as steroids (see Historical Highlights). If an analytical method has been developed and the retention time for a particular anabolic steroid has been determined, how might you use this method to determine the possibility of the use of anabolic steroids by an athlete?

HISTORICAL HIGHLIGHTS

Who's Taking What? Analysis of Biological Fluids for Illegal Substances

A star athlete on your favorite team has just been suspended for the remainder of the season. A champion has been stripped of the medal won in Olympic competition. You bet on a loser at the race track, but the horse won and you stood to win enough to pay for your college education; yet you did not collect a dime. Your friend's boss was just fired without warning and for no obvious reason.

What happened in all these cases? You probably can guess the answer: The athletes, including the horse, and the boss all failed a drug test because their urine contained traces of illegal substances. In the case of the athletes, the drugs likely were performance-enhancing, whereas your friend's boss may have been using one or more "recreational drugs" like marijuana or cocaine. Use of performance-enhancing or mood-affecting drugs, legal or illegal, is certainly not limited to athletes and executives, of course, as evidenced by the males who have made Viagra and its analogs "cash cows" for their producer and natives in the high Andes who chew coca leaves as a means to allow them to continue working in thin air and under brutally cold conditions (see the Historical Highlights at the end of Chapter 20).

It is not only in modern times that humans have attempted to improve their performances through the use of various medicinals. Indeed, records from the second century B.C. show that athletes in the first Olympiads consumed exotic mushrooms and seeds in an effort to be the "best of the best." Interestingly, public awareness of drug testing for athletes is mainly associated with the Olympic games and the Tour de France, but it is only since the 1960s that the International Olympic Committee (IOC) and other supervisory organizations have instituted random testing for substances that these groups have deemed as prohibited. The substances banned by for use by athletes are determined by the World Anti-Doping Agency, and the number of prohibited substances

is constantly increasing. At the time of the 2004 Summer Olympic Games in Athens, there were over 125 compounds listed.

The number of Olympians subjected to random testing has increased dramatically since the testing program was initiated in 1968, when a total of 753 tests were performed in the summer and winter games. The corresponding combined figure for the 2002 Winter Games in Salt Lake City and the 2004 Summer Games in Athens was 4737, an increase of over 600%. Gratifyingly, the increased testing has not resulted in a corresponding increase in the number of athletes found to be using banned substances. For example, only one competitor was caught using a prohibited drug in the Summer Games in Mexico City (1968), and this was a pentathlete who had consumed an alcoholic beverage to steady his hand in a shooting competition: Although you may not think of ethanol as a sedative, it actually is when consumed in small amounts. The numbers of athletes violating the rules on banned substances grew to 7 at the Munich Summer Games (1972) and to 12 at the Los Angeles Summer Games (1984). Only 2 athletes were found in violation of the rules at the 1996 Summer Games in Atlanta, but the Sydney Summer Games (2000) were marred by the banning of 6 athletes for use of prohibited substances, 5 of whom lost their medals as a result. A dozen athletes failed drug tests during the Athens games and were not allowed to compete.

Violations associated with the use of banned substances by athletes participating in the Winter Olympic Games are much fewer, even when the fact that only about 20% as many individuals are involved is considered. For example, a sum total of only 5 athletes were banned from the games over the nine different competitions preceding that in Salt Lake City in 2002, when 12 athletes unfortunately were found to have violated the rules.

(continued)

Caffeine

Pseudoephedrine
(threo)

11-Nor-Δ^8-tetrahydrocannabinol-
9-carboxylic acid (THCA)

Classes of substances currently banned by the IOC include stimulants (amphetamines, cocaine, caffeine, pseudoephedrine), narcotics (heroin, methodone), anabolic agents (testosterone, nandrolone), diuretics (acetazolamide, spironolactone), and peptide hormones and their mimetics and analogs (erythropoietin, human growth hormone). Alcohol and marijuana at specified levels are also prohibited. For the latter, a level of as little as 15 ng/mL of 11-nor-Δ^8-tetrahydrocannabinol-9-carboxylic acid is a violation of the rules.

The presence of substances like caffeine and pseudoephedrine on the list of banned substances may surprise you. Caffeine is present in coffee, tea, and many types of soft drinks, among other liquids that an athlete might drink. However, the specified limit for caffeine is such to make it unlikely that a consumer would unwittingly exceed the limit: Some eight cups of coffee would have to be drunk within about two hours prior to collection of the urine sample to violate the rules. Pseudoephedrine is found in a number of over-the-counter nasal decongestants such as Dimetapp™ and Sudafed™, but once again, the levels that trigger a violation are such that it would be difficult to do so unwittingly. A violation associated with pseudoephedrine, by the way, was the reason Andreea

Raducan, a female Romanian gymnast, was stripped of her gold medal in the 2000 Summer Olympics in Sydney in a highly publicized and controversial ruling. Her team doctor prescribed the use of a product containing this substance because Raducan allegedly had a cold; fittingly, the IOC banned the doctor from participating in the Games until 2004.

One of the more interesting recent controversies surrounding drug testing is associated with nandrolone (17β-hydroxy-19-nor-4-androsten-3-one). This is an anabolic steroid—a steroid that contributes to the building of muscle tissue—that naturally occurs in the body, albeit in miniscule amounts. The allowed threshold level set by the IOC for nandrolone in urine, in the form of its metabolite, 19-norandrosterone, is 2 ng/mL. Some athletes have been found to have levels some 100 times higher than this, a result that suggests illegal use of the steroid. Some creative alibis have been provided by implicated individuals: One claimed that his high reading was the result of having consumed a serving of spaghetti bolognese in which the meat sauce contained beef from cattle that had been fed anabolic drugs; another cited his having had sex with his pregnant wife as the cause of his elevated value! However, most of those who have

Nandrolone

19-Norandrosterone

Creatine

(continued)

been accused cite their use of legal dietary supplements like "weight-gain" protein milkshakes and the α-amino acid creatine as the cause of their apparent violation, and recent studies suggest that this might be possible. In one of them, three volunteers gave urine specimens prior to taking the suspect dietary supplements; none of the specimens showed a level of 19-norandrostrone that exceeded 2 ng/mL. They then took the supplements and, 24 hours later, provided a second urine sample. Two of the volunteers, neither of whom had exercised during this period, again had only a low level of the metabolite in their urine. However, the third individual, who had exercised, had a level of 10 ng/mL, which exceeds the allowed threshold level. Thus there may be a relationship between consumption of the dietary supplements often used by athletes, their training regimens, and the production of nandrolone and its metabolite. Further studies are needed to unravel this confusing picture.

Just how are these drugs or their metabolites detected in urine, a fluid that contains a myriad of compounds? The answer to this question is found in a powerful combination of the techniques of extraction (Chap. 5), gas-liquid chromatography (Sec. 6.4) and mass spectrometry (Sec. 8.5). The aqueous solution (urine) is extracted with an organic solvent such as dichloromethane, and the extracts are subjected to analysis by GC-MS (Sec. 6.4). Through meticulous comparison of the retention times and fragmentation patterns of the analyte with those of known standards, subject substances may be easily identified.

A major challenge to the analytical chemist in testing for the presence of performance-enhancing drugs is the fact that new substances are constantly becoming available, and experimental protocols must be developed for detecting them. Moreover, athletes are becoming more adept at masking their drug use by consuming substances that interfere with the analytical procedure, rendering it inconclusive. In other words, detecting violations of rules governing the use of performance-enhancing drugs is a moving target, one requiring continuing development of new methods to ensure that violaters are identified unambiguously and that nonviolaters are not wrongly prosecuted because of a "false-positive" test.

Relationship of Historical Highlight to Chapter

The analysis of the components of complex mixtures remains one of the greatest challenges to the experimentalist. In this context, the development of new chromatographic techniques has contributed significantly to solving many of the most formidable problems in achieving analyses of such mixtures. The combination of gas chromatography with mass spectrometry in the form of GS-MS instruments represents an effective strategy for taking advantage of the separating ability of chromatography with the analytical power of a mass spectrometer. This strategy has been extended to liquid chromatography as well, in the form of instruments that link a liquid chromatograph with a mass spectrometer, a technique termed LC-MS.

See more on *Drug Testing*

See more on *Pseudoephedrine*

See more on *Nandrolone*

See more on *Narandrosterone*

See more on *Creatine*

See more on *Caffeine*

14

EXPERIMENT 30

Chromic Acid Oxidation of Alcohols

Chromic acid oxidation of an alcohol
Kinetics
Ultraviolet-visible spectrophotometry

The chemical reaction of interest in this experiment is the oxidation of an alcohol to the corresponding aldehyde by an acidic solution of potassium dichromate:

$$3\ RCH_2OH + Cr_2O_7{}^{2-} + 8\ H^+ \longrightarrow 3\ R{-}\overset{\displaystyle O}{\overset{\|}{C}}{-}H + 2\ Cr^{3+} + 7\ H_2O$$

Normally, the aldehyde formed is also susceptible to oxidation by the dichromate ion, yielding the corresponding acid:

$$3\ R{-}\overset{\displaystyle O}{\overset{\|}{C}}{-}H + Cr_2O_7{}^{2-} + 8\ H^+ \longrightarrow 3\ R{-}\overset{\displaystyle O}{\overset{\|}{C}}{-}OH + 2\ Cr^{3+} + 4\ H_2O$$

In this experiment, however, the alcohol is present in large excess, and the likelihood that the second reaction will take place is thereby greatly reduced. A secondary alcohol is oxidized to a ketone by a similar process. A ketone is not easily oxidized further by the dichromate reagent.

$$3\ R{-}\underset{\displaystyle R'}{\overset{\displaystyle }{\underset{|}{CH}}}{-}OH + Cr_2O_7{}^{2-} + 8\ H^+ \longrightarrow 3\ R{-}\overset{\displaystyle O}{\overset{\|}{C}}{-}R' + 2\ Cr^{3+} + 7\ H_2O$$

Although various mechanisms have been proposed to explain how dichromate ion oxidizes alcohols, the most commonly accepted mechanism is the one F. H. Westheimer first proposed in 1949. In acid solution, dichromate ion forms two molecules of chromic acid, H_2CrO_4:

$$2\ H_3O^+ + Cr_2O_7{}^{2-} \overset{fast}{\rightleftarrows} 2\ H_2CrO_4 + H_2O \qquad \text{step 1}$$

The chromic acid, in a rapid, reversible step, forms a chromate ester with the alcohol:

$$RCH_2OH + H_2CrO_4 \underset{}{\overset{fast}{\rightleftharpoons}} R-CH_2-O-\overset{\overset{\displaystyle O}{\|}}{\underset{\underset{\displaystyle O}{\|}}{Cr}}-OH + H_2O \qquad \text{step 2}$$

The chromate ester undergoes a rate-determining decomposition by a two-electron transfer with cleavage of the α-carbon-hydrogen bond, as seen in step 3.

$$R-\overset{\overset{\displaystyle H}{|}}{\underset{\underset{\displaystyle H}{|}}{C}}-O-\overset{\overset{\displaystyle O}{\|}}{\underset{\underset{\displaystyle O}{\|}}{Cr}}-OH \xrightarrow{\text{slow}} R-\overset{}{\underset{\underset{\displaystyle H}{|}}{C}}=O + H_2CrO_3 \qquad \text{step 3}$$

Cr in +6   Cr in +4
oxidation state   oxidation state

The H_2CrO_3 is further reduced to Cr^{3+} by interaction with chromium in various oxidation states and by further interaction with the alcohol. All these subsequent steps are very rapid relative to step 3. Consequently, they are not involved in the rate-determining step of the mechanism and need not be considered further.

The rate-determining step, step 3, involves only one molecule of the chromate ester, which in turn arises from a prior equilibrium involving the combination of one molecule of alcohol and one molecule of chromic acid (step 2). As a result, this reaction, which is first-order in chromate ester, turns out to be *second-order* for the reacting alcohol and the dichromate reagent. The kinetic equation therefore is

$$-\frac{d[Cr_2O_7^{2-}]}{dt} = k[RCH_2OH][Cr_2O_7^{2-}] \qquad (1)$$

The presence of the chromium atom strongly affects the distribution of electrons in the remainder of the chromate ester molecule. Electrons need to be transferred to the chromium atom during the cleavage step. If the R group includes an electron-withdrawing group, it diminishes the necessary electron density needed for reaction. Consequently, the reaction proceeds more slowly. An electron-releasing group would be expected to have the opposite effect.

THE EXPERIMENTAL METHOD

The rate of the reaction is measured by following the rate of disappearance of the dichromate ion as a function of time. The dichromate ion, $Cr_2O_7^{2-}$, is yellow orange, absorbing light at 350 and 440 nm. The chromium is reduced to the green Cr^{3+} during the reaction. The ion Cr^{3+} does not absorb light significantly at 350 or 440 nm, but rather at 406, 574, and 666 nm. Therefore, if we measure the amount of light absorbed at a single wavelength, such as 440 nm, we can follow the rate of disappearance of dichromate ion without any interfering absorption of light by the ion Cr^{3+}.

The instrument used to measure the amount of light absorbed at a particular wavelength, when that light lies within the visible region of the electromagnetic spectrum, is a **spectrophotometer.** This type of instrument can be described simply. Ordinary visible light is passed through the sample and then through a prism, where the light of the particular wavelength being studied is selected. This selected light is directed against a photocell, where its intensity is measured. A meter provides a visible display of the intensity of the light of the desired wavelength.

The true rate equation for this reaction is second-order. However, because a large excess of alcohol will be used, its concentration will change imperceptibly during the reaction. The rate equation, under these conditions, will simplify to that of a pseudo first-order reaction. The mathematics involved will become much simpler as a result.

The rate equation for a first-order (or a pseudo first-order) reaction is

$$-\frac{d[A]}{dt} = k[A] \tag{2}$$

In this experiment, the rate equation becomes

$$-\frac{d[Cr_2O_7^{2-}]}{dt} = k[Cr_2O_7^{2-}] \tag{3}$$

Let a equal the initial concentration of dichromate ion. At some time t, an amount x moles/L of dichromate will have undergone reaction, and x moles/L of aldehyde will have been produced. The remaining concentration of dichromate at that value of time equals $a - x$. The rate equation becomes

$$-\frac{dx}{dt} = k(a - x) \tag{4}$$

Integration provides

$$\ln\left(\frac{a}{a - x}\right) = kt \tag{5}$$

Converting to base 10 logarithms gives

$$2.303 \log\left(\frac{a}{a - x}\right) = kt \tag{6}$$

This equation is of the form appropriate for a straight line with intercept equal to zero. If the reaction is indeed first-order, a plot of $\log [a/(a - x)]$ versus t will provide a straight line whose slope is $k/2.303$.

Because it is experimentally difficult to measure directly how much dichromate ion is consumed during this reaction, evaluating the term $[a/(a - x)]$ requires an indirect approach. What is needed is some measurable quantity from which the concentration of dichromate can be derived. Such a quantity is the amount of light absorbed by the solution at wavelength 440 nm.

The Beer–Lambert Law relates the amount of light absorbed by a molecule or an ion to its concentration, according to the equation

$$A = \epsilon cl \tag{7}$$

where A is the absorbance of the solution, ϵ is the molar absorptivity (a measure of the efficiency with which the sample absorbs the light), c is the concentration of the solution, and l is the path length of the cell in which the solution is contained. The absorbance is read by the spectrophotometer.

At the initial concentration a of dichromate ion, we may write

$$A_0 = \epsilon al \tag{8}$$

or

$$a = \frac{A_0}{\epsilon l} \tag{9}$$

The amount of dichromate ion remaining unreacted at any particular time t, which equals $a - x$ becomes

$$A_t = \epsilon(a - x)l \tag{10}$$

or

$$a - x = \frac{A_t}{\epsilon l} \tag{11}$$

Substituting absorbance values for concentrations and canceling provides

$$\frac{a}{a - x} = \frac{A_0}{\epsilon l}\, \frac{\epsilon l}{A_t} \tag{12}$$

or

$$\frac{a}{a - x} = \frac{A_0}{A_t} \tag{13}$$

At this point, a correction must be introduced. When the reaction reaches completion, at "infinite" time, a certain degree of absorption of 440-nm light remains. In other words, at time $t = \infty$, the value A_∞ does not equal zero. Therefore, this residual absorbance must be subtracted from each of the absorbance terms written in Equation 13. The difference $A_0 - A_\infty$ gives the actual amount of dichromate ion present initially, and the difference $A_t - A_\infty$ gives the actual amount of dichromate ion remaining unreacted at a value t of time. Introducing these corrections, we have

$$\frac{a}{a-x} = \frac{A_0 - A_\infty}{A_t - A_\infty} \tag{14}$$

The integrated rate equation becomes

$$2.303 \log\left(\frac{A_0 - A_\infty}{A_t - A_\infty}\right) = kt \tag{15}$$

Because the dimensions of the cell and the molar absorptivity cancel out of this equation, it is not necessary to have any particular knowledge of these parameters.

A plot of $\ln\left[(A_0 - A_\infty)/(A_t - A_\infty)\right]$ versus time (see figure) will provide a straight line whose slope equals k. The slope is determined as shown on the graph. If time is measured in seconds, the units of k are $\sec^{-1}$. The experimental points plotted on the graph may contain a certain amount of scatter, but the line drawn is the best **straight line** (use some mathematical method such as the method of averages or least squares).

One other value often cited in kinetic studies is the **half-life, τ,** of the reaction. The half-life is the time required for half of the reactant to undergo conversion to products. Dur-

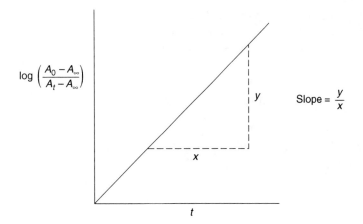

A plot of $\log\left[(A_0 - A_\infty)/(A_t - A_\infty)\right]$ versus time provides a straight line with slope equal to $k/2.303$.

ing the first half-life, 50% of the available reactant is consumed. At the end of the second half-life, 75% of the reactant has been consumed. For a first-order reaction, the half-life is calculated by

$$\tau = \frac{\ln 2}{k} = \frac{0.69315}{k} \tag{16}$$

The class will study several alcohols in this experiment. The class data will be compared in determining the relative reactivities of the alcohols. Two particular alcohols, 2-methoxyethanol and 2-chloroethanol, react more slowly than the other alcohols used in this experiment. In spite of this lower reactivity, the reactions will not be followed for more than a few minutes, because in these compounds, the second reaction—the oxidation of the aldehyde product to the corresponding carboxylic acid—becomes more important over longer periods. As a result of this second reaction, dichromate ion becomes consumed more rapidly than the calculations would suggest, and the graph of $\log [(A_0 - A_\infty)/(A_t - A_\infty)]$ versus time becomes curved. So that this complication is avoided, only the first few minutes of the reaction are used to calculate an initial reaction rate, which corresponds to the reaction being studied in this experiment. The other alcohols are sufficiently reactive that the second reaction does not introduce any significant error.

Required Reading

Review: Read the sections on kinetics in your lecture textbook.

New: Essay   Detection of Alcohol: The Breathalyzer

Special Instructions

Primary and secondary alcohols are oxidized in this experiment to aldehydes and ketones, respectively. The experimental procedure is identical for both types of alcohols. This experiment should be done by pairs of students in order to distribute the workload of preparing solutions and making the measurements. There are two alternative methods that are available in this experiment. Experiment 30A uses a Bausch & Lomb Spectronic 21 spectrophotometer to collect data. Experiment 30B is similar to Experiment 30A except that it has been written for use with a Hewlett-Packard 8452 Diode-Array UV-VIS spectrophotometer. Each kinetic run requires about 1.5 to 2 hours.

> **Caution:** Potassium dichromate solutions have been determined to be potential carcinogens.

This experiment involves using an acidic solution of potassium dichromate. The dichromate solution will be prepared as a stock solution for the entire class to use. This stock solution should be stored in a hood. Students should wear gloves and use pipet bulbs when using this stock solution.

The Occupational Safety and Health Administration is considering regulating the use of 2-methoxyethanol because there is mounting evidence that it is a reproductive toxin. When using this substance, use gloves and avoid breathing the vapors. All the alcohols should be stored in a hood for use by the class.

Suggested Waste Disposal

Dispose of all aqueous solutions containing chromium in a container designated for chromium wastes. Use gloves when handling this waste.

EXPERIMENT 30A

Chromic Acid Oxidation of Alcohols— Visible Spectrophotometer Method

Procedure

Preparation of Reagents. Select an alcohol from one of the following: ethanol, 1-propanol, 2-propanol, 2-methoxyethanol, 2-chloroethanol, ethylene glycol, and 1-phenylethanol (methylbenzyl alcohol). A stock solution of 3.9 M sulfuric acid and a carefully prepared solution of 0.0196 M potassium dichromate solution (prepared using distilled water in a volumetric flask) should be available for the entire class to use.

Instrument Preparation. Turn on the instrument and allow it to warm up. Select the tungsten lamp as the light source. Select an operating mode that allows the instrument to operate at a fixed wavelength of 440 nm and to record data as absorbance.

Running the Experiment. Using a small flask, prepare the test solution by transferring 1 mL of the stock dichromate solution and 10 mL of the stock sulfuric acid solution into the flask with volumetric pipets supplied by the instructor. (**Caution:** *Use pipet bulbs.*) Shake the solution well. Rinse a sample cuvette three times with this acidic dichromate solution and then fill the cell. Wipe the cuvette clean and dry. Place the cuvette into the sample cell compartment and place a cuvette filled with distilled water into the reference cell compartment. Close the cell compartment lid and allow the chromic acid solution to reach temperature equilibrium by allowing it to remain in the instrument (with the instrument running) for 20 minutes. This preheating minimizes the problem of the solution being slowly heated during the experiment by the tungsten lamp, which is the light source in the spectrophotometer. Such heating would tend to accelerate the reaction as time passed.

At the end of the preheating, record the absorbance A_0 of the chromic acid solution, along with a time value of 0.0 minutes. Withdraw a 10.0-μL sample of the alcohol being studied into a hypodermic syringe and transfer it rapidly to the chromic acid solution. As the transfer is made, start the timer. Withdraw the sample cuvette from the cell compartment, shake it vigorously for 20 to 30 seconds, and return it to the cell compartment. Be sure to wipe off the cell again. Close the compartment lid. The measurements can now be taken.

Take readings of the absorbance A_t and the corresponding time at 1-minute intervals over a 6-minute period (8 minutes for 2-propanol). At the end of this time, remove the cuvette from the cell compartment of the spectrophotometer and allow the solution in the cuvette to stand undisturbed for at least 1 hour (another student may use the instrument during this time). After this period, return the cuvette to the cell compartment (warm up the instrument first, if it was turned off) and read the absorbance value. This final value corresponds to "infinite" time A_∞.

The instructor may require each student to perform a duplicate run. If so, repeat the experiment under precisely the same conditions used for the first run.

Analysis of Data. Plot the data according to the method described in the introductory section of the experiment. A table of sample data is shown on page 253. Report the value of each rate constant determined in this experiment (and the average of the rate constants, if duplicate determinations were made). Also, report the value of the half-life τ. Include all data and graphs in the report. The results from the entire class may be compared, at the option of the instructor.

E X P E R I M E N T   3 0 B

Chromic Acid Oxidation of Alcohols— UV-VIS Spectrophotometer Method

Procedure

Preparation of Reagents. Prepare the reagents according to the procedure given in Experiment 30A, page 250.

Instrument Setup. Turn on the spectrophotometer and the computer connected to it. The Hewlett-Packard program should appear on the screen. Using the arrow keys, move the highlight bar down to **OPERATOR NAME** and press **ENTER**. Input an operator name, press **ENTER**, move the highlight bar up to **GENERAL SCANNING,** and press **ENTER**. Make sure that the flow cell has been removed from the beam path and that the cuvette holder has been installed. The spectrometer setup screen should be displayed at this time, with a listing of function-key (F1 . . . F10) commands listed below. Select **ACQUISITION** (F4) and move the highlighted bar down to **STANDARD DEVIATION**. If an **X** does not appear in the brackets to the left of **STANDARD DEVIATION,** then press **ENTER**. Press **ESC** to return to the setup screen. Select **SAMP. INPUT** (F8), highlight **MANUAL INPUT,** and press **ENTER**. Press **ESC** to exit. Move to the **OPTIONS** selection (F5) and choose **OVERLAY SPECTRA**. While still in the setup mode, insert a cuvette filled with deionized water (DI-H$_2$O) into the sample cell holder and select **MEAS. BLANK** by pressing **F2**.

Sample Scans. A spectrum of DI-H$_2$O should appear on the screen in what is known as the Graphics mode. Select **REGISTERS** (F5) and then press **F3** to clear all registers. The blank scan is automatically stored to another file and does not need to be included in the sample spectrum. Press **ESC** to return to the Graphics mode. The spectrometer is now ready for sample scans to take place. The same cuvette used for the blank scan should also be used for the experimental portion to maintain consistency.

Using a small flask, prepare the test solution by transferring 1 mL of the stock dichromate solution and 10 mL of the stock sulfuric acid solution into the flask with the volumetric pipet supplied. Shake the solution well. Rinse a sample cuvette three times with this acidic dichromate solution and then fill the cell. Wipe the cuvette clean and dry. Place the cuvette into the sample cell compartment.

Withdraw a 10.0-μL sample of ethanol into a hypodermic syringe and transfer it rapidly to the chromic acid solution. Simultaneously, as you transfer the sample, press

F1. This starts the timer and records the value of absorbance, A_0. Withdraw the sample cuvette from the cell compartment, shake it vigorously for 20–30 seconds, and return it to the cell compartment. Be sure to wipe off the cell again. Close the compartment lid.

Once the experiment is initiated, all that is required is to press **F1 (MEAS. SAMPLE)** at each time interval for the time-dependent part of the experiment. Only the time need be recorded; the absorbance and other data can be obtained later when time is not a constraint. Each time **F1** is pressed, a spectrum will be displayed, overlayed on top of the last scan(s) taken.

Take readings of the absorbance A_t and the corresponding time at 1-minute intervals over a 6-minute period. At the end of this time, it will be necessary to wait for approximately 1 hour to allow the reaction to go to completion. After the waiting period, read the final absorbance value. This final value corresponds to "infinite" time, A_∞.

Data Workup. The peak of interest for this experiment is the absorbance value found at 440 nm. Select the **RESCALE** (F3) function and highlight **ZOOM IN.** Press **ENTER** and a cursor will appear on the screen. Move the cursor, using the arrow keys, to a point below and to the left of the area you wish to zoom in on. Press **ENTER** and move the cursor above and to the right of the area to be isolated, drawing a box around the area. Pressing **ENTER** will bring the portion of the spectrum into view. If a mistake is made, select **RESCALE** (F3) again and choose **ZOOM OUT.** This will return the full spectrum to the screen, and the zooming process can be repeated.

Each peak in this portion of the spectrum can be marked using the cursor feature. Select **CURSOR** (F2) and an arrow should appear on Register A. (See just below the spectrum for a description of the arrow placement and on which spectrum it is located.) The left and right arrow keys will move the arrow along the spectrum, while the up and down arrow keys will move the arrow to a different register/spectrum. Place the arrow in Register A, which should correspond to the spectrum at time = 0.0 minutes. Move the arrow to the peak at 440 nm and press **MARK** (F1). Move down to Register B, mark the peak at 440 nm and repeat for all of the remaining spectra. Once all of the peak(s) are marked, press **LIST MARKS** (F3) to display the absorbances for each peak at 440 nm. Exit the cursor mode and return to the Graphics mode by selecting **RETURN** (F10).

To obtain a printout of the spectrum and the absorbances, select **HARDCOPY** (F9), highlight **PRINT SPECTRA,** and press **RETURN.** (*NOTE: Do not* select **TABULATE SPECTRA** or you will receive about 30 seconds of useless material!)

Analysis of Data. Plot the data according to the method described in Experiment 30A, page 251. Report the value of the rate constant determined in this experiment. Also, report the value of the half-life, τ. Include all data and graphs in the report. The results from the entire class may be compared, at the option of the instructor.

REFERENCES

Lanes, R. M., and Lee, D. G. "Chromic Acid Oxidation of Alcohols." *Journal of Chemical Education, 45* (1968): 269.

Pavia, D. L., Lampman, G. M., and Kriz, G. S. *Introduction to Spectroscopy: A Guide for Students of Organic Chemistry,* 3rd ed. Philadelphia: Saunders, 2001. Chap. 7.

Westheimer, F. H. "The Mechanism of Chromic Acid Oxidations." *Chemical Reviews, 45* (1949): 419.

Westheimer, F. H., and Nicolaides, N. "Kinetics of the Oxidation of 2-Deuterio-2-Propanol by Chromic Acid." *Journal of the American Chemical Society, 71* (1949): 25.

QUESTIONS

1. Plot the data given in the table. Determine the rate constant and the half-life for this example.

Oxidation of Ethanol

Time (min)	Absorbance (440 nm)	$A_t - A_\infty$	$\dfrac{A_0 - A_\infty}{A_t - A_\infty}$	$\log\left(\dfrac{A_0 - A_\infty}{A_t - A_\infty}\right)$
0.0	0.630	0.578	1.000	0.000
1.0	0.535	0.483	1.197	0.078
2.0	0.440	0.388	1.490	0.173
3.0	0.365	0.313	1.847	0.266
4.0	0.298	0.246	2.350	0.371
5.0	0.247	0.195	2.964	0.472
6.0	0.202	0.150	3.853	0.586
66.0 (∞)	0.052	0.000	. . .	. . .

2. Using data collected by the class, compare the relative rates of ethanol, 1-propanol, and 2-methoxyethanol. Explain the observed order of reactivities in terms of the mechanism of the oxidation reaction.

3. Using data collected by the class, compare the relative rates of 1-propanol and 2-propanol. Account for any differences that might be observed.

4. Balance the following oxidation–reduction reactions:

a. $HO\text{—}CH_2CH_2\text{—}OH + K_2Cr_2O_7 \xrightarrow{H_2SO_4}$ (glyoxal) $+ Cr^{3+}$

b. (toluene) $+ KMnO_4 \longrightarrow$ (benzoate) $+ MnO_2$

c. $HO\text{—}CH_2CH_2CH_2CH_2\text{—}OH + K_2Cr_2O_7 \xrightarrow{H_2SO_4}$ (product) $+ Cr^{3+}$

d. $CH_3CH_2CH_2CH{=}CH_2 + KMnO_4 \xrightarrow{KOH} CH_3CH_2CH_2C\text{—}O^- + CO_2 + MnO_2$ (with C=O)

e. (1-methylcyclohexene) $+ KMnO_4 \xrightarrow{KOH} CH_3\text{—}C\text{—}CH_2CH_2CH_2CH_2\text{—}C\text{—}O^- + MnO_2$ (with C=O groups)

15

E X P E R I M E N T   5 4

Isolation of Casein and Lactose from Milk

Isolation of a protein
Isolation of a sugar

In this experiment, you will isolate several of the chemical substances found in milk. First, you will isolate a phosphorus-containing protein, casein (Experiment 54A). The remaining milk mixture will then be used as a source of a sugar, α-lactose (Experiment 54B). After you isolate the milk sugar, you will make several chemical tests on this material. Fats, which are present in whole milk, are not isolated in this experiment because powdered non-fat milk is used.

Here is the procedure you will follow. First, the casein is precipitated by warming the powdered milk and adding dilute acetic acid. It is important that the heating not be excessive or the acid too strong, because these conditions also hydrolyze lactose into its components, glucose and galactose. After the casein has been removed, the excess acetic acid is neutralized with calcium carbonate, and the solution is heated to its boiling point to precipitate the initially soluble protein, albumin. The liquid containing the lactose is poured away from the albumin. Alcohol is added to the solution, and any remaining protein is removed by centrifugation. α-Lactose crystallizes on cooling.

Lactose is an example of a disaccharide. It is made up of two sugar molecules: galactose and glucose. In the preceding structures, the galactose portion is on the left, and glucose is on the right. Galactose is bonded through an acetal linkage to glucose.

Notice that the glucose portion can exist in one of two isomeric hemiacetal structures: α-lactose and β-lactose. Glucose can also exist in a free aldehyde form. This aldehyde form (open form) is an intermediate in the equilibration (interconversion) of α- and β-lactose. Very little of this free aldehyde form exists in the equilibrium mixture. The isomeric α- and β-lactose are diastereomers because they differ in the configuration at one carbon atom, called the anomeric carbon atom.

The sugar α-lactose is easily obtainable by crystallization from a water–ethanol mixture at room temperature. However, β-lactose must be obtained by a more difficult process, which involves crystallization from a concentrated solution of lactose at temperatures about 93.5°C. In the present experiment, α-lactose is isolated because the experimental procedure is easier.

α-Lactose undergoes numerous interesting reactions. First, α-lactose interconverts, via the free aldehyde form, to a large extent, to the β-isomer in aqueous solution. This causes a change in the rotation of polarized light from +92.6° to +52.3° with increasing time. The process that causes the change in optical rotation with time is called **mutarotation.**

A second reaction of lactose is the oxidation of the free aldehyde form by Benedict's reagent. Lactose is referred to as a reducing sugar because it reduces Benedict's reagent (copper[II] ion to copper[I] ion) and produces a red precipitate (Cu_2O). In the process, the aldehyde group is oxidized to a carboxyl group. The reaction that takes place in Benedict's test is

$$R-CHO + 2\,Cu^{2+} + 4\,OH^- \longrightarrow RCOOH + Cu_2O + 2\,H_2O$$

A third reaction of lactose is the oxidation of the galactose part by the mucic acid test. In this test, the acetal linkage between galactose and glucose units is cleaved by the acidic medium to give free galactose and glucose. Galactose is oxidized with nitric acid to the dicarboxylic acid, galactaric acid (mucic acid). Mucic acid is an insoluble, high-melting solid that precipitates from the reaction mixture. On the other hand, glucose is oxidized to a di-acid (glucaric acid), which is more soluble in the oxidizing medium and does not precipitate.

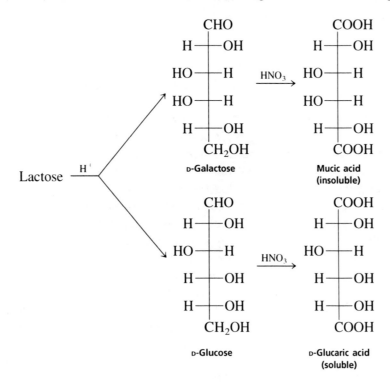

Required Reading

Review: Technique 8   Filtration

New: Essay   Chemistry of Milk

Special Instructions

Experiments 54A and 54B should both be performed during one laboratory period. The lactose solution must be allowed to stand until the following laboratory period. Casein must dry for 2 or 3 days.

Suggested Waste Disposal

Place residues left from the Benedict's test in the container designated for the disposal of copper wastes. Dispose of solid materials obtained from milk in a trash container. Aqueous wastes, including those that contain ethanol, should be poured into the aqueous waste container.

EXPERIMENT 54A

Isolation of Casein from Milk

Procedure

Precipitation of Casein.   Place 4.0 g of powdered milk and 10 mL of water into a 100-mL beaker. Heat the mixture in a water bath to 40°C. Check the temperature of the milk solution with a thermometer. Place 1.0 mL of dilute acetic acid solution in a small flask for temporary storage.[1] When the mixture has reached 40°C, add the dilute acetic acid dropwise to the warm milk. After every 5 drops, stir the mixture gently using a glass stirring rod with an attached rubber policeman. Using the rubber policeman, push the casein up onto the side of the beaker so that most of the liquid drains from the solid. Then transfer the congealed casein to another small beaker in portions. If any liquid separates from the casein in the small beaker, use a Pasteur pipet to transfer the liquid back into the reaction mixture. Continue to add dropwise the remainder of the 1.0 mL of dilute acetic acid to the milk mixture in the 100-mL beaker to precipitate the casein fully. Remove as much of the casein as possible and transfer it to the small beaker. Avoid adding an excess of acetic acid to the milk solution, as this will cause the lactose in the milk to hydrolyze into glucose and galactose.

When you have removed most of the casein from the milk solution, add 0.2 g of calcium carbonate to the milk in the 100-mL beaker. Stir the mixture for a few minutes and save it for use in Experiment 54B. Use this mixture as soon as possible during the laboratory period. This beaker contains lactose and albumins.

Isolation of Casein.   Transfer the casein from the beaker to a Büchner funnel (Technique 8, Section 8.3, p. 651, and Figure 8.5, p. 652). Draw a vacuum on the casein to remove as much liquid as possible (about 5 minutes). Press the casein with a spatula during this time. Transfer the casein to a piece of filter paper (about 7 cm). Using a spatula, move the solid around on the paper so that the remaining liquid is absorbed into the filter paper. When most of the liquid has been removed, transfer the solid to a watch glass to complete the drying operation. Allow the casein to air dry completely for 2 to 3 days before weighing the product. You must remove the casein from the filter paper, or it will become "glued" to the paper. (You have nearly prepared white glue.) Submit the casein in a labeled vial to the instructor. Calculate the percentage weight of the casein isolated from the powdered milk.

---

[1] The laboratory instructor should prepare a large batch for the class in the ratio of 2 mL glacial acetic acid to 20 mL of water.

EXPERIMENT 54B

Isolation of Lactose from Milk

Procedure

Precipitation of Albumins. Heat the mixture directly on a hot plate in the 100-mL beaker that you saved from Experiment 54A to approximately 75°C for about 5 minutes. This heating operation results in a nearly complete separation of the albumins from the solution. Decant the liquid in the beaker away from the solid into a clean centrifuge tube. You may need to hold the solid with a spatula while transferring the liquid. Press the albumins with a spatula to remove as much liquid as possible and pour the liquid into the centrifuge tube (save the albumins in the original beaker for the procedure in the next paragraph). You should have about 7 mL of liquid. When the liquid has cooled to about room temperature, centrifuge the contents of the tube for 2–3 minutes. Be sure to place another tube in the centrifuge to balance the unit. Following centrifugation, decant the liquid away from the solid into a beaker and save it for use in the next section, "Precipitation of Lactose."

Allow the albumins to dry for 2–3 days in the original beaker. Break up the solid and weigh it. Calculate the percentage weight of albumins isolated from the powdered milk.

Precipitation of Lactose. Add 15 mL of 95% ethanol to the beaker containing the centrifuged and decanted liquid. Solids will precipitate. Heat this mixture to about 60°C, placing it directly on the hot plate, to dissolve some of the solid. Pour the *hot* liquid into a 40-mL centrifuge tube (or two 15-mL tubes) and centrifuge the hot solution as soon as possible before the solution cools appreciably. Centrifuge the mixture for 2–3 minutes. Be sure to place another tube in the centrifuge to balance the unit. It is important to centrifuge this mixture while it is warm to prevent premature crystallization of the lactose. A considerable quantity of solid forms in the bottom of the centrifuge tube. This solid is not lactose.

Remove the warm supernatant liquid from the tube using a Pasteur pipet and transfer the liquid to a small Erlenmeyer flask. Discard the solid remaining in the centrifuge tube. Stopper the flask and allow the lactose to crystallize for at least 2 days. Granular crystals will form during this time.

Isolation of Lactose. Collect the lactose by vacuum filtration on a Büchner funnel. Use about 3 mL of 95% ethanol to aid the transfer and to wash the product. α-Lactose crystallizes with one water of hydration, $C_{12}H_{22}O_{11} \cdot H_2O$. Weigh the product after it is thoroughly dry. Submit the α-lactose in a labeled vial to the instructor unless it is to be used in the following optional tests. Calculate the percentage weight of the lactose isolated from the powdered milk.

Optional Exercise: Benedict's Test. Prepare a hot water bath (above 90°C) for this experiment. Dissolve about 0.01 g of your lactose in 1 mL of water in a test tube. Heat the mixture to dissolve most of the lactose (some cloudiness remains). Place about 1 mL each of 1% solutions of glucose and galactose in separate test tubes. Add to each of the three test tubes 2 mL of Benedict's reagent.[2] Place the test tubes in the hot water bath for 2 minutes. Remove the tubes and note the results. The formation of an orange to brownish red precipitate indicates a positive test for a reducing sugar. This test is described on page 449 in Experiment 52.

Optional Exercise: Mucic Acid Test. Prepare a hot water bath (above 90°C) for this experiment or use the one prepared for the Benedict's test. Place 0.1 g of the isolated lactose, 0.05 g of glucose (dextrose), and 0.05 g of galactose in 3 separate test tubes. Add 1 mL of water to each tube and dissolve the solids, with heating if necessary. The lactose solution may be somewhat cloudy but will clear when the nitric acid is added. Add 1 mL of concentrated nitric acid to each tube. Heat the tubes in the hot water bath for 1 hour in a hood (nitrogen oxide gases are evolved). Remove the tubes and allow them to cool slowly after the heating period. Scratch the test tubes with clean stirring rods to induce crystallization. After the test tubes are cooled to room temperature, place them in an ice bath. A fine precipitate of mucic acid should begin to form in the galactose and lactose tubes about 30 minutes after the tubes are removed from the water bath. Allow the test tubes to stand until the next laboratory period to complete the crystallization. Confirm the insolubility of the solid formed by adding about 1 mL of water and then shaking the resulting mixture. If the solid remains, it is mucic acid.

QUESTIONS

1. A student decided to determine the optical rotation of mucic acid. What should be expected as a value? Why?

2. Draw a mechanism for the acid-catalyzed hydrolysis of the acetal bond in lactose.

3. β-Lactose is present to a larger extent in an aqueous solution when the solution is at equilibrium. Why is this to be expected?

4. Very little of the free aldehyde form is present in an equilibrium mixture of lactose. However, a positive test is obtained with Benedict's reagent. Explain.

5. Outline a separation scheme for isolating casein, albumin, and lactose from milk. Use a flowchart like that shown in the Advance Preparation and Laboratory Records section in Technique 2.

---

[2] Dissolve 34.6 g of hydrated sodium citrate and 20.0 g of anhydrous sodium carbonate in 160 mL of distilled water by heating. Filter the solution, if necessary. Add to it a solution of 3.46 g of copper(II) sulfate $CuSO_4 \cdot 5H_2O$ dissolved in 20 mL of distilled water. Dilute the combined solutions to 200 mL.

Polymers

See more on
Polymers

See more on
Biopolymers

Bigger is better? You may think so after performing experiments in this chapter because they will give you the opportunity to explore various aspects of the chemistry of **polymers,** molecules having molar masses in the tens of thousands. In addition to your everyday use of polymers in a variety of forms, including the fibers in the clothing you wear and the adhesive on Post-It™ notes that you stick on everything, you, yourself, are constantly manufacturing **biopolymers,** in the form of hair, skin, DNA, and RNA, for example. Although we can provide only a small sampling of the wealth of chemistry surrounding polymers in this chapter, it should give you a sense of this fascinating branch of organic chemistry.

22.1 INTRODUCTION

See more on
Polysaccharides

See more on
Proteins

See more on
Nucleic Acids

See more on
Terpenes

See more on
Plastics

See more on
Elastomers

See more on
Fibers

Polymers are a class of molecules characterized by their high molar masses, which range from the thousands to the hundreds of thousands, and by the presence of simple repeating structural units called **monomers.** Because of their large size, polymers are often referred to as **macromolecules.** A polymer comprised of a *single* recurring monomer, M, is termed a **homopolymer,** whereas one containing at least two structurally distinct monomeric units, M_1 and M_2, distributed at random in the molecule is called a **heteropolymer** or **copolymer.** These two classes of macromolecules are represented by **1** and **2,** respectively.

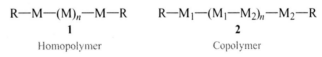

$$R—M—(M)_n—M—R \qquad R—M_1—(M_1—M_2)_n—M_2—R$$

1   **2**

Homopolymer   Copolymer

Polymers are found in nature and may also be produced by laboratory synthesis. Important examples of naturally occurring macromolecules, or **biopolymers,** are **proteins, polysaccharides, terpenes,** and **nucleic acids.** General representations of these substances are provided by structures **3–6,** respectively, in which the monomeric subunits of an α-amino acid, **3,** a pyranose, **4,** an isoprene, **5,** and a ribonucleotide phosphate, **6,** are seen. Synthetic, or "man-made," polymers are represented by the myriad of **plastics, elastomers,** and **fibers** that are commonplace in contemporary society.

Two primary methods are commonly used to convert monomers into synthetic polymers. In the older literature, these techniques are referred to as **addition** and **condensation polymerization,** but because of ambiguities in these terms, the preferred names now are **chain-reaction polymerization** and **step-growth**

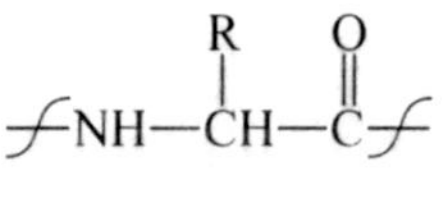

3

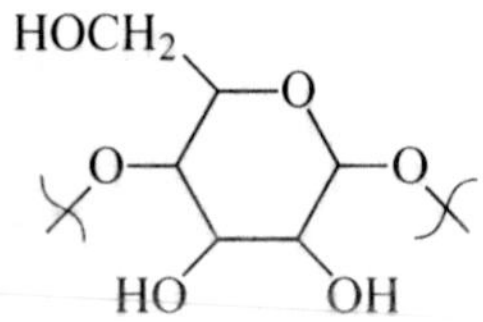

4

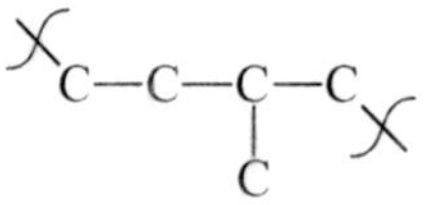

5

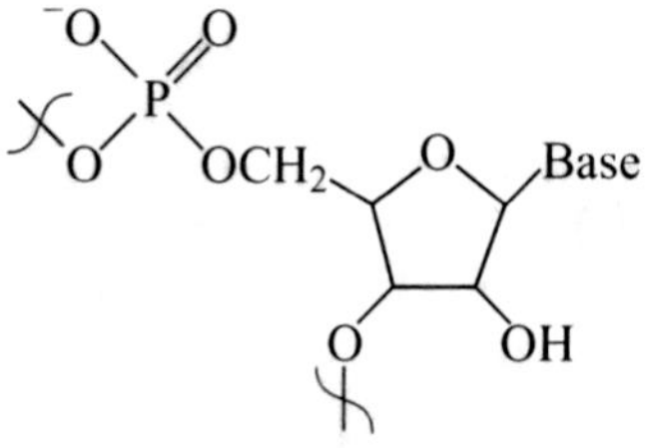

6

(Base = purine or pyrimidine)

polymerization, respectively. As discussed in Sections 22.2 and 22.3, the major distinction between these two types of polymerization is the general mechanism by which the polymer forms.

The term *addition polymerization* arose because such polymers are produced by combining a large number of monomer molecules through addition reactions. For example, the self-addition of thousands of ethylene molecules yields polyethylene (**7**), a homopolymer (Eq. 22.1). Another homopolymer is polystyrene (**9**), which is formed by self-addition of styrene (**8**) as shown in Equation 22.2. We note that representation of the molecular formula of the polymer as essentially *n* times that of the monomer, as shown in these two equations, is only a slight oversimplification of the actual formula. Because *n* is such a large number, inclusion of the elemental compositions of the end-groups, R, that appear at the termini of the polymeric chain makes an insignificant change in the molecular formula in comparison with the rest of the molecule.

$$n \ CH_2{=}CH_2 \ \xrightarrow[\text{and/or heat}]{\text{catalyst}} \ {+}CH_2{-}CH_2{\big)}_n \qquad (22.1)$$

Ethylene

7

$n= 10,000{-}30,000$
Polyethylene

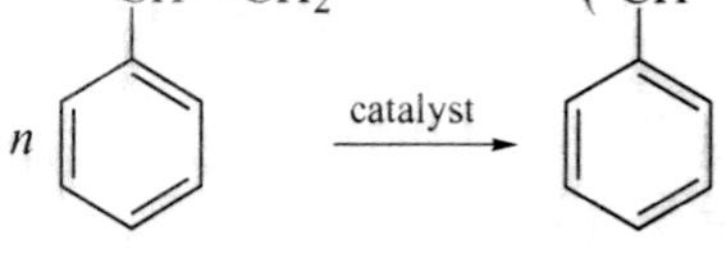

$$(22.2)$$

8

Styrene

9

Polystyrene

Some other common addition polymers have trade names that do not indicate their structure. For example, Teflon is a homopolymer of tetrafluoroethylene (**10**), and Plexiglas™ is a polymer of methyl methacrylate (**11**).

$$CF_2{=}CF_2$$

10

Tetrafluoroethylene

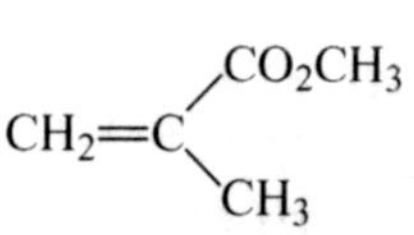

$$CH_2{=}C \begin{matrix} CO_2CH_3 \\ \\ CH_3 \end{matrix}$$

11

Methyl methacrylate

See more on
Copolymers

See more on
Block Copolymers

Copolymers are produced from a *mixture* of monomers, as was noted earlier. For example, saran (**14**), a widely used plastic film, is made by polymerizing a mixture of vinyl chloride (**12**) and vinylidene chloride (**13**), as depicted in Equation 22.3. You should be aware that the abbreviated formula of **14** is not meant to imply that the two monomeric units appear as a sequence of two distinct blocks, each of which individually represents a homopolymer. Although such **block copolymers** can be produced by special techniques, copolymers usually have the two monomers distributed randomly along the chain, as in **15**.

$$n\ CH_2{=}CH \underset{Cl}{\vert} \ + \ m\ CH_2{=}CCl_2 \longrightarrow \left(\!\!\left(CH_2{-}CH\underset{Cl}{\vert}\right)_{\!\!n}\!\!\left(CH_2{-}CCl_2\right)\!\!\right)_{\!\!m} \quad (22.3)$$

       12   **13**   **14**

Vinyl chloride   Vinylidene chloride   Saran

$$R{-}M_1{-}(M_2{-}M_2{-}M_1{-}M_2{-}M_1{-}M_1{-}M_1)_n{-}M_2{-}R$$
15

The term *condensation polymerization* originally was used because this form of polymerization involves condensation reactions. Such transformations normally involve combining two functionalized molecules through an addition-elimination process, termed nucleophilic acyl substitution (Sec. 20.1), that results in the loss of a small molecule, H–L, such as water (Eq. 22.4). The aldol condensation (Sec. 18.3) and esterification (Sec. 20.2) are examples of such reactions. In the case of condensation or step-growth polymerization, *di*functionalized substrates are required as monomers as illustrated in Equation 22.5.

$$R{-}\overset{\overset{\displaystyle O}{\|}}{C}{-}L \ + \ HNu{:} \longrightarrow R{-}\overset{\overset{\displaystyle O}{\|}}{C}{-}Nu{:} \ + \ HL \qquad (22.4)$$

$$L{-}\overset{\overset{\displaystyle O}{\|}}{C}\text{wwww}\overset{\overset{\displaystyle O}{\|}}{C}{-}L \ + \ HN\ddot{u}\text{wwww}N\ddot{u}H \longrightarrow \left(\overset{\overset{\displaystyle O}{\|}}{C}\text{wwww}\overset{\overset{\displaystyle O}{\|}}{C}{-}N\ddot{u}\text{wwww}N\ddot{u}\right)_{\!\!n} \quad (22.5)$$

The following sections contain discussions of the mechanisms of chain-reaction and step-growth polymerization. The associated experimental procedures illustrate the preparation of polymers derived from each type of polymerization.

22.2 CHAIN-REACTION POLYMERIZATION

As the name implies, *chain-reaction polymerization* is a chain reaction in which the initiator may be a cation, anion, or free radical. An example of **cationic polymerization** is found in the polymerization of isobutylene (2-methylpropene) in the presence of protic or Lewis acid catalysts to give poly(isobutylene) (**16**) as depicted in Equation 22.6. The conversion of acrylonitrile to poly(acrylonitrile) (**17**) using sodium amide, a strong base, represents **anionic polymerization** (Eq. 22.7).

$$(CH_3)_2C=CH_2 \xrightarrow{H^+} (CH_3)_2\overset{+}{C}-CH_3 \xrightarrow{H_2C=C(CH_3)_2} (CH_3)_3C-CH_2\overset{+}{C}\overset{CH_3}{\underset{CH_3}{}}$$

Isobutylene

See more on
Poly(isobutylene)

$$n\ H_2C=C(CH_3)_2 \qquad (22.6)$$

$$(CH_3)_3C\left(CH_2\overset{CH_3}{\underset{CH_3}{C}}\right)_n CH_2\overset{|}{C}-R$$

16

Poly(isobutylene)

$$CH_2=CHCN \xrightarrow{H_2N^-} \overset{NH_2}{\underset{|}{CH_2}}-\overset{-}{CHCN} \xrightarrow{CH_2=CHCN} H_2NCH_2CH-CH_2\overset{CN}{\underset{}{C^-}}-H$$

Acrylonitrile

See more on
Poly(acrylonitrile)

$$n\ CH_2=CHCN \qquad (22.7)$$

$$H_2N\left(CH_2\overset{CN}{\underset{}{CH}}\right)_n CH_2\overset{CN}{\underset{}{CH}}-R$$

17

Poly(acrylonitrile)

See more on
Free Radicals

Free-radical polymerization is a widely used method to induce chain-reaction polymerization, and its mechanistic course is parallel to that of the free-radical halogenation of hydrocarbons (Sec. 9.2). In the experiment in this section, you will perform the free-radical polymerization of styrene to give polystyrene (**24**, Eq. 22.12).

The reaction is started by the thermal decomposition of an *initiator,* which in our experiment is *tert*-butyl peroxybenzoate (**18**); this compound produces the free radicals **19** and **20** when heated (Eq. 22.8). If In• stands for one or both of these free radicals, the course of the polymerization may be illustrated as shown in Equations 22.9–22.12. Equation 22.9 indicates the function of the free radicals in **initiating** the polymerization. Equations 22.10a and 22.10b represent the **propagation** of the growing polymer chain. Equations 22.11 and 22.12 show possible **termination** processes. In Equation 22.11, the free-radical end of one growing polymer chain abstracts a hydrogen atom from the carbon atom next to the end of another polymer radical to produce the unsaturated and saturated polymer molecules **22** and **23**, respectively, in a process termed **disproportionation**. For the termination reaction illustrated by Equation 22.12, Rad• may be one of the initiating radicals, In•, or another growing polymer chain.

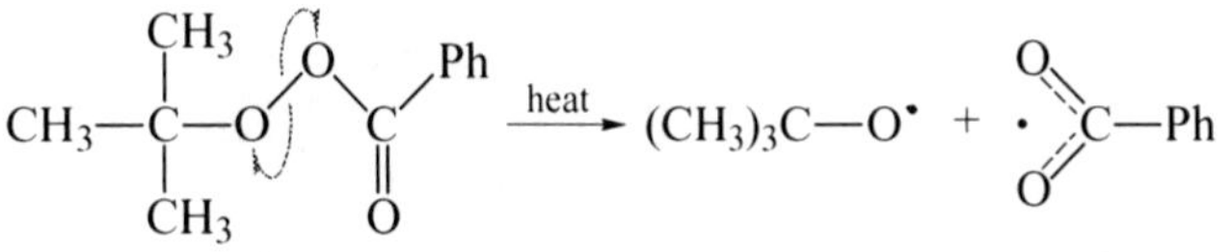

$$\text{(22.8)}$$

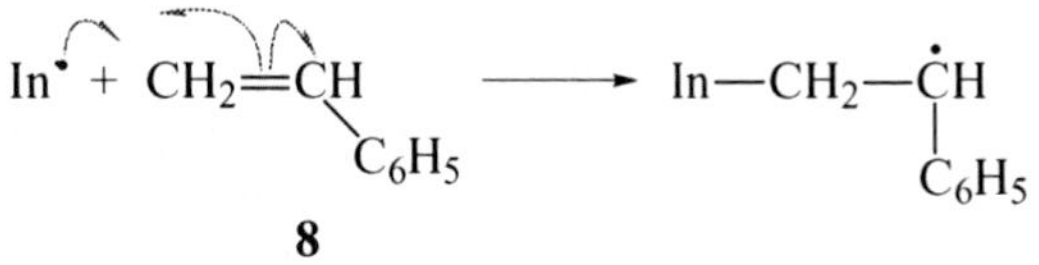

$$\text{In}^\bullet + \text{CH}_2=\text{CH} \longrightarrow \text{In}-\text{CH}_2-\overset{\bullet}{\text{CH}} \qquad \text{(22.9)}$$

8

$$\text{(22.10a)}$$

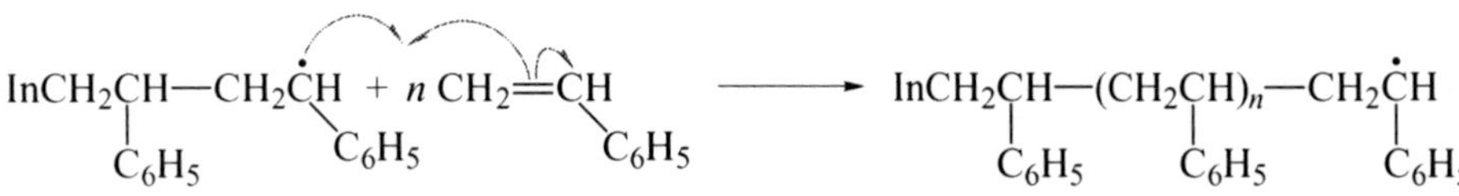

21

$$\text{(22.10b)}$$

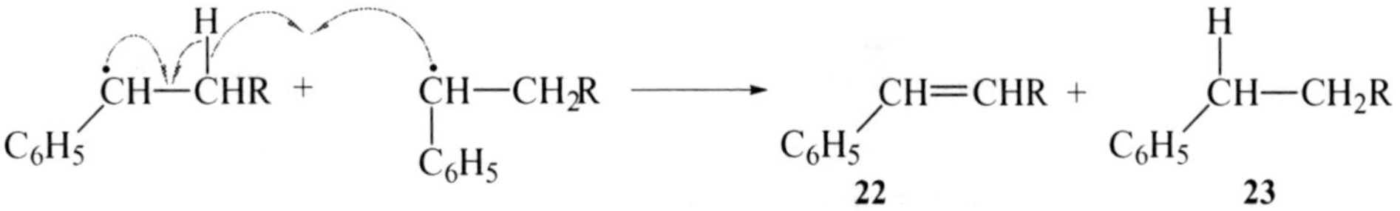

21

$$\text{(22.11)}$$

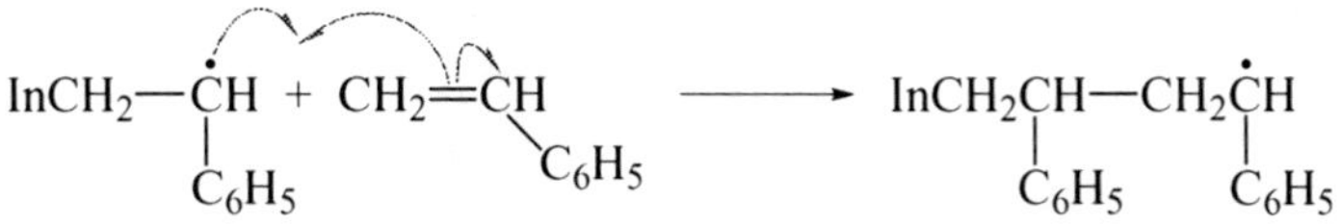

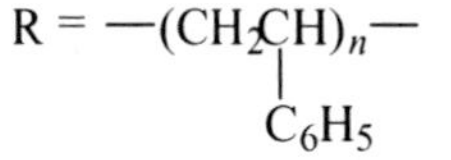

22   **23**

$$R = -(CH_2CH)_n-$$
$$\qquad\quad C_6H_5$$

$$\text{(22.12)}$$

24

The commercially available styrene used in our experiments contains *tert*-butylcatechol (**25**), a phenol that stabilizes styrene by functioning as a **radical scavenger.** The catechol does this by donating a hydrogen atom to reactive free radicals to convert them into nonradical products as shown in Equation 22.13. The resulting phenoxy radical **26** is relatively unreactive as an initiator of a free-radical chain reaction. The stabilizer is necessary to prevent premature polymerization of styrene during storage or shipment, because it is so readily polymerized by traces of substances such as atmospheric oxygen.

(22.13)

25
tert-Butycatechol
26

In the discovery experiment that follows, you will explore an important aspect of polymer chemistry by preparing polystyrene (**24**) under different reaction conditions and to test whether it, like many polymers, may be produced in a variety of physical forms such as an amorphous solid, a film, and a clear glass.

EXPERIMENTAL PROCEDURES

Preparation of Polystyrene

Discovery Experiment

Purpose To demonstrate the synthesis of polystyrene by free-radical polymerization under different conditions.

SAFETY ALERT

The free-radical initiator *tert*-butyl peroxybenzoate is a safe material to use in this experiment because it decomposes at a moderate rate when heated. Nonetheless, do not heat this catalyst excessively when performing the polymerization.

Miniscale Procedure

See Pre-Lab Exercises and MSDSs

Preparation Answer the Pre-Lab Exercises on page PL. 167. Read the MSDSs for chemicals used in this procedure. Review Sections 2.9, 2.17, 2.19, 2.21, and 2.22.

Apparatus A separatory funnel, small soft-glass test tube, 25-mL round-bottom flask, microburner, apparatus for magnetic stirring, heating under reflux, and *flameless* heating.

A ▪ REMOVAL OF THE INHIBITOR FROM COMMERCIAL STYRENE

Place about 10 mL of commercial styrene in a small separatory funnel and add 4 mL of 3 M sodium hydroxide and 15 mL of water. Shake the mixture thoroughly, allow the layers to separate, and withdraw the aqueous layer. Wash the organic layer sequentially with two 8-mL portions of water, carefully separating the aqueous layers after each wash. Dry the styrene by pouring it into a small Erlenmeyer flask containing a little anhydrous calcium chloride and then swirling the flask.

Allow the mixture to stand for 5–10 min, decant the liquid from the drying agent, and use the dried styrene in the following experiments.

Analysis Obtain IR and NMR spectra of styrene and compare them with those of an authentic sample (Figs. 22.1 and 22.2).

WRAPPING IT UP

Allow the volatiles to evaporate from the *calcium chloride* by placing it on a tray in the hood; then discard it in the container for nontoxic solids. Neutralize the *aqueous layers* before flushing them down the drain.

B ▪ POLYMERIZATION OF PURE STYRENE

Place about 2–3 mL of dry styrene in a small soft-glass test tube, and add 2 or 3 drops of *tert*-butyl peroxybenzoate. Clamp the test tube in a *vertical* position over a wire gauze, insert a thermometer so that its bulb is in the liquid, and heat the styrene and catalyst with a *small* burner flame. When the temperature reaches 140 °C, temporarily remove the flame. If boiling stops, resume heating to maintain gentle boiling. The exothermicity of the polymerization increases the rate of formation of free radicals by thermal decomposition of the initiator, and this in turn increases the rate of polymerization. Thus be watchful for a rapid increase in the rate of boiling and remove the flame if the refluxing liquid nears the top of the test tube.

After the onset of polymerization the temperature should rise to 180–190 °C, much above the boiling point of styrene. The viscosity of the liquid will increase rapidly during this time. As soon as the temperature begins to decrease, remove the thermometer and pour the polystyrene onto a watchglass. Do not touch the thermometer *before* the temperature decreases because moving it in the boiling liquid might cause a sudden "bump," which could throw hot liquid out of the tube. Note the formation of fibers as the thermometer is pulled out of the polymer. The rate of solidification of the polystyrene depends on the amount of catalyst used, the temperature, and the length of time the mixture is heated.

C ▪ SOLUTION POLYMERIZATION OF STYRENE

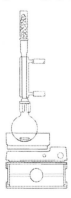

Place about 2 mL of dry styrene and 5 mL of xylene in a 25-mL round-bottom flask and add 7 drops of *tert*-butyl peroxybenzoate from a Pasteur pipet. Assemble the apparatus for heating under reflux and heat the mixture under reflux for 20 min. Cool the solution to room temperature and then pour about *half* of it into 25 mL of methanol. Collect the white precipitate of polystyrene that forms by decantation or, if decantation is not practical, by vacuum filtration. Resuspend the polystyrene in fresh methanol and stir it vigorously; collect the polystyrene by filtration and allow it to dry in the hood.

Pour the remaining *half* of the polystyrene solution onto a watchglass or the bottom of a large inverted beaker, and allow the solvent to evaporate. A clear film of polystyrene should form.

Optional Discovery Experiments   Two of the following experiments allow you to explore whether polystyrene is stable toward different organic solvents and to assess the effect that an ionic polymer, sodium polyacrylate (**27**), may have on the properties of water. The third lets you investigate the change in the properties of a polymer when it is cross-linked with other strands of itself or other polymers.

Discovery Experiment   *Stability of Polystyrene toward Organic Solvents*

Styrofoam® is a "puffed-up" form of **24** that is produced by polymerizing styrene in the presence of a "blowing agent" like pentane. The heat of the polymerization causes the agent to vaporize, and it is temporarily trapped in the polymerizing material, forming a bubble or cell if the viscosity of the material is high enough to prevent the gases to escape. The final polymer has many of these cells, resulting in a "foam-like" material. The foam is a good semirigid shock absorber and also serves as an insulator because air is not very effective at transferring heat or cold. As a consequence of these physical properties, Styrofoam may be used in a variety of ways, ranging from packaging materials to ice chests.

Work in groups of at least two on this experiment and carefully observe what happens as you perform it. All of the results should be compiled and separately interpreted by each member of the team.

Working at the fume hood and away from any flames and hot plates, fill a petri dish about half-full with an organic solvent. Place a Styrofoam cup bottom down in the solvent and record what happens. Use a glass stirring rod to explore what remains of the cup. Some solvents that might be tested are acetone, 95% ethanol, dichloromethane, and toluene. Properly dispose of all liquids and solids remaining at the completion of this experiment.

Discovery Experiment   *Polymers and Water*

Most polymers are water-insoluble even though they may contain polar, but neutral, substituents along the carbon backbone. Sodium polyacrylate, however, is a cross-linked ionic polymer that is water-soluble or, equivalently, is a solid polymer in which water is soluble. It is used in products as diverse as disposable diapers and an alternative to plant soils. (You may learn more about this latter application at http://www.plantgel.com.) Just what happens when this polymer and water are combined is the subject of this experiment.

See more on
Sodium
Poly(acrylate)

$$-(CH_2-CH)_n-$$
$$| $$
$$CO_2^- \ Na^+$$

Sodium poly(acrylate)

Weigh out approximately 0.5 g of sodium polyacrylate and transfer it to a *dry* 250-mL Erlenmeyer flask. Add 100 mL of water and immediately stir the mixture. Record your observations.

Discovery Experiment   *Cross-Linking of Polymers*

Poly(vinyl alcohol), like sodium poly(vinyl acrylate), is another water-soluble polymer and is comprised of repeating units of vinyl alcohol. In contrast to the acrylate, however, the solubility is not due to a charged polar functionality; rather, extensive hydrogen-bonding involving the hydroxyl groups accounts for the water solubility.

See more on
Poly(vinyl alcohol)

$$-(CH_2-CH)_n-$$
$$|$$
$$OH$$

Poly(vinyl alcohol)

When sodium tetraborate is dissolved in water, an equilibrium is established according to the equation below, resulting in the formation of a buffer having a pH of about 9. The protonated borate ion reacts with the hydroxyl groups of one strand of the poly(vinyl alcohol) and subsequently with the hydroxyl groups of another strand, possibly with the elimination of water. The resulting array may be represented in a general way as shown below. By joining strands of the polymer through such cross-links, a measure of rigidity is imparted to the molecular array that has been formed. In addition to the cross-links, the molecules have extensive intra- and intermolecular hydrogen-bonding, which also effects a form of cross-linking, albeit a weak one. Breaking and reforming of the hydrogen bonds presumably accounts for the viscoelastic properties of the material that is produced. This material can be formed into a ball, but you should see what happens when it is left untouched.

$$B_4O_7^{2-}{}_{(aq)} + H_2O \rightleftharpoons HB_4O_7^-{}_{(aq)} + HO^-{}_{(l)}$$

$$-(CH_2-CH)_n-$$
$$|$$
$$O \qquad O$$
$$\diagdown B \diagup \quad (CH-CH_2)_n-$$
$$\diagup X \diagdown \qquad |$$

Apparatus A 100-mL and a 250-mL beaker, thermometer, glass stirring rod, and apparatus for magnetic stirring and *flameless* heating.

Setting Up Add 50 mL of distilled water into the 250-mL beaker equipped with a stirbar. Heat the water with stirring but do *not* exceed a temperature of 90 °C.

Gel Formation With continued stirring and warming, slowly sprinkle 2 g of poly-(vinyl alcohol) having an average molar mass of at least 10^5 g/mol onto the surface of the water; this procedure prevents the formation of a sticky mass of polymer that is difficult to dissolve. Combine the poly(vinyl alcohol) solution and 5 mL of a 4% (by mass) aqueous solution of sodium tetraborate, $Na_2B_4O_7$, in the 100-mL beaker, and stir the mixture vigorously with the glass rod. A material that you may consider to be "slime" should form almost immediately.

This cross-linked polymer is a gel that has interesting physical properties. You may explore some of them by forming your material into a ball and then seeing what happens when you carefully tip it in the palm of your hand. If a long column of polymer forms, jerk it abruptly and record the result. Be creative and test the properties of the gel in other ways!

Wrapping It Up The beaker and stirring rod used to prepare the gel may be cleaned with soap and water. Mix the solution of polymer with a copious amount of water and flush the mixture down the drain. The gel itself should be discarded in the container for nonhazardous waste.

WRAPPING IT UP

Place the *filtrate* containing a mixture of xylene and methanol in the container for nonhalogenated organic liquids. Flush the *methanolic filtrate* obtained after resuspension of the polystyrene down the drain.

EXERCISES

1. *tert*-Butylcatechol (**25**) is capable of reacting with *two* equivalents of a radical, R•, to produce two moles of RH and a stable non-radical oxidation product of **25**. Propose a structure for this product and write a stepwise reaction mechanism for its formation. Use curved "fish-hook" arrows to symbolize the flow of electrons.

2. The use of phenols such as *tert*-butylcatechol as free-radical scavengers is based on the fact that phenolic hydrogens are readily abstracted by radicals, producing relatively stable phenoxyl radicals, which interrupt chain processes of oxidation and polymerization. Alcohols such as cyclohexanol, on the other hand, do *not* function as radical scavengers. Explain why the two types of molecules differ in their abilities to donate a hydrogen atom to a radical, R•.

3. Write an equation for the reaction involved in the removal of *tert*-butylcatechol from styrene by extraction with sodium hydroxide.

4. Why is it necessary to remove *tert*-butylcatechol from commercially available styrene prior to preparing polystyrene?

5. Why is *tert*-butyl peroxybenzoate a good radical initiator?

6. Explain why only a catalytic amount of the radical initiator is required in a free-radical-chain polymerization reaction.

7. Why is the polymerization of styrene an exothermic reaction? Explain in terms of a calculation based on the following equation using these bond dissociation energies: PhCH(R)–H, 83 kcal/mol; CH_2=CHPh, 53 kcal/mol (π-bond only); $PhCH_2CH_2$–CH(CH_3)Ph, 73 kcal/mol.

$$PhCH-H \ + \ CH_2=CH \longrightarrow PhCH-CH_2CHPh$$
$$\quad\ \ |\qquad\qquad\quad\ \ |\qquad\qquad\qquad |\qquad\quad |$$
$$\quad CH_3\qquad\qquad\ Ph\qquad\qquad\quad CH_3\quad\ H$$

8. Explain why polystyrene is soluble in xylene but insoluble in methanol.

9. What effect would using a smaller proportion of catalyst to styrene have on the average molar mass of polystyrene?

10. In principle, radicals could add to styrene at the carbon atom bearing the phenyl group rather than the other one, yet they do not. Explain the basis of this selectivity for the addition reaction.

11. Specify whether polystyrene is a condensation polymer, a homopolymer, a copolymer or a block polymer.

12. Some monomers polymerize to produce a polymer having centers of chirality (Chap. 7). If there is no preference for one configuration over another, the configuration of the centers will be random throughout the polymer. This type of polymer is called *atactic*. When the stereocenters are nonrandom, the polymer may be either *syndiotactic* or *isotactic* (see your lecture textbook for a definition of these terms).

   a. Write a portion of polystyrene containing two monomeric units and circle any stereocenters that are present.

   b. Would you expect the polystyrene generated in this experiment to be *atactic, syndiotactic,* or *isotactic?*

13. Circle the monomeric unit in the polysaccharide shown below.

14. Teflon is produced from the polymerization of tetrafluoroethene. Write the structure of Teflon showing the monomeric unit in parenthesis.

15. Why does the nucleophilic attack of isobutylene on the $(CH_3)_3C^+$ cation in Equation 22.6 form a new carbon-carbon bond at C(2) of isobutylene instead of C(1)?

16. Super Glue™ is a polymer formed via an anionic polymerization of methyl cyanoacrylate, $CH_2=(C\equiv N)CO_2CH_3$. Predict the structure of this glue.

Refer to Tables 8.1–8.8 as needed for answering the following questions on spectroscopy.

See Spectra   17. Consider the spectral data for styrene (Figs. 22.1 and 22.2).

   a. In the functional group region of the IR spectrum, specify the absorptions associated with the carbon-carbon double bond and the aromatic ring. Also specify the absorptions in the fingerprint region that are characteristic for the terminal vinyl group.

   b. In the ^1H NMR spectrum, assign the various resonances to the hydrogen nuclei responsible for them.

   c. For the ^{13}C NMR data, assign the various resonances to the carbon nuclei responsible for them.

See Spectra   8. Discuss the differences in the IR spectrum of styrene and polystyrene that are consistent with the loss of the vinyl group during the polymerization of styrene in this experiment.

Starting Material and Product

The IR spectrum of polystyrene is provided in Figure 8.9.

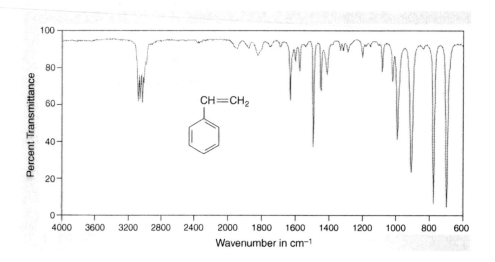

Figure 22.1
IR spectrum of styrene (neat).

(a) ^{1}H NMR spectrum (300 MHz).

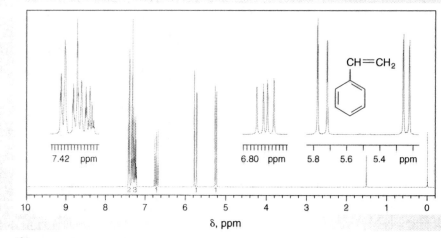

Figure 22.2
NMR data for styrene (CDCl$_3$).

(b) ^{13}C NMR data: δ 113.5, 126.2, 127.8, 128.5, 137.0, 137.7.

22.3 STEP-GROWTH POLYMERIZATION

Step-growth polymerization typically involves the reaction between two different, *difunctionalized* monomers. Both functionalities of each monomer react, and this leads to the formation of polymers. For example, a diacid such as terephthalic acid (**27**) can react with a diol such as ethylene glycol (**28**) in the presence of an acid catalyst to produce a polyester, as shown in Equation 22.14.

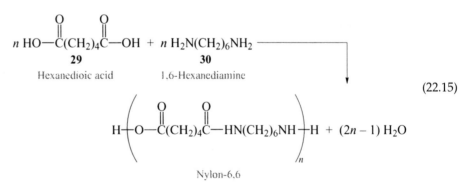

$$n \ HO_2C-\!\!\!\!\!\!\!\!\!\bigcirc\!\!\!\!\!\!\!\!\!-CO_2H \xrightarrow[\quad n \ HOCH_2CH_2OH \quad]{H^+}$$

(22.14)

27   **28**
Terephthalic acid   Ethylene glycol

$$H-\!\!\left(\!O-\overset{\overset{O}{\|}}{C}-\!\!\!\!\!\bigcirc\!\!\!\!\!-\overset{\overset{O}{\|}}{C}-O-CH_2CH_2\!\right)_{\!\!n}\!\!OH \ + \ (2n-1) \ H_2O$$

A polyester

See more on
*Step-growth
Polymerization*

See more on
Polyesters

See more on
Nylon

See more on
Fibers

Chain growth is initiated by the acid-catalyzed reaction of a carboxyl group of the diacid with a hydroxy function of the diol to provide an ester and a molecule of water. The free carboxyl group or hydroxyl group of the resulting dimer then reacts with an appropriate functional group in another monomer or dimer, and the process is repeated in such *steps* until all of the monomers are converted into dimers, trimers, tetramers, and, eventually, polymers. Step-growth polymerization processes are much slower than chain-reaction processes. Because they also typically have higher activation energies, heating is often required to attain satisfactory rates of polymerization. Finally, step-growth polymers generally have lower average molar masses than polymers formed by chain-reaction polymerization.

Polyamides are one type of useful polymer that is produced by a step-growth process, and a variety of such polymers are preparable from various diacids and diamines. Nylon-6,6™ was the first commercially successful polyamide and is derived from the two monomers, hexanedioic acid (**29**) and 1,6-hexanediamine (**30**), as shown in Equation 22.15. Its trade name reflects the presence of six carbon atoms in each of the monomeric units that comprise the polymer. Of interest regarding the commercial importance of the nylons is the fact that the tremendous financial success enjoyed by E. I. Du Pont and Company from these types of polymers stems from the firm's patent on a method to draw the substance into fibers rather than from a patent on the molecular composition of the polymer itself. (See the Historical Highlights at the end of this chapter.)

$$n \ HO-\overset{\overset{O}{\|}}{C}(CH_2)_4\overset{\overset{O}{\|}}{C}-OH \ + \ n \ H_2N(CH_2)_6NH_2 \quad\longrightarrow$$

29   **30**
Hexanedioic acid   1,6-Hexanediamine

(22.15)

$$H-\!\!\left(\!O-\overset{\overset{O}{\|}}{C}(CH_2)_4\overset{\overset{O}{\|}}{C}-HN(CH_2)_6NH\!\right)_{\!\!n}\!\!H \ + \ (2n-1) \ H_2O$$

Nylon-6,6

In the typical industrial process for preparing polyamides, equimolar amounts of the diacid and diamine are mixed to give a salt, which is then heated to high temperature under vacuum to eliminate the water. The resulting polymer has a molar mass of about 10,000 and a melting point of about 250 °C. Fibers may be spun from melted polymer, and if the fibers are stretched to several times their original length, they become very strong. This "cold-drawing" orients the polymer molecules parallel to one another so that hydrogen bonds form between C–O and N–H groups on adjacent polymer chains, as shown in **31**, greatly increasing the strength of the fibers. The strength of the fibers of silk, a well-known biopolymer involving protein molecules, is ascribed to the same stabilizing factor.

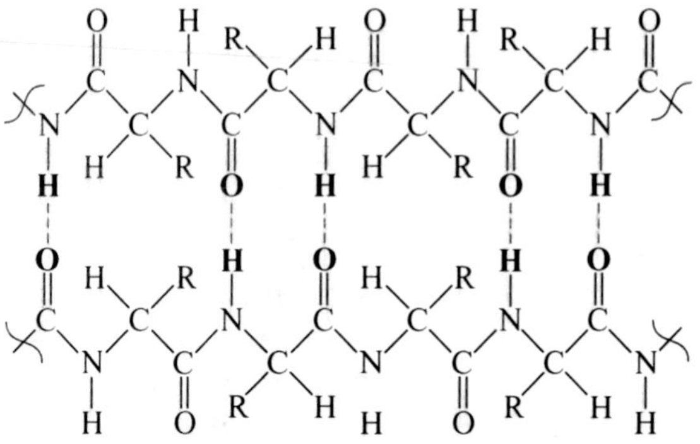

31

The preparation of Nylon-6,10™, rather than Nylon-6,6, has been chosen to illustrate step-growth polymerization for the present experiment. This polyamide is commercially produced from decanedioic acid (**32**) and 1,6-hexanediamine (**30**), as shown in Equation 22.16. To facilitate forming the polyamide under simple laboratory conditions, however, the diacid dichloride of **32** is used because it is more reactive toward diamine **30**. Using the diacid dichloride means that the small molecule eliminated in this step-growth polymerization is hydrogen chloride rather than water (Eq. 22.17). Sodium carbonate is added to neutralize the acid formed to prevent consumption of the expensive diamine via an acid-base reaction. If the base were not added, an excess of diamine would be required for complete polymerization.

$$\underset{\substack{\mathbf{32}\\ \text{Decanedioic acid}}}{n\ HO-\overset{O}{\overset{\|}{C}}(CH_2)_8\overset{O}{\overset{\|}{C}}-OH} + \underset{\mathbf{30}}{n\ H_2N(CH_2)_6NH_2} \longrightarrow \underset{\text{Nylon-6,10}}{H\!\left(O-\overset{O}{\overset{\|}{C}}(CH_2)_8\overset{O}{\overset{\|}{C}}-HN(CH_2)_6NH\right)_{\!n}\!H} + (2n-1)\ H_2O \qquad (22.16)$$

$$\underset{\substack{\text{Decanedioyl dichloride}\\ \text{(Sebacoyl chloride)}}}{Cl\overset{O}{\overset{\|}{C}}(CH_2)_8\overset{O}{\overset{\|}{C}}Cl} + H_2NCH_2-R \longrightarrow Cl\overset{O}{\overset{\|}{C}}(CH_2)_8\overset{O}{\overset{\|}{C}}-NHCH_2-R \qquad (22.17)$$

The reactivity of the diacid chloride toward nucleophilic acyl substitution (Eq. 22.17) allows this polymerization to be performed under mild conditions. When a solution of the diacid chloride in a water-immiscible solvent is brought into contact

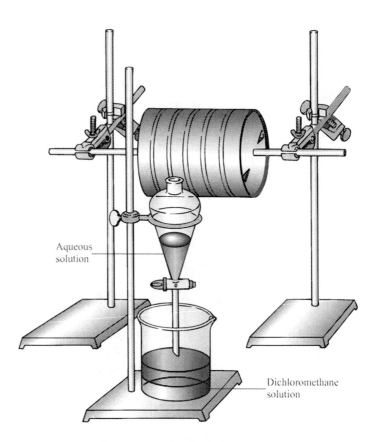

Figure 22.3
Apparatus for the "Nylon Rope Trick."

Aqueous
solution

Dichloromethane
solution

with an aqueous solution of the aliphatic diamine, a film of polymer of high molar mass instantly forms at the interface between the two solutions. The film is thin but strong, and can be pulled from the interface, where it is immediately and continuously replaced by additional polymer. In this way a long cord or rope of polyamide can be produced, much as a magician pulls a string of silk handkerchiefs out of a top hat. When this experiment was first described by two Du Pont chemists, they characterized it as the "Nylon Rope Trick." It does seem to be almost magic that a polymer can attain an average molar mass in the range 5000–20,000 in a fraction of a second!

To perform this experiment properly, the necessary equipment must be assembled so the polymer rope can be pulled from the reaction zone rapidly. A convenient way to do this is illustrated in Figure 22.3. A can, preferably with a diameter of 10 cm or more, makes a good drum on which to wind the polymer. After puncturing the can in the center of each end, a wooden or metal rod is passed through the center holes to make an axle for the drum. The rod is supported horizontally by clamps attached to ring stands in the usual way.

The circumference of the drum should be measured and a reference point should be marked on the drum so that an estimate of the length of the nylon rope can be made by counting the revolutions made as the rope is produced. A length of 6 m or more can usually be obtained with the procedure described here.

If instructed to do so, a much simpler procedure may be used to draw a polymeric fiber, but it will not allow you to determine the length of the fiber easily. Thus, you may dip a glass stirring rod or copper wire into the polymerizing mixture, lift the rod or wire out, and wind the fiber around it as the polymerization proceeds.

The dry polymer obtained in this experiment does not appear to have the properties expected of a nylon; it is fragile and of low density. However, fibers produced from it are much more dense, and have the appearance and strength more characteristic of a typical polyamide. You will make fibers and films from the dry polymer so you can compare the properties of the different forms of the polymer.

EXPERIMENTAL PROCEDURES

Preparation of Nylon-6,10

Purpose To demonstrate step-growth polymerization by the synthesis of Nylon-6,10.

SAFETY ALERT

1. **If Pasteur pipets are used instead of syringes to measure the reactants, use a rubber bulb to draw up the liquid.**

2. **Do not handle the polymer rope with your bare hands more than is necessary until it has been washed free of solvent and reagents. Use latex gloves, tongs, or forceps to manipulate it. If you touch the crude polymer, immediately wash your hands with soap and warm water.**

3. **If you use formic acid to form a film, do not let it get on your skin, because it causes deep skin burns that are not immediately obvious. If the acid does accidentally come in contact with your skin, wash the affected area immediately with 5% sodium bicarbonate solution and then with copious amounts of water.**

Miniscale Procedure

See Pre-Lab Exercises and MSDSs

Preparation Answer the Pre-Lab Exercises on page PL. 169. Read the MSDSs for chemicals used in this procedure. Discuss the experiment with your lab partner.

Apparatus A 250-mL beaker, a 5-mL syringe, separatory funnel, apparatus for the "Nylon Rope Trick."

Setting Up Measure 2 mL of decanedioyl dichloride into a 250-mL beaker using the syringe. *The size of the beaker is important:* In smaller beakers the polymer tends to stick to the walls, whereas in larger beakers poor "ropes" are obtained unless larger amounts of reagents are used. Dissolve the decanedioyl dichloride in 100 mL of dichloromethane. Place 1.1 g of crystalline 1,6-hexanediamine or 1.3 mL of its commercially available 80–95% aqueous solution in a separatory funnel, and add 2.0 g of sodium carbonate and 50 mL of water. Gently shake the mixture to dissolve both reactants. Arrange the drum onto which the polymer is to be wound at a height such that the beaker containing the decanedioyl dichloride solution can be placed on the lab bench about 40 cm beneath and slightly in front of the drum (Fig. 22.3). Support the separatory funnel containing the other reagents so the lower tip of the funnel is centered no more than a centimeter above the surface of the dichloromethane solution of the decanedioyl dichloride.

Reaction Open the stopcock of the separatory funnel slightly so the aqueous solution runs *slowly and gently* onto the surface of the organic solution. A film of polymer will form immediately at the interface of the two solutions. Use long forceps or tongs to grasp the *center* of the polymer film and pull the rope that forms up to the front of the drum, loop it over the drum, and rotate the drum away from you to wind the rope onto the drum. For the first turn or two it may be necessary for you to use your fingers to secure the rope to the drum. Continue to rotate the drum and rapidly wind the nylon rope onto the drum until the reactants are consumed, remembering to count the revolutions of the drum as you wind.

Work-Up and Isolation Replace the beaker with a large dish or pan containing about 200 mL of 50% aqueous ethanol, and unwind the nylon rope into the wash solution. After stirring the mixture gently, decant the wash solution, and transfer the polymer to a filter on a Büchner funnel. Press the polymer as dry as possible, and then place it in your desk until the next laboratory period. When the nylon is thoroughly dry, weigh it and calculate the yield. Note the decrease in the bulk of polymer upon drying.

Film Formation To produce a film of Nylon-6,10, dissolve the dry polymer in about 10 times its weight of 90–100% formic acid (*Caution:* see item 3 of the Safety Alert) by stirring the mixture at *room temperature;* heating to achieve dissolution degrades the polymer. Spread the viscous solution on a glass plate. Leave the plate *in a hood* until the next laboratory period to allow evaporation of the formic acid.

Alternative Procedure

Apparatus A 100-mL beaker, 10-mL graduated cylinder, Pasteur pipet, glass rod or 15-cm length of copper wire.

Setting Up Pour 10 mL of a 5% aqueous solution of 1,6-hexanediamine into the beaker and add 10 drops of 20% aqueous sodium hydroxide solution. Stir the solution to ensure homogeneity.

Reaction Carefully pour 10 mL of a 5% solution of decanedioyl dichloride into the beaker to produce a biphasic mixture. Touch the tip of the glass rod or end of the copper wire to the interface between the two layers and gently remove the rod or wire from the mixture, pulling the fiber of polymer along with it. Twist the rod or wire to spin the fiber around it.

Work-Up and Isolation Follow the procedure described for the "Nylon Rope Trick."

Fiber Formation Form fibers by carefully melting the dry polymer in a metal spoon or spatula with gentle heating over a very small burner flame or a hot plate, and then drawing fibers from the melt with a small glass rod. If necessary, combine your polymer with that of several students to provide enough material to be melted and drawn successfully. Do not heat the polymer much above the melting temperature because it becomes discolored and charred.

Obtain IR and NMR spectra of your starting materials and compare them to those of authentic specimens (Figs. 22.4–22.7).

WRAPPING IT UP

After the rope has been drawn, stir the remaining reaction mixture thoroughly until no more *polymer* forms. Isolate any additional polymer and, after thoroughly washing it with water, put it in the container for nonhazardous organic solids. Separate the *dichloromethane and aqueous layers* of the reaction mixture. Pour the *dichloromethane* into the container for halogenated organic liquids. Flush the *aqueous layer and all aqueous solutions* down the drain.

EXERCISES

1. Explain why the preparation of Nylon-6,10 occurs under milder conditions when decanedioyl dichloride is used instead of decanedioic acid.

2. Using curved arrows to symbolize the flow of electrons, write the stepwise mechanism for the condensation reaction between decandioyl dichloride and 1,6-hexanediamine.

3. Write an equation for the formation of the salt produced from one molecule of hexanedioic acid and two molecules of 1,6-hexanediamine.

4. Why is sodium carbonate used in the reaction to prepare Nylon-6,10?

5. There is a large decrease in the bulk of the rope of Nylon-6,10 upon drying. Explain this observation.

6. Using full structural formulas, draw a typical portion of a Nylon-6,6 molecule; that is, expand a portion of the formula given in Equation 22.15. Show at least two hexanedioic acid units and two 1,6-hexanediamine units.

7. Draw formulas that illustrate the hydrogen bonding that may exist between two polyamide molecules after fibers have been "cold-drawn."

8. Nylons undergo *de*polymerization when heated in aqueous acid. Propose a reaction mechanism that accounts for this fact, using curved arrows to symbolize the flow of electrons.

9. Nylon-6 is produced from caprolactam by adding a small amount of aqueous base and then heating the mixture to about 270 °C.

Caprolactam

   a. Draw a representative portion of the polyamide molecule.

   b. Suggest a mechanism for the polymerization, using curved arrows to symbolize the flow of electrons, and indicate whether it is of the chain-reaction or step-growth type.

10. Would you expect polyesters to be stabilized by hydrogen bonding? Explain.

11. Proteins are polyamides formed from α-amino acids.

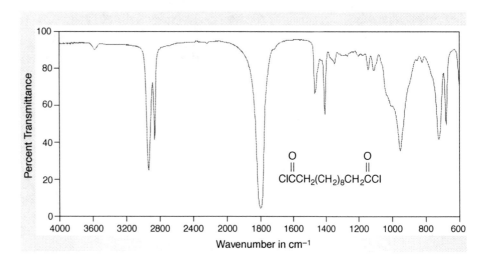

An α-amino acid

    a. Write a partial structure of a protein by drawing three monomeric units of it.

    b. Are proteins *chain-reaction* or *step-growth* polymers?

Refer to Tables 8.1.–8.8 as needed for answering the following questions on spectroscopy.

See Spectra   **12.** Consider the spectral data for decanedioyl dichloride (Figs. 22.4 and 22.5).

    a. In the functional group region of the IR spectrum, specify the absorptions associated with the carbonyl component of the acid chloride.

    b. In the ^{1}H NMR spectrum, assign the various resonances to the hydrogen nuclei responsible for them.

    c. For the ^{13}C NMR data, assign the various resonances to the carbon nuclei responsible for them.

See Spectra   **13.** Consider the spectral data for 1,6-hexanediamine (Figs. 22.6 and 22.7).

    a. In the IR spectrum, specify the absorptions associated with the amino group.

    b. In the ^{1}H NMR spectrum, assign the various resonances to the hydrogen nuclei responsible for them.

    c. For the ^{13}C NMR data, assign the various resonances to the carbon nuclei responsible for them.

SPECTRA

Starting Materials and Products

Figure 22.4
IR spectrum of decanedioyl dichloride (neat).

[IR spectrum plot: Percent Transmittance (y-axis, 0–100) vs Wavenumber in cm⁻¹ (x-axis, 4000–600). Structure shown on plot:]

$$\text{ClCCH}_2(\text{CH}_2)_8\text{CH}_2\text{CCl}$$

with carbonyl groups (O double-bonded to each terminal C)

(a) ^{1}H NMR spectrum (300 MHz).

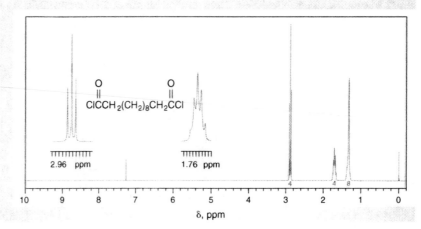

Figure 22.5
NMR data for decanedioyl dichloride (CDCl$_3$).

(b) ^{13}C NMR data: δ 24.7, 27.9, 28.4, 46.7, 173.2.

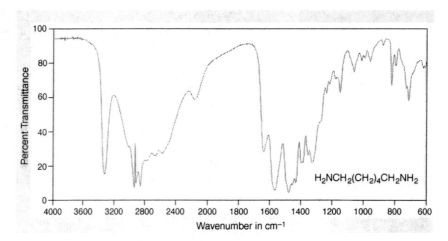

Figure 22.6
IR spectrum of 1,6-hexanediamine (neat).

(a) ^{1}H NMR spectrum (300 MHz).

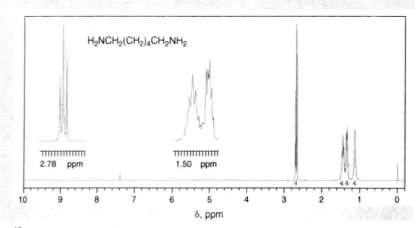

Figure 22.7
NMR data for 1, 6-hexanediamine (CDCl

(b) ^{13}C NMR data: δ 26.0, 33.0, 41.4.

HISTORICAL HIGHLIGHTS

Discovery of Polyethylene and Nylon

Polyethylene, or "polythene," as its British inventors called it, and the nylons are two types of polymers that have particularly interesting histories of discovery that bear repeating here. Both stories illustrate the role of serendipity in scientific achievements of great importance.

Polyethylene was discovered accidentally by British chemists at Imperial Chemicals Industries (I.C.I.) as an unexpected result of experiments on chemical reactions at very high pressures. In 1933, a reaction of benzaldehyde and ethylene at 170 °C and 1400 atmospheres gave no adducts involving the two reagents and was considered a complete failure. However, an observant chemist noticed a thin layer of "white waxy solid" on the walls of the reaction vessel used for the experiment. This was recognized as a polymer of ethylene, but additional experiments with ethylene alone to produce the same polymer only resulted in violent decompositions that destroyed the equipment.

Two years elapsed before better and stronger equipment was available for further experimentation. When ethylene was heated to 180 °C in this new equipment, the pressure in the apparatus dropped unexpectedly, so more ethylene was pumped in. Then, when the reaction vessel was opened, the I.C.I. chemists found a large amount of white powdery solid, which was the long-sought polyethylene. Because they knew that the polymerization could not account for all of the pressure drop that had been observed, they suspected a leak in one of the joints of the apparatus. This idea led to the proposal that the polymerization had been catalyzed by oxygen in the air that had leaked into the apparatus, and this hypothesis was confirmed by experiments in which air was intentionally included with the ethylene. Oxygen can act as a radical initiator and catalyze the polymerization by a chain-reaction mechanism analogous to Equations 22.7–22.10.

The polyethylene produced by the oxygen-catalyzed, high-pressure, high-temperature process developed by I.C.I. in the mid-1930s was ideal for many applications, including insulation of radar equipment, where it was used to great advantage by the Allies in World War II. Referring to the contribution radar made to naval operations, the British

Commander-in-Chief said it enabled the Home Fleet to "find, fix, fight, and finish the *Scharnhorst* (the pride of Hitler's navy)."

The group of polymers called nylons was first produced in 1939 as a material for women's hose and other garments and was the world's first totally synthetic fiber. Nylon hose were an instant hit with the buying public: 800,000 pairs were sold on May 15, 1940, the first day they were on the market! With the onset of World War II and the involvement of the United States. By 1941, nylon was taken off the domestic market because it was found to be the best available material for military parachutes.

The first nylon to be produced industrially was Nylon-6,6. The remarkable fact about the discovery of this polymer is not how it was first prepared from the two monomers, but how it was first prepared in a form suitable for a textile fiber. This depended on invention of the "cold-drawing process," and this technique was discovered almost completely by accident, as we shall see.

Wallace Hume Carothers was brought to Du Pont to direct its new basic chemical research program because his faculty mentors at the University of Illinois, where he earned his Ph.D., and his colleagues at Harvard University, where he served on the faculty, recommended him as the most brilliant chemist they knew. An incentive for his move from academia to industry in 1927 might well have been the fact that his salary was doubled—to all of $6,000 per year. Carothers initiated a program aimed at understanding the composition of the high polymers of nature such as cellulose, silk, and rubber, and of producing synthetic materials like them. By 1934 his group had contributed valuable fundamental knowledge in these areas, but Carothers had just about decided that their efforts to produce a synthetic fiber like silk was a failure. It was a shrewd observation made during some "horseplay" among Carothers's chemists in the laboratory that turned this failure to compete with nature into the enormous success ultimately advertised at the 1939 New York World's Fair as "Nylon, the Synthetic Silk Made from Coal, Air, and Water!"

The Carothers group had learned how to make Nylon-6,6, but even though this polyamide had a molecular structure similar to that of silk, they had

(continued)

"put it on the back shelf" without patent protection because the polymer did not have the tensile strength of silk, a necessary criterion for a good textile fiber. The group continued its research by investigating a series of polyester polymers that were more soluble, easier to handle, and thus simpler to work with in the laboratory. It was while working with one of these softer materials that Julian Hill noted that if he gathered a small ball of such a polymer on the end of a glass stirring rod and drew a thread out of the mass, the thread of polymer so produced became very silky in appearance. This attracted his attention and that of the others working with him, and it is reported that one day while Carothers was in downtown Wilmington, Hill and his cohorts tried to see how far they could stretch one of these samples. One chemist put a little ball of the polymer on a stirring rod and a second chemist touched a glass rod to the polymer ball and then ran down the hall to see how far he could stretch the thread of polymer. While doing this they noticed not only the silky appearance of the extended strands, but also their increased strength. They soon realized that this additional strength might be the result from some special orientation of the polymer molecules produced by the stretching procedure.

Because the polyesters they were working with at that time had melting points too low for use in textile products, a deficiency that has since been removed, the researchers returned to the polyamides (nylons) that had earlier been put aside. They soon found that these polymers, too, could be "cold-drawn" to increase

their tensile strength so much that they could be made into excellent textiles. Filaments, gears, and other molded objects could also be made from the strong polymer produced by cold-drawing.

The alignment of the long polyamide molecules in a manner that produces extensive intermolecular hydrogen-bonding (**31**, Sec. 22.3) binds the individual polymer molecules together in much the same way that separate strands in a rope, when twisted together, form a cable. This association of linear polymer molecules through hydrogen bonding is responsible for the greatly increased strength of the nylon fibers. We believe that the same principle accounts for the strength of silk fibers; the natural polyamide molecules of silk are oriented in such a way that hydrogen bonds hold the individual molecules together. Interestingly, the silkworms accomplish the equivalent of "cold-drawing" as they extrude the viscous silk filaments to produce cocoons!

Relationship of Historical Highlight to Experiments

The experiments in this chapter represent examples of chain-reaction polymerization to produce polystyrene (Sec. 22.2) and step-growth polymerization (Sec. 22.3) to yield a nylon. The procedures of Section 22.2 provide an opportunity to observe formation of the same polymer in three physically different forms, whereas that of Section 22.3 illustrates how strong hydrogen-bonded fibers can result from the "cold-drawing" technique patented by Du Pont.

See more on *Polyethylene*
See more on *Nylon*
See more on *Free Radicals*
See *Who was Wallace Carothers?*
See *Who was Julian Hill?*

Dehydrating Cyclohexanol

prepared by **Carl T. Wigal**, Lebanon Valley College

PURPOSE OF THE EXPERIMENT

Dehydrate cyclohexanol to prepare cyclohexene. Characterize cyclohexene by using ammonium cerium (IV) nitrate test, bromine test, infrared spectroscopy and/or refractive index.

EXPERIMENTAL OPTIONS

BACKGROUND REQUIRED

You should be familiar with basic laboratory techniques for measuring volumes and masses. You should know how to conduct a simple distillation. For product characterization, you should know how to measure refractive index and/or obtain and interpret an infrared spectrum.

BACKGROUND INFORMATION

Elimination reactions involve the loss of a small molecule (H–X) from adjacent carbon atoms, resulting in pi-bond formation. Consequently, elimination reactions are good synthetic methods for producing alkenes or alkynes. These reactions occur through a process called heterolytic bond cleavage. **Heterolytic bond cleavage** occurs when one atom leaves a compound with both electrons of the original bond, resulting in the formation of ions. For example, elimination of H–X from an organic molecule involves the loss of a proton (H^+) and a leaving group (X^-), as shown in Figure 1. The leaving group departs with both electrons from the original C–X bond. The electrons in the adjacent C–H bond form the new pi bond of the alkene, with loss of the proton.

Figure 1 Elimination of HX from an organic molecule

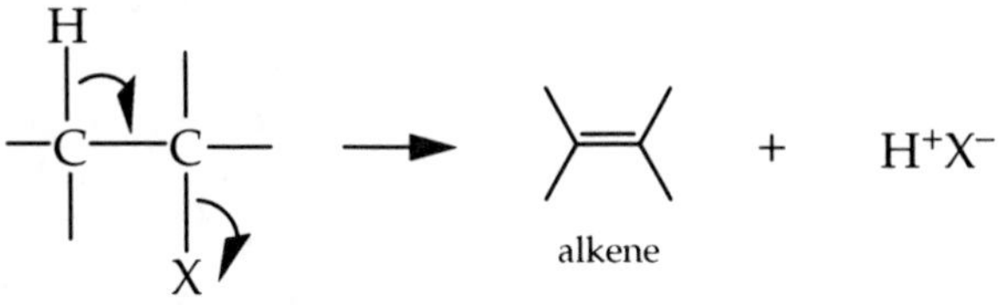

The elimination of water (H–OH) from alcohols was one of the earliest organic reactions studied. This reaction, still widely used, is called a **dehydration reaction**. In many cases, alcohol dehydration is an acid-catalyzed reaction that proceeds by an elimination mechanism

02 01 00 99 — 15 14 13 12 11 10 9 8 7 6 5 4 3 2

called **E1**. The E1 mechanism for the dehydration of 2-methyl-2-butanol is shown in Figure 2.

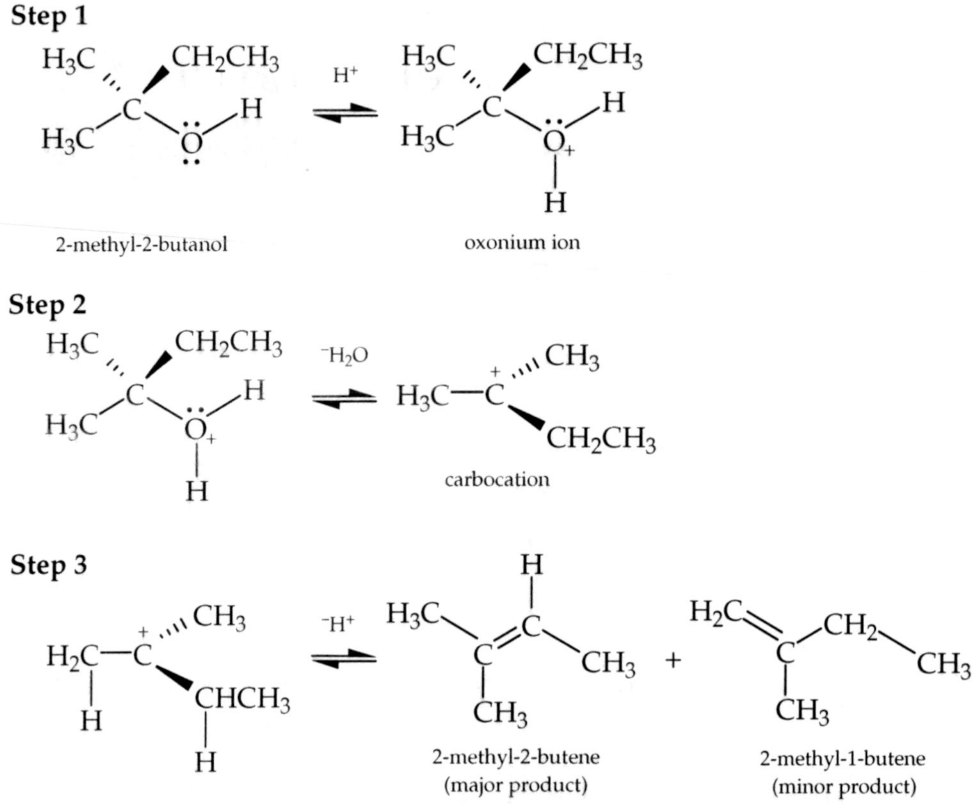

Step 1

2-methyl-2-butanol   oxonium ion

Step 2

carbocation

Step 3

2-methyl-2-butene (major product)   +   2-methyl-1-butene (minor product)

Figure 2   E1 mechanism for the dehydration of 2-methyl-2-butanol

The first step of dehydration is a proton transfer from the acid catalyst to the oxygen atom of the alcohol. This protonation forms an **oxonium ion**, the conjugate acid of the alcohol. Weak bases are good leaving groups, so changing the leaving group from hydroxide to water favors the reaction.

The second step of the dehydration reaction is loss of water from the oxonium ion forming a positively charged **carbocation**. This step of the mechanism is rate-determining.

Not all alcohols dehydrate at the same rate. Alcohols are classified according to the number of alkyl groups attached to the carbon bearing the hydroxyl group. The terminology used to describe the degree of substitution is **tertiary (3°), secondary (2°),** and **primary (1°)**. Experimental evidence shows that the ease of alcohol dehydration follows the trend 3° > 2° > 1°. This reactivity directly relates to the stability of the carbocation intermediate formed during the rate-determining step of the reaction.

In the third and final step, a proton is released from a carbon atom adjacent to the positively charged carbon. The electrons previously comprising the C–H bond form the new carbon–carbon pi bond.

The formation of two isomeric alkenes is possible in elimination reactions where a proton can be lost from either of two different carbon atoms. **Saytzeff's rule** states that the orientation of the double bond favors the more thermodynamically stable alkene; that is, the alkene with the greatest number of alkyl groups bonded to the carbons of the double bond. Thus, dehydrating 2-methyl-2-butanol produces primarily 2-methyl-2-butene, a trisubstituted alkene, rather than 2-methyl-1-butene, a disubstituted alkene.

In this experiment, you will dehydrate cyclohexanol to form cyclohexene. Because cyclohexene has a lower boiling point than cyclohexanol, the cyclohexene can be distilled away as it forms. You will isolate and characterize the cyclohexene by performing qualitative tests for alcohols and alkenes. Your laboratory instructor will tell you whether to further characterize the cyclohexene by measuring its refractive index and/or by generating infrared spectra for both cyclohexanol and cyclohexene.

Qualitative Tests   The presence of the hydroxyl group of an alcohol can be determined by observing the reaction of an alcohol with ammonium cerium(IV) nitrate, $(NH_4)_2Ce(NO_3)_6$. A positive test for an alcohol is indicated as the yellow $(NH_4)_2Ce(NO_3)_6$ solution turns red when complexed with an alcohol, as shown in Figure 3. Even small contaminating amounts of alcohol can cause a slight color change.

Figure 3   Reaction of ammonium cerium(IV) nitrate with an alcohol

$$(NH_4)_2Ce(NO_3)_6 \ + \ R\text{-}OH \longrightarrow [alcohol + reagent]$$

yellow   alcohol   red complex

The presence of a carbon–carbon double bond of an alkene can be determined by observing the reaction between bromine and an alkene, as shown in Figure 4. Bromine is a reddish-brown color. A positive test is indicated by the decolorization of the bromine solution.

Figure 4   Reaction of bromine with an alkene

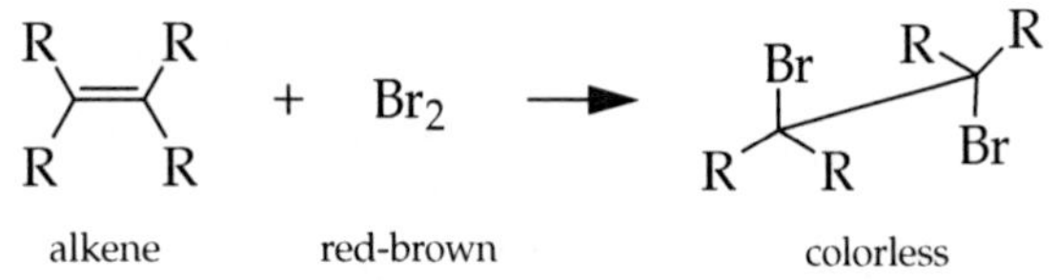

alkene   red-brown   colorless

Semi-Microscale Dehydration

Equipment

100-mL beaker	magnetic stir bar
distillation apparatus	2 Pasteur pipets, with latex bulb
condenser, with tubing	5-mL sample vial
distilling head	sand bath[†]
10-mL round-bottom flask	13 × 100-mm test tube[‡]
receiver flask*	support ring
thermometer, –10 to 260 °C,	2 support stands
or equivalent, with adapter	3 utility clamps
vacuum adapter	wire gauze
10-mL graduated cylinder	

*10-mL vial or 10-mL round-bottom flask

[†]stirring hot plate with crystallizing dish filled with sand or magnetic stirrer and electric flask heater filled with sand

[‡]or centrifuge tube

Reagents and Properties

substance	quantity	molar mass (g/mol)	bp (°C)	d (g/mL)
calcium chloride anhydrous	0.25 g	110.99		
cyclohexanol	2.84 g	100.16	160	0.948
cyclohexene*		82.15	83	0.811
phosphoric acid, 85%	4.0 mL	98.00		1.685
sulfuric acid, concentrated	0.2 mL	98.08		1.840

*product

Preview

- Assemble the distillation apparatus
- Add cyclohexanol, sulfuric acid, and phosphoric acid to the flask
- Distill the reaction mixture and collect the distillate in a receiver
- Transfer the distillate to a test tube
- Remove the bottom layer of the distillate
- Dry the top layer with anhydrous calcium chloride
- Tare a sample vial
- Transfer the cyclohexene to the sample vial
- Weigh the cyclohexene

PROCEDURE   **Chemical Alert**

anhydrous calcium chloride—*irritant and hygroscopic*
cyclohexanol—*irritant and hygroscopic*
cyclohexene—*flammable and irritant*
phosphoric acid—*corrosive*
sulfuric acid—*toxic and oxidizer*

Caution: Wear departmentally approved safety goggles at all times while in the chemistry laboratory.

1. Using Distillation to Dehydrate Cyclohexanol

Caution: Concentrated sulfuric acid (H_2SO_4) is toxic and an oxidizer. Phosphoric acid (H_3PO_4) is corrosive. Prevent eye, skin, clothing, and combustible materials contact. Cyclohexanol is an irritant and hygroscopic. Avoid inhaling vapors and ingesting these compounds. Use a *fume hood*.

Assemble the distillation apparatus shown in Figure 5. If necessary, use substitute glassware as directed by your laboratory instructor. Remove the 10-mL round-bottom flask from the apparatus. Place 4.0 mL of 85% H_3PO_4 and 2.84 g (3.0 mL) of cyclohexanol in the round-bottom flask. Add 5 drops of concentrated H_2SO_4 to the flask and add a magnetic stir bar.

Figure 5 Distillation apparatus for semi-microscale dehydration

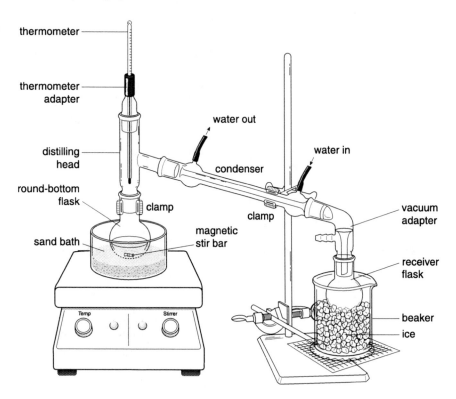

Reattach the round-bottom flask to the distillation apparatus. Start the flow of water through the condenser.

Turn on the magnetic stirrer. Heat the reaction mixture while stirring until the product starts to distill. Continue the distillation, collecting the product in the receiver flask until no more liquid distills or until the temperature of the thermometer rises above 85 °C.

Turn off the heat. Allow the apparatus to cool. Turn off the magnetic stirrer.

Remove the receiver flask from the distillation assembly. Use a Pasteur pipet to transfer the distillate into a centrifuge tube or small test tube.

2.   Isolating Cyclohexene **Caution:**   Cyclohexene is flammable and irritating. Keep away from flames or other heat sources. Prevent eye, skin, and clothing contact. Avoid inhaling vapors. Use a *fume hood*.

Notice that as the distillate in the tube cools, two layers form. Use the Pasteur pipet to remove the majority of the bottom layer. Place the bottom layer into the container labeled "Recovered Acid Layer", provided by your laboratory instructor.

Caution: Anhydrous calcium chloride is irritating and hygroscopic. Avoid inhaling dust.

Dry the top organic layer by placing about 0.25 g of anhydrous calcium chloride into the test tube. Let the test tube stand for 5 min.

Weigh a clean 5-mL sample vial. Using a clean dry Pasteur pipet, remove the liquid from the test tube, and transfer the liquid to the tared sample vial. Weigh your product.

Characterize your cyclohexene using the methods in the Product Characterization section designated by your laboratory instructor.

3. **Cleaning Up** Place your recovered materials in the appropriate labeled collection containers as directed by your laboratory instructor. Clean your glassware with soap or detergent.

Caution: Wash your hands thoroughly with soap or detergent before leaving the laboratory.

Microscale Dehydration

Using Glassware with Elastomeric Connectors

Equipment

100-mL beaker	2 Pasteur pipets, with latex bulb
distillation apparatus	receiver vial
elastomeric connectors	5-mL sample vial
distilling head–air condenser	sand bath*
5-mL round-bottom flask	support ring
thermometer, –10 to 260 °C,	support stand
or equivalent	10 × 75-mm test tube[†]
10-mL graduated cylinder	2 utility clamps
magnetic stir bar	wire gauze

*stirring hot plate with crystallizing dish filled with sand or magnetic stirrer and electric flask heater filled with sand

[†]or centrifuge tube

Reagents and Properties

substance	quantity	molar mass (g/mol)	bp (°C)	d (g/mL)
calcium chloride, anhydrous	0.25 g	110.99		
cyclohexanol	1.422 g	100.16	160	0.948
cyclohexene*		82.15	83	0.811
phosphoric acid, 85%	1.5 mL	98.00		1.685
sulfuric acid, concentrated	0.12 mL	98.08		1.840

*product

Preview

- Assemble the distillation apparatus

- Add cyclohexanol, sulfuric acid, and phosphoric acid to the flask

- Distill the reaction mixture and collect the distillate in a receiver

- Transfer the distillate to a test tube

- Remove the bottom layer of the distillate

- Dry the top layer with anhydrous calcium chloride

- Tare a sample vial
- Transfer the cyclohexene to the sample vial
- Weigh the cyclohexene

PROCEDURE

Chemical Alert

anhydrous calcium chloride—*irritant and hygroscopic*
cyclohexanol—*irritant and hygroscopic*
cyclohexene—*flammable and irritant*
phosphoric acid—*corrosive*
sulfuric acid—*toxic and oxidizer*

Caution: Wear departmentally approved safety goggles at all times while in the chemistry laboratory.

1. Using Distillation to Dehydrate Cyclohexanol

Caution: Concentrated sulfuric acid (H_2SO_4) is toxic and an oxidizer. Phosphoric acid (H_3PO_4) is corrosive. Prevent eye, skin, clothing, and combustible materials contact. Cyclohexanol is an irritant and hygroscopic. Avoid inhaling vapors and ingesting these compounds. Use a *fume hood*.

Assemble the distillation apparatus shown in Figure 6. Remove the 5-mL round-bottom flask from the apparatus. Place 1.5 mL of 85% H_3PO_4 and 1.422 g (1.5 mL) of cyclohexanol into the flask. Add 3 drops of concentrated H_2SO_4 to the flask and add a magnetic stir bar. Reattach the round-bottom flask to the distillation apparatus.

Figure 6 Distillation apparatus for microscale dehydration using glassware with elastomeric connectors

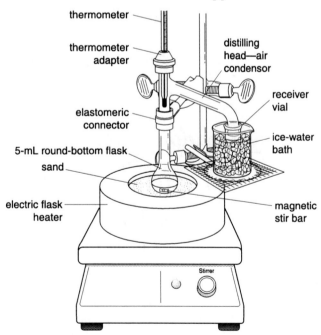

Turn on the magnetic stirrer. Heat the reaction mixture while stirring until the product starts to distill. Continue the distillation, collecting the product in the receiver vial until no more liquid distills or until the temperature of the thermometer rises above 85 °C.

Turn off the heat. Allow the apparatus to cool. Turn off the magnetic stirrer.

Remove the receiver vial from the distillation assembly. Use a Pasteur pipet to transfer the distillate into a centrifuge tube or small test tube.

2. **Isolating Cyclohexene** ***Caution:*** Cyclohexene is flammable and irritating. Keep away from flames or other heat sources. Prevent eye, skin, and clothing contact. Avoid inhaling vapors. Use a ***fume hood.***

Notice that as the distillate in the tube cools, two layers form. Use the Pasteur pipet to remove the majority of the bottom layer. Place the bottom layer into the container labeled "Recovered Acid Layer", provided by your laboratory instructor.

Caution: Anhydrous calcium chloride is irritating and hygroscopic. Avoid inhaling dust.

Dry the top organic layer by placing about 0.25 g of anhydrous calcium chloride in the test tube. Let the test tube stand for 5 min.

Weigh a clean 5-mL sample vial. Using a clean dry Pasteur pipet, remove the liquid from the tube and transfer the liquid to the tared sample vial. Weigh your product.

Characterize your cyclohexene using the methods in the Product Characterization section designated by your laboratory instructor.

3. **Cleaning Up** Place your recovered materials in the appropriate labeled collection containers as directed by your laboratory instructor. Clean your glassware with soap or detergent.

Caution: Wash your hands thoroughly with soap or detergent before leaving the laboratory.

Microscale Dehydration

Using a Hickman Still Assembly

Equipment

5-mL conical vial	support stand
10-mL graduated cylinder	10 × 75-mm test tube[†]
Hickman still	thermometer, –10 to 150 °C,
magnetic spin vane	with adapter[‡]
2 Pasteur pipets, with latex bulb	thermometer, –10 to 260 °C, or
3-mL sample vial	equivalent
sand bath*	2 utility clamps

*stirring hot plate with crystallizing dish filled with sand or magnetic stirrer and electric flask heater filled with sand

[†]or centrifuge tube

[‡]to fit Hickman still

Reagents and Properties

substance	quantity	molar mass (g/mol)	bp (°C)	d (g/mL)
calcium chloride anhydrous	0.25 g	110.99		
cyclohexanol	1.422 g	100.16	160	0.948
cyclohexene*		82.15	83	0.811
phosphoric acid, 85%	1.5 mL	98.00		1.685
sulfuric acid, concentrated	0.12 mL	98.08		1.840

*product

Preview

- Assemble the distillation apparatus

- Add cyclohexanol, sulfuric acid, and phosphoric acid to the vial

- Distill the reaction mixture into the still collar

- Transfer the distillate to a test tube

- Remove the bottom layer of the distillate

- Dry the top layer with anhydrous calcium chloride

- Tare a sample vial

- Transfer the cyclohexene to the sample vial

- Weigh the cyclohexene

PROCEDURE **Chemical Alert**

anhydrous calcium chloride—*irritant and hygroscopic*

cyclohexanol—*irritant and hygroscopic*

cyclohexene—*flammable and irritant*

phosphoric acid—*corrosive*

sulfuric acid—*toxic and oxidizer*

Caution: Wear departmentally approved safety goggles at all times while in the chemistry laboratory.

1. Using Distillation to Dehydrate Cyclohexanol

Caution: Concentrated sulfuric acid (H_2SO_4) is toxic and an oxidizer. Phosphoric acid (H_3PO_4) is corrosive. Prevent eye, skin, clothing, and combustible materials contact. Cyclohexanol is an irritant and hygroscopic. Avoid inhaling vapors and ingesting these compounds. Use a *fume hood*.

Assemble the distillation apparatus shown in Figure 7 on the next page.

Figure 7 Distillation apparatus for microscale dehydration using a Hickman still

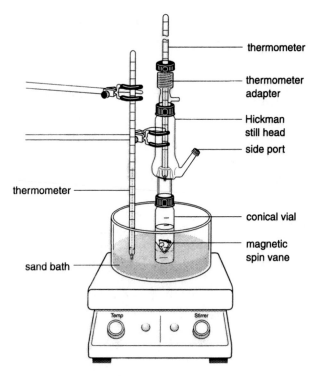

Remove the 5-mL conical vial from the apparatus. Place 1.5 mL of 85% H_3PO_4 and 1.422 g (1.5 mL) of cyclohexanol into the vial. Add 3 drops of concentrated H_2SO_4 to the vial and add a magnetic spin vane. Reattach the vial to the distillation apparatus.

Turn on the magnetic stirrer. Heat the reaction mixture while stirring until the product starts to distill. As the product starts to collect in the still, use a Pasteur pipet to remove the liquid from the still. [NOTE 1] Transfer the liquid into a centrifuge tube or a small test tube. Continue the distillation and collection until no more liquid distills or until the temperature of the thermometer rises above 85 °C.

Turn off the heat. Allow the apparatus to cool. Turn off the magnetic stirrer.

NOTE 1: If your Hickman still is not equipped with a side port, prepare a bent-tip Pasteur pipet as directed by your laboratory instructor.

2.   Isolating Cyclohexene   ***Caution:***   Cyclohexene is flammable and irritating. Keep away from flames or other heat sources. Prevent eye, skin, and clothing contact. Avoid inhaling vapors. Use a ***fume hood.***

Notice that as the distillate in the test tube or vial cools, two layers form. Use the Pasteur pipet to remove the majority of the bottom layer. Place the bottom layer into the container labeled "Recovered Acid Layer", provided by your laboratory instructor.

Caution: Anhydrous calcium chloride is irritating and hygroscopic. Avoid inhaling dust.

Dry the top organic layer by placing about 0.25 g of anhydrous calcium chloride into the test tube. Let the test tube stand for 5 min.

Weigh a clean 3-mL sample vial. Using a clean dry Pasteur pipet, remove the liquid from the test tube and transfer the liquid to the tared sample vial. Weigh your product.

Characterize your cyclohexene using the methods in the Product Characterization section designated by your laboratory instructor.

3. Cleaning Up Place your recovered materials in the appropriate labeled collection containers as directed by your laboratory instructor. Clean your glassware with soap or detergent.

Caution: Wash your hands thoroughly with soap or detergent before leaving the laboratory.

Product Characterization

Equipment

5 Pasteur pipets, with latex bulb   white spot plate
3 test tubes, 10 × 75-mm

Reagents and Properties

substance	quantity	molar mass (g/mol)	bp (°C)
ammonium cerium(IV) nitrate test reagent	0.6 mL		
bromine test reagent	0.24 mL		
cyclohexanol	0.16 mL	100.16	160
cyclohexene	0.16 mL	82.15	83
dichloromethane	2.4 mL	84.93	40
1,4-dioxane	0.36 mL	88.11	100–102

Preview

- Test standards and product for presence of alcohol using ammonium cerium(IV) nitrate reagent

- Test standards and product for presence of alkene using bromine reagent

- Compare cyclohexanol and cyclohexene product using infrared analysis

- Measure refractive index of cyclohexene product

PROCEDURE *Chemical Alert*

ammonium cerium(IV) nitrate—*irritant and oxidizer*
bromine—*highly toxic and oxidizer*
cyclohexanol—*irritant and hygroscopic*
cyclohexene—*flammable and irritant*
dichloromethane—*toxic and irritant*
1,4-dioxane—*flammable and suspected carcinogen*

Caution: Wear departmentally approved safety goggles at all times while in the chemistry laboratory.

© 1998 Chemical Education Resources

1. Using Ammonium Cerium(IV) Nitrate to Test for Alcohols

Caution: Ammonium cerium(IV) nitrate, $(NH_4)_2Ce(NO_3)_6$, is irritating and an oxidizer. 1,4-Dioxane is flammable and a suspected carcinogen. Keep 1,4-dioxane away from flames or other heat sources. Prevent eye, skin, and clothing contact. Avoid inhaling vapors. Use 1,4-dioxane in a ***fume hood.***

Cyclohexanol is irritating and hygroscopic. Cyclohexene is flammable and irritating. Keep cyclohexene away from flames or other heat sources. Prevent eye, skin, and clothing contact. Avoid inhaling vapors.

NOTE 1: 1,4-Dioxane is used as a solvent.

Place 5 drops of the $(NH_4)_2Ce(NO_3)_6$ test reagent and 3 drops of 1,4-dioxane in each of three wells of a white spot plate. [NOTE 1]   Add 2 drops of cyclohexanol to the first well and stir. Observe any color change and record your results.

Add 2 drops of cyclohexene from the reagent bottle to the second well and stir. Observe any color change and record your results.

Add 2 drops of your cyclohexene product to the third well and stir. Observe any color change and record your results.

2. Using Bromine to Test for Alkenes

Caution: Bromine (Br_2) is highly toxic. Dichloromethane is toxic and irritating. Cyclohexanol is irritating and hygroscopic. Cyclohexene is flammable and irritating. Keep cyclohexene away from flames or other heat sources. Prevent eye, skin, and clothing contact. Avoid inhaling vapors. Use these reagents in a ***fume hood.***

Label three small test tubes "cyclohexanol", "cyclohexene", and "product". Place 2 drops of cyclohexanol into the tube labeled "cyclohexanol". Place 2 drops of cyclohexene into the tube labeled "cyclohexene". Place 2 drops of your product into the tube labeled "product".

NOTE 2: Dichloromethane is used as a solvent.

Add 20 drops of dichloromethane into each test tube, and stir. [NOTE 2]. Add 2 drops of the Br_2 test reagent to each tube and stir. Observe any color change. Record your results.

3. Using Infrared Analysis to Compare Cyclohexanol and Your Cyclohexene Product

Obtain the operating instructions for using the infrared spectrometer from your laboratory instructor. Obtain a set of KBr, NaCl, or AgCl salt plates and a holder. [NOTE 3]   Place 1 drop of your cyclohexanol between the salt plates. Gently press the plates together to remove any air bubbles. Place the plates in the holder and secure the plates. Run and plot the IR spectrum according to your operating instructions.

NOTE 3: Salt plates are fragile and hygroscopic. ***Do not use water to wipe the plates.*** Even moisture from your fingers will attack the plates. Use gloves and only handle the plates by the edges.

Repeat this procedure for your cyclohexene product. Examine the region of the spectrum above $1500\ cm^{-1}$. Assign the bonds that give rise to these absorptions.

4. Using Refractive Index to Characterize Your Cyclohexene Product

Obtain the operating instructions for the refractometer from your laboratory instructor. Measure the refractive index for your cyclohexene product. Measure the laboratory temperature in °C. Make temperature corrections, if necessary. [NOTE 4]   Compare your refractive index to the literature values shown in Table 1.

NOTE 4: The refractive index at 20 °C is calculated by using the following equation, where T is the ambient temperature in degrees Celsius and n_D^T is the refractive index measured at ambient temperature.

$$n_D^{20} = n_D^T + 0.00045\,(T - 20\ °C)$$

Table 1   Refractive indices (20 °C)

water	1.3329
cyclohexanol	1.4650
cyclohexene	1.4460

5. **Cleaning Up**   Place your recovered materials in the appropriate labeled collection containers as directed by your laboratory instructor. Clean your glassware with soap or detergent.

Caution: Wash your hands thoroughly with soap or detergent before leaving the laboratory.

Post-Laboratory Questions

1. Calculate the percent yield that you obtained from this reaction.
2. Did your product cause a color change with $(NH_4)_2Ce(NO_3)_6$ test reagent? Explain your results.
3. Did your product cause a color change with the Br_2 test reagent? Explain your results.
4. Compare the IR spectra for cyclohexanol and your product. What IR evidence do you have that your product is cyclohexene and not cyclohexanol? Briefly explain.
5. (a) Calculate the refractive index of your product at 20 °C.

    (b) Compare the refractive index of your product to the data of Table 1. Does the result indicate that your product is pure? Briefly explain.

    (c) If the refractive index of your product differs from the listed value, what is the most likely contaminant in your product, as indicated by the refractive index? Briefly explain.
6. What would be the major product obtained from the E1 dehydration of 2-methylcyclohexanol?
7. Outline a mechanism for the dehydration of 1-methyl-1-cyclohexanol. Would you predict this reaction to be faster or slower than the reaction you performed?

NAME   SECTION   DATE

REAC 712/Dehydrating Cyclohexanol

Pre-Laboratory Assignment

1. What safety precautions must be observed when using concentrated H_2SO_4 and H_3PO_4?

2. (a) Write the chemical equation for the dehydration of cyclohexanol.

   (b) Using the following information, calculate the theoretical yield for the dehydration of 3.0 mL of cyclohexanol.

substance	molar mass (g/mol)	d (g/mL)
cyclohexanol	100.16	0.948
cyclohexene	82.15	0.811

3. When 2-butanol undergoes E1 dehydration, three alkenes are obtained. Draw the structures for these alkenes. Which alkene would you predict to be formed in greatest abundance?

ISBN 0-87540-712-9

Synthesizing Aspirin: The Acetylation of Salicylic Acid

Prepared by Joe Jeffers, Ouachita Baptist University

PURPOSE OF THE EXPERIMENT

Prepare acetylsalicylic acid by the esterification of salicylic acid. Test the product by reaction with iron(III) chloride.

EXPERIMENTAL OPTIONS

Semi-Microscale Synthesis
Microscale Synthesis

BACKGROUND REQUIRED

You should be familiar with reflux, vacuum filtration, and melting point measurement.

BACKGROUND INFORMATION

The curative powers of willow tree bark have been known for centuries. Studies on extracts of the willow bark indicated that it is a pain reliever, a fever reducer, and an anti-inflammatory agent.

The active ingredient in willow bark, salicylic acid, was synthesized in 1853 by the French chemist Charles Gerhardt. Unfortunately, many people experience serious side effects with salicylic acid. In 1893, Felix Hoffmann, a German chemist, synthesized the acetyl derivative, acetylsalicylic acid. A few years later, the Bayer Company began marketing acetylsalicylic acid under the trade name aspirin.

Salicylic acid contains a phenol group. The phenol group can react with acetic anhydride to form an ester, as shown in Equation 1 on the next page. Phosphoric acid is used to catalyze the reaction.

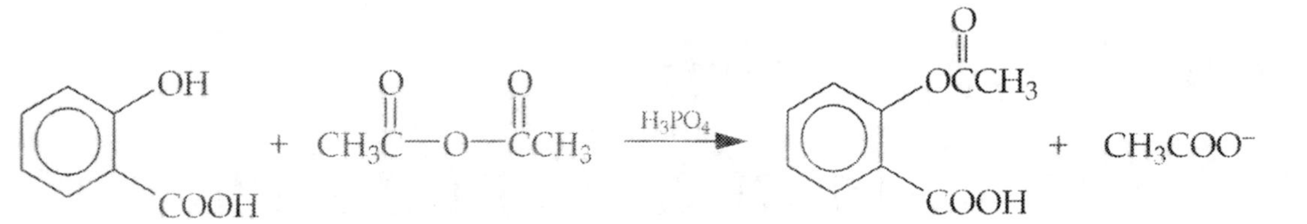

salicylic acid   acetic anhydride   acetylsalicylic acid   acetate

Over time, commercial aspirin reacts with moisture in the air to hydrolyze into salicylic acid and acetic acid.

Iron(III) chloride ($FeCl_3$) reacts with phenols to form brightly colored complexes, ranging from red to violet. Thus, $FeCl_3$ reacts with salicylic acid because of its phenol group. Acetylsalicylic acid does not react because the phenol group is acetylated. The $FeCl_3$ test provides an easy method to test acetylsalicylic acid sold as aspirin to see if any of the acetylsalicylic acid has degraded to salicylic acid and acetic acid.

In this experiment, you will synthesize aspirin from salicylic acid and acetic anhydride. You will characterize your product by melting point and by reaction with $FeCl_3$.

SEMI-MICROSCALE SYNTHESIS

Equipment

25-mL beaker
250-mL beaker*
25-mL filter flask,
  with vacuum tubing
filter paper
glass rod
10-mL graduated cylinder
Hirsch funnel, with adapter
magnetic stir bar
melting point capillary tube
microspatula
mortar and pestle

2 Pasteur pipets, with latex bulb
standard taper glassware
  condenser
  10-mL round-bottom flask
stirring hot plate
support stand
4 test tubes, 13 × 100-mm[†]
18 × 150-mm test tube
−10 to 260 °C thermometer
transfer pipet, 2-mL
2 utility clamps
watch glass

*for hot-water bath and ice-water bath
[†]plus an additional test tube for each commercial aspirin tablet tested

Reagents and Properties

substance	quantity	molar mass (g/mol)	mp (°C)	bp (°C)
acetic anhydride	1.2 mL	102.09		138
acetylsalicylic acid*		180.16	138	
commercial aspirin tablets				
iron(III) chloride, 1%	4 drops			
phosphoric acid, 85%	2 drops			
salicylic acid	0.500 g	138.12	158	

* product

Preview

- Prepare a 50 °C hot-water bath
- Add salicylic acid, acetic anhydride, and phosphoric acid to a reflux apparatus
- Use the hot-water bath to reflux the reaction for 15 min
- Crystallize the product
- Collect the product by vacuum filtration
- Measure the melting point
- Test the product, salicylic acid, and acetylsalicylic acid with 1% iron(III) chloride
- Test commercial aspirin tablets with 1% iron(III) chloride

PROCEDURE

CAUTION

Wear departmentally approved safety goggles at all times while in the chemistry laboratory.

Always use caution in the laboratory. Many chemicals are potentially harmful. Prevent contact with your eyes, skin, and clothing. Avoid ingesting any of the reagents.

1. Setting Up the Reaction

Prepare a hot-water bath by placing approximately 100 mL of water into a 250-mL beaker. Use a stirring hot plate to heat the water to 50 °C.

Assemble a reflux apparatus, as shown in Figure 1. Add a magnetic stir bar to the 10-mL round-bottom flask.

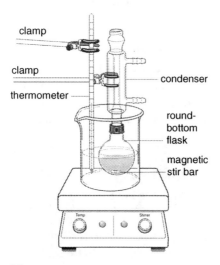

Figure 1
Semi-microscale reflux apparatus

CAUTION

Acetic anhydride is corrosive and a lachrymator. 85% Phosphoric acid is corrosive. Salicylic acid is a teratogen and irritating.

Put 0.500 g (500 mg) of salicylic acid into the round-bottom flask. Add 1.2 mL of acetic anhydride. Use a Pasteur pipet to add two drops of 85% phosphoric acid. Reassemble the reflux apparatus without delay.

2. Conducting the Reaction [NOTE 1]

NOTE 1: The reflux condenser is used to prevent loss of any reactants during the reaction. Boiling will not occur.

Place the reaction flask in the 50 °C hot-water bath. Clamp the flask in place. Turn on the stirrer. Stir the reaction to dissolve the salicylic acid.

If the reaction mixture clumps and stops the stirring, use a microspatula to restart the stir bar. Once the salicylic acid has dissolved, continue heating the reaction mixture for an additional 15 min.

3. Recovering the Product

Remove the reaction flask from the hot-water bath. Transfer the reaction mixture, while it is still warm, to a 25-mL-beaker. Allow the reaction mixture to cool to room temperature.

In the meantime, prepare an ice-water bath using the 250-mL beaker. Put 10 mL of distilled or deionized water into a large test tube. Chill the water in the ice-water bath.

If product crystals have not appeared, scratch the walls of the 25-mL beaker with a glass rod to induce crystallization. When the crystals appear, transfer the beaker into the ice-water bath to complete the crystallization.

Add 5 mL of *cold* distilled water to the crystals. Stir thoroughly.

Set up a vacuum filtration apparatus using a Hirsch funnel and a 25-mL filter flask connected to a filter trap and an aspirator. Wet the filter paper with water and turn on the aspirator.

NOTE 2: A drying oven set at 100–110 °C may be used to dry the crystals. If the crystals are air dried, it is best to dry them overnight.

Collect the product crystals by vacuum filtration. Pour the crystals into the Hirsch funnel. Rinse the beaker with 1 mL of cold water and add the rinse to the Hirsch funnel. Rinse the crystals with an additional 1 mL of cold water.

Transfer the crystals to a watch glass. Allow the crystals to dry. [NOTE 2]

4. Characterizing the Product

NOTE 3: Do not weigh the compounds for the characterization tests. Use the demonstration quantity provided by your laboratory instructor to estimate the amounts.

Measure the melting point of your product. Record the results.

Label four test tubes 1–4. Put 0.5 mL of distilled water in each tube.

Add a few milligrams of salicylic acid to tube 1. [NOTE 3] Add a few milligrams of acetylsalicylic acid to tube 2. Add a few milligrams of your product to tube 3. Use tube 4 as a control.

CAUTION

Iron(III) chloride (FeCl$_3$) is toxic and corrosive.

Shake tubes 1–3 to dissolve the crystals. Add one drop of 1% FeCl$_3$ to each of the four tubes. Record the results.

If your laboratory instructor provides commercial aspirin samples, label an additional test tube for each tablet. Crush the tablets. Dissolve a few milligrams of each sample in 0.5 mL of distilled water. Test the samples with 1% $FeCl_3$. Record the results.

5. Cleaning Up   Use the labeled collection containers provided by your laboratory instructor.

CAUTION

Wash your hands thoroughly with soap or detergent before leaving the laboratory.

MICROSCALE SYNTHESIS

Equipment

250-mL beaker*
25-mL filter flask,
    with vacuum tubing
filter paper
glass rod
10-mL graduated cylinder
Hirsch funnel, with adapter
melting point capillary tube
micropipet, 100 to 1000-μL
microspatula
2 Pasteur pipets, with latex bulb
reflux glassware, elastomeric
    connectors assembly[†]
        air condenser
        elastomeric connectors
        magnetic stir bar

5-mL round-bottom flask,
    long-neck
5-mL vial or 10-mL beaker
reflux glassware, conical vial
    assembly[†]
    condenser
    5-mL conical vial
    magnetic spin vane
stirring hot plate
support stand
5 test tubes, 13 × 100-mm[‡]
−10 to 260°C thermometer
2 utility clamps
watch glass

*for hot-water bath and ice-water bath
[†]use glassware provided by your laboratory instructor
[‡]plus an additional test tube for each commercial aspirin tablet tested

Reagents and Properties

substance	quantity	molar mass (g/mol)	mp°C)	bp (°C)
acetic anhydride	0.350 mL	102.09		138
acetylsalicylic acid*		180.16	138	
commercial aspirin tablets				
iron(III) chloride, 1%	4 drops			
phosphoric acid, 85%	1 drop			
salicylic acid	0.150 g	138.12	158	

* product

Preview

- Prepare a 50 °C hot-water bath
- Add salicylic acid, acetic anhydride, and phosphoric acid to a reflux apparatus
- Use the hot-water bath to reflux the reaction for 5 min
- Crystallize the product
- Collect the product by vacuum filtration
- Measure the melting point
- Test the product, salicylic acid, and acetylsalicylic acid with 1% iron(III) chloride
- Test commercial aspirin tablets with 1% iron(III) chloride

PROCEDURE

CAUTION

Wear departmentally approved safety goggles at all times while in the chemistry laboratory.

Always use caution in the laboratory. Many chemicals are potentially harmful. Prevent contact with your eyes, skin, and clothing. Avoid ingesting any of the reagents.

---

1. Setting Up the Reaction

Prepare a hot-water bath by placing approximately 100 mL of water into a 250-mL beaker. Use a stirring hot plate to heat the water to 50 °C.

Assemble the apparatus shown in Figure 2 that corresponds to your glassware. Add a magnetic stir bar or spin vane.

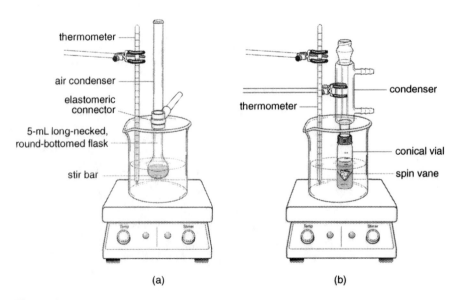

Figure 2
Reflux apparatus for (a) glassware with elastomeric connectors or (b) conical vial

Acetic anhydride is corrosive and a lachrymator. 85% Phosphoric acid is corrosive. Salicylic acid is a teratogen and irritating.

Put 0.150 g (150 mg) of salicylic acid into the 5-mL round-bottom flask or 5-mL conical vial. Add 0.350 mL of acetic anhydride. Use a Pasteur pipet to add one drop of 85% phosphoric acid. Reassemble the reflux apparatus without delay.

2. Conducting the Reaction [NOTE 1]

NOTE 1: The reflux condenser is used to prevent loss of any reactants during the reaction. Boiling will not occur.

Place the reaction flask (or vial) in the 50 °C hot-water bath. Clamp the flask (or vial) in place. Turn on the stirrer. Stir the reaction to dissolve the salicylic acid.

If the reaction mixture clumps and stops the stirring, use a microspatula to restart the stir bar (or spin vane). Once the salicylic acid has dissolved, continue heating the reaction mixture for an additional 5 min.

3. Recovering the Product

Remove the reaction flask (or vial) from the hot-water bath. If you used a round-bottom flask, transfer the reaction mixture, while it is still warm, to a vial or small beaker. Allow the reaction mixture to cool to room temperature.

In the meantime, prepare an ice-water bath using the 250-mL beaker. Put 5 mL of distilled or deionized water into a test tube. Chill the water in the ice-water bath.

If product crystals have not appeared, scratch the walls of the vial or beaker with a glass rod to induce crystallization. When crystals appear, put the vial (or beaker) into the ice-water bath to complete the crystallization.

Add 2 mL of *cold* distilled water to the crystals. Stir thoroughly.

Set up a vacuum filtration apparatus using a Hirsch funnel and a 25-mL filter flask connected to a trap and an aspirator. Wet the filter paper with water and turn on the aspirator.

NOTE 2: A drying oven set at 100–110 °C may be used to dry the crystals. If the crystals are air dried, it is best to dry them overnight.

Collect the product crystals by vacuum filtration. Pour the crystals into the Hirsch funnel. Rinse the vial (or beaker) with 0.5–1 mL of cold distilled water and add the rinse to the Hirsch funnel. Rinse the crystals with an additional 0.5–1 mL of cold water.

Transfer the crystals to a watch glass. Allow the crystals to dry. [NOTE 2]

4. Characterizing the Product

NOTE 3: Do not weigh the compounds for the characterization tests. Use the demonstration quantity provided by your laboratory instructor to estimate the amounts.

Measure the melting point of your product. Record the results.

Label four test tubes 1–4. Put 0.5 mL of distilled water in each tube.

Add a few milligrams of salicylic acid to tube 1. [NOTE 3]. Add a few milligrams of acetylsalicylic acid to tube 2. Add a few milligrams of your product to tube 3. Use tube 4 as a control.

Iron(III) chloride (FeCl₃) is toxic and corrosive.

Shake tubes 1–3 to dissolve the crystals. Add one drop of 1% $FeCl_3$ to each of the four tubes. Record the results.

If your laboratory instructor provides commercial aspirin samples, label an additional test tube for each tablet. Crush the tablets. Dissolve a few milligrams of each sample in 0.5 mL of distilled water. Test the samples with 1% $FeCl_3$. Record the results.

5. Cleaning Up

Use the labeled collection containers provided by your laboratory instructor.

CAUTION

Wash your hands thoroughly with soap or detergent before leaving the laboratory.

POST-LABORATORY QUESTIONS

1. Calculate your percent yield of acetylsalicylic acid. Remember to adjust your theoretical yield to the actual amount of salicylic acid you used in the experiment.

2. Does your measured melting point indicate that your product is pure? Briefly explain.

3. **(a)** Describe the results of the reactions you conducted with 1% $FeCl_3$.

   (b) What do the results indicate about your product? Briefly explain.

Name _____   Section _____   Date _____

Pre-Laboratory Assignment

1. What precautions should you take when working with:

   (a) acetic anhydride?

   (b) phosphoric acid?

2. What would happen if you placed your product in a drying oven set near 138 °C?

3. What is the limiting reagent in this reaction? (Acetic anhydride density is $d = 1.082$ g/mL.) Show your calculations here and in your laboratory notebook.

4. Calculate the theoretical yield of acetylsalicylic acid in this experiment. Show your calculations here and in your laboratory notebook.

5. Will acetylsalicylic acid give a colored complex with $FeCl_3$? Briefly explain.

6. Tablets from a bottle of commercial aspirin gave a negative test with $FeCl_3$. Several months later, tablets from the same bottle gave a positive test with $FeCl_3$. How do you account for this result? Briefly explain.

7. Salicylic acid reacts with acetic anhydride at the phenol group rather than at the carboxylic acid group. Briefly explain why the phenol site is preferred over the carboxylic acid site.

EXPERIMENT 16

Isolation of Chlorophyll and Carotenoid Pigments from Spinach

Isolation of a natural product
Extraction
Column chromatography
Thin-layer chromatography

Photosynthesis in plants takes place in organelles called **chloroplasts.** Chloroplasts contain a number of colored compounds (pigments) that fall into two categories: **chlorophylls** and **carotenoids.**

Carotenoids are yellow pigments that are also involved in the photosynthetic process. The structures of **α-** and **β-carotene** are given in the essay preceding this experiment. In addition, chloroplasts also contain several oxygen-containing derivatives of carotenes, called **xanthophylls.**

In this experiment, you will extract the chlorophyll and carotenoid pigments from spinach leaves using acetone as the solvent. The pigments will be separated by column chroma-

Chlorophyll a

Phytyl = $-CH_2-CH=C(CH_3)-CH_2-(CH_2-CH_2-CH(CH_3)-CH_2)_2-CH_2-CH_2-CH(CH_3)-CH_3$

tography using alumina as the adsorbent. Increasingly more polar solvents will be used to elute the various components from the column. The colored fractions collected will then be analyzed using thin-layer chromatography. It should be possible for you to identify most of the pigments already discussed on your thin-layer plate after development.

In this experiment, you will extract the chlorophyll and carotenoid pigments from spinach leaves using acetone as the solvent. The pigments will be separated by column chromatography using alumina as the adsorbent. Increasingly more polar solvents will be used to elute the various components from the column. The colored fractions collected will then be analyzed using thin-layer chromatography. It should be possible for you to identify most of the pigments already discussed on your thin-layer plate after development.

Chlorophylls are the green pigments that act as the principal photoreceptor molecules of plants. They are capable of absorbing certain wavelengths of visible light that are then converted by plants into chemical energy. Two different forms of these pigments found in plants are **chlorophyll *a*** and **chlorophyll *b*.** The two forms are identical, except that the methyl group that is shaded in the structural formula of chlorophyll *a* is replaced by a — CHO group in chlorophyll *b*. **Pheophytin *a*** and **pheophytin *b*** are identical to chlorophyll *a* and chlorophyll *b*, respectively, except that in each case the magnesium ion Mg^{2+} has been replaced by two hydrogen ions $2H^+$.

Required Reading

Review:	Techniques 5 and 6	
	Technique 7	Reaction Methods, Section 7.10
	Technique 12	Extractions, Separations, and Drying Agents, Sections 12.7 and 12.9
	Technique 20	Thin-Layer Chromatography
New:	Technique 19	Column Chromatography
	Essay	The Chemistry of Vision

Special Instructions

Hexane and acetone are both highly flammable. Avoid the use of flames while working with these solvents. Perform the thin-layer chromatography in the hood. The procedure calls for a centrifuge tube with a tight-fitting cap. If this is not available, you can use a vortex mixer for mixing the liquids. Another alternative is to use a cork to stopper the tube; however, the cork will absorb some liquid.

Fresh spinach is preferable to frozen spinach. Because of handling, frozen spinach contains additional pigments that are difficult to identify. Because the pigments are light-sensitive and can undergo air oxidation, you should work quickly. Samples should be stored in closed containers and kept in the dark when possible. The column chromatography procedure takes less than 15 minutes to perform and cannot be stopped until it is completed. It is very important, therefore, that you have all the materials needed for this part of the experiment prepared in advance and that you are thoroughly familiar with the procedure before running the column. If you need to prepare the 70% hexane–30% acetone solvent mixture, be sure to mix it thoroughly before using.

Suggested Waste Disposal

Dispose of all organic solvents in the container for nonhalogenated organic solvents. Place the alumina in the container designated for wet alumina.

Notes to the Instructor

The column chromatography should be performed with activated alumina from EM Science (No. AX0612-1). The particle sizes are 80–200 mesh, and the material is Type F-20. Dry the alumina overnight in an oven at 110°C and store it in a tightly sealed bottle. Alumina more than several years old may need to be dried for a longer time at a higher temperature. Depending on how dry the alumina is, solvents of different polarity will be required to elute the components from the column.

For thin-layer chromatography, use flexible silica gel plates from Whatman with a fluorescent indicator (No. 4410 222). If the TLC plates have not been purchased recently, place them in an oven at 100°C for 30 minutes and store them in a desiccator until used.

If you use different alumina or different thin-layer plates, try out the experiment before using it in class. Materials other than those specified here may give different results than indicated in this experiment.

Procedure

PART A.   EXTRACTION OF THE PIGMENTS

Weigh about 0.5 g of fresh (or 0.25 g of frozen) spinach leaves (avoid using stems or thick veins). Fresh spinach is preferable, if available. If you must use frozen spinach, dry the thawed leaves by pressing them between several layers of paper towels. Cut or tear the spinach leaves into small pieces and place them in a mortar along with 1.0 mL of cold acetone. Grind with a pestle until the spinach leaves have been broken into particles too small to be seen clearly. If too much acetone has evaporated, you may need to add an additional portion of acetone (0.5–1.0 mL) to perform the following step. Using a Pasteur pipet, transfer the mixture to a centrifuge tube. Rinse the mortar and pestle with 1.0 mL of cold acetone and transfer the remaining mixture to the centrifuge tube. Centrifuge the mixture (be sure to balance the centrifuge). Using a Pasteur pipet, transfer the liquid to a centrifuge tube with a tight-fitting cap (see "Special Instructions" if one is not available).

Add 2.0 mL of hexane to the tube, cap the tube, and shake the mixture thoroughly. Then add 2.0 mL of water and shake thoroughly with occasional venting. Centrifuge the mixture to break the emulsion, which usually appears as a cloudy, green layer in the middle of the mixture. Remove the bottom aqueous layer with a Pasteur pipet. Using a Pasteur pipet, prepare a column containing anhydrous sodium sulfate to dry the remaining hexane layer, which contains the dissolved pigments. Place a plug of cotton into a Pasteur pipet ($5\frac{3}{4}$-inch) and tamp it into position using a glass rod. The correct position of the cotton is shown in the figure. Add about 0.5 g of powdered or granular anhydrous sodium sulfate and tap the column with your finger to pack the material.

Clamp the column in a vertical position and place a dry test tube (13-mm × 100-mm) under the bottom of the column. Label this test tube with an "**E**" for "extract" so that you don't confuse it with the test tubes you will be working with later in this experiment. With a Pasteur pipet, transfer the hexane layer to the column.

When all the solution has drained, add 0.5 mL of hexane to the column to extract all the pigments from the drying agent. Evaporate the solvent by placing the test tube in a warm water bath (40–60°C) and directing a stream of nitrogen gas (or dry air) into the tube. Dissolve the residue in 0.5 mL of hexane. Stopper the test tube and place it in your drawer until you are ready to run the alumina chromatography column.

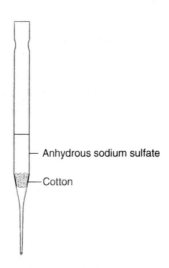

Column for drying extract.

PART B. COLUMN CHROMATOGRAPHY

Introduction. The pigments are separated on a column packed with alumina. Although there are many different components in your sample, they usually separate into two main bands on the column. The first band to pass through the column is yellow and consists of the carotenes. This band may be less than 1 mm wide, and it may pass through the column very rapidly. It is easy to miss seeing the band as it passes through the alumina. The second band consists of all the other pigments discussed in the introduction to this experiment. Although it consists of both green and yellow pigments, it appears as a green band on the column. The green band spreads out on the column more than the yellow band, and it moves more slowly. Occasionally, the yellow and green components in this band will separate as the band moves down the column. If this begins to occur, you should change to a solvent of higher polarity so that the components come out as one band. As the samples elute from the column, collect the yellow band (carotenes) in one test tube and the green band in another test tube.

Because the moisture content of the alumina is difficult to control, different samples of alumina may have different activities. The activity of the alumina is an important factor in determining the polarity of the solvent required to elute each band of pigments. Several solvents with a range of polarities are used in this experiment. The solvents and their relative polarities follow:

Hexane	increasing
70% hexane–30% acetone	polarity
Acetone	
80% acetone–20% methanol ↓	

A solvent of lower polarity elutes the yellow band; a solvent of higher polarity is required to elute the green band. In this procedure, you first try to elute the yellow band with hexane. If the yellow band does not move with hexane, you then add the next more polar solvent. Continue this process until you find a solvent that moves the yellow band. When you find the appropriate solvent, continue using it until the yellow band is eluted from the column. When the yellow band is eluted, change to the next more polar solvent. When you find a solvent that moves the green band, continue using it until the green band is eluted. Remember that occasionally a second yellow band will begin to move down the column before the green band moves. This yellow band will be much wider than the first one. If this occurs, change to a more polar solvent. This should bring all the components in the green band down at the same time.

Advance Preparation. Before running the column, assemble the following glassware and liquids. Obtain five dry test tubes (16-mm × 100-mm) and number them 1 through 5. Prepare two dry Pasteur pipets with bulbs attached. Calibrate one of them to deliver a volume of about 0.25 mL (Technique 5, Section 5.4, p. 607). Place 10.0 mL of hexane, 6.0 mL of 70% hexane–30% acetone solution (by volume), 6.0 mL of acetone, and 6.0 mL of 80% acetone–20% methanol (by volume) into four separate containers. Clearly label each container.

Prepare a chromatography column packed with alumina. Place a *loose* plug of cotton in a Pasteur pipet ($5\frac{3}{4}$-inch) and push it *gently* into position using a glass rod (see figure on p. 127 for the correct position of the cotton). Add 1.25 g of alumina (EM Science, No. AX0612-1) to the pipet while tapping the column gently with your finger. When all the alumina has been added, tap the column with your finger for several seconds to ensure that the alumina is tightly packed. Clamp the column in a vertical position so that the bottom of the column is just above the height of the test tubes you will be using to collect the fractions. Place test tube 1 under the column.

> **Note:** Read the following procedure on running the column. The chromatography procedure takes less than 15 minutes, and you cannot stop until all the material is eluted from the column. You must have a good understanding of the whole procedure before running the column.

Running the Column. Using a Pasteur pipet, slowly add about 3.0 mL of hexane to the column. The column must be completely moistened by the solvent. Drain the excess hexane until the level of hexane reaches the top of the alumina. Once you have added hexane to the alumina, the top of the column must not be allowed to run dry. If necessary, add more hexane.

Note: It is essential that the liquid level not be allowed to drain below the surface of the alumina at any point during the procedure.

When the level of the hexane reaches the top of the alumina, add about half (0.25 mL) of the dissolved pigments to the column. Leave the remainder in the test tube for the thin-layer chromatography procedure. (Put a stopper on the tube and place it back in your drawer). Continue collecting the eluent in test tube 1. Just as the pigment solution penetrates the column, add 1 mL of hexane and drain until the surface of the liquid has reached the alumina.

Add about 4 mL of hexane. If the yellow band begins to separate from the green band, continue to add hexane until the yellow band passes through the column. If the yellow band does not separate from the green band, change to the next more polar solvent (70% hexane–30% acetone). When changing solvents, do not add the new solvent until the last solvent has nearly penetrated the alumina. When the appropriate solvent is found, add this solvent until the yellow band passes through the column. Just before the yellow band reaches the bottom of the column, place test tube 2 under the column. When the eluent becomes colorless again (the total volume of the yellow material should be less than 2 mL), place test tube 3 under the column.

Add several mL of the next more polar solvent when the level of the last solvent is almost at the top of the alumina. If the green band moves down the column, continue to add this solvent until the green band is eluted from the column. If the green band does not move or if a diffuse yellow band begins to move, change to the next more polar solvent. Change solvents again if necessary. Collect the green band in test tube 4. When there is little or no green color in the eluent, place test tube 5 under the column and stop the procedure.

Using a warm water bath (40–60°C) and a stream of nitrogen gas, evaporate the solvent from the tube containing the yellow band (tube 2), the tube containing the green band (tube 4), and the tube containing the original pigment solution (tube E). As soon as all the solvent has evaporated from each of the tubes, remove them from the water bath. Do not allow any of the tubes to remain in the water bath after the solvent has evaporated. Stopper the tubes and place them in your drawer.

PART C. THIN-LAYER CHROMATOGRAPHY

Preparing the TLC Plate. Technique 20 describes the procedures for thin-layer chromatography. Use a 10-cm × 3.3-cm TLC plate (Whatman Silica Gel Plates No. 4410 222). These plates have a flexible backing but should not be bent excessively. Handle them carefully, or the adsorbent may flake off them. Also, you should handle them only by the edges; the surface should not be touched. Using a lead pencil (not a pen), *lightly* draw a line across the plate (short dimension) about 1 cm from the bottom (see figure). Using a centimeter ruler, move its index about 0.6 cm in from the edge of the plate and lightly mark off three 1-cm intervals on the line. These are the points at which the samples will be spotted.

Prepare three micropipets to spot the plate. The preparation of these pipets is described and illustrated in Technique 20, Section 20.4, page 822. Prepare a TLC development chamber with 70% hexane–30% acetone (see Technique 20, Section 20.5, p. 823). A beaker covered with aluminum foil or a wide-mouth, screw-cap bottle is a suitable container to use (see Figure 20.4, p. 824). The backing on the TLC plates is very thin, so if they touch the filter paper liner of the development chamber *at any point,* solvent will begin to diffuse onto the absorbent surface at that point. To avoid this, be sure that the filter paper liner does not go completely around the inside of the container. A space about 2 inches wide must be provided.

Using a Pasteur pipet, add two drops of 70% hexane–30% acetone to each of the three test tubes containing dried pigments. Swirl the tubes so that the drops of solvent dissolve as much of the pigments as possible. The TLC plate should be spotted with three samples: the extract, the yellow band from the column, and the green band. For each of the three samples, use a different micropipet to spot the sample on the plate. The correct method of spotting a TLC plate is described in Technique 20, Section 20.4, page 822. Take up part of the sample in the pipet (don't use a bulb; capillary action will draw up the liquid). For the extract (tube E) and the green band (tube 4), touch the plate once *lightly* and let the solvent evaporate. The spot should be no longer than 2 mm in diameter and should be a fairly dark green. For the yellow band (tube 2), repeat the spotting technique 5–10 times, until the spot is a definite yellow color. Allow the solvent to evaporate completely between successive applications and spot the plate in exactly the same position each time. Save the samples in case you need to repeat the TLC.

Developing the TLC Plate.   Place the TLC plate in the development chamber, making sure that the plate does not come in contact with the filter paper liner. Remove the plate when the solvent front is 1–2 cm from the top of the plate. Using a lead pencil, mark the position of the solvent front. As soon as the plates have dried,

Preparing the TLC plate.

outline the spots with a pencil and indicate the colors. This is important to do soon after the plates have dried, because some of the pigments will change color when exposed to the air.

Analysis of the Results. In the crude extract, you should be able to see the following components (in order of decreasing R_f values):

> Carotenes (1 spot) (yellow orange)
>
> Pheophytin *a* (gray, may be nearly as intense as chlorophyll *b*)
>
> Pheophytin *b* (gray, may not be visible)
>
> Chlorophyll *a* (blue green, more intense than chlorophyll *b*)
>
> Chlorophyll *b* (green)
>
> Xanthophylls (possibly 3 spots: yellow)

Depending on the spinach sample, the conditions of the experiment, and the amount of sample spotted on the TLC plate, you may observe other pigments. These additional components can result from air oxidation, hydrolysis, or other chemical reactions involving the pigments discussed in this experiment. It is very common to observe other pigments in samples of frozen spinach. It is also common to observe components in the green band that were not present in the extract.

Identify as many of the spots in your samples as possible. Determine which pigments were present in the yellow band and in the green band. Draw a picture of the TLC plate in your notebook. Label each spot with its color and its identity, where possible. Calculate the R_f values for each spot produced by chromatography of the extract (see Technique 20, Section 20.9, p. 827). At the instructor's option, submit the TLC plate with your report.

QUESTIONS

1. Why are the chlorophylls less mobile on column chromatography, and why do they have lower R_f values than the carotenes?

2. Propose structural formulas for pheophytin *a* and pheophytin *b*.

3. What would happen to the R_f values of the pigments if you were to increase the relative concentration of acetone in the developing solvent?

4. Using your results as a guide, comment on the purity of the material in the green and yellow bands.